GOLDSMITH'S WORKS

THE WORKS

OF

OLIVER GOLDSMITH

EDITED BY

PETER CUNNINGHAM, F.S.A.

IN FOUR VOLUMES

Volume II.—INQUIRY INTO THE PRESENT STATE OF POLITE LEARNING

THE CITIZEN OF THE WORLD

NEW YORK

HARPER & BROTHERS, FRANKLIN SQUARE

1881

ADVERTISEMENT.

THIS volume contains the "Inquiry into the State of Polite Literature in Europe," published in 1759, when Goldsmith was young and unknown; and the series of Letters, entitled "The Citizen of the World," written for the columns of a newspaper—afterwards collected by the author himself, and esteemed among the most delightful of his works.

In this volume, as in the preceding one, I have been careful to mark all Goldsmith's own notes with his name—a duty which no other editor has deemed it worth while to perform. It is true that, in some instances, the author's notes have been retained by his editors, who have in such cases, however, invariably adopted them as their own, or have at least omitted all indication that they are his. Other notes, and those at times curiously illustrative of the text, have been most unaccountably omitted. I have restored all.

PETER CUNNINGHAM.

CONTENTS OF VOL. II.

AN INQUIRY

INTO

THE PRESENT STATE OF POLITE LEARNING

IN EUROPE.

Εμοι προς φιλοσοφους εστι φιλια· προς μεν τοι σοφιστας η
γραμματιστας ουτε νυν εστι φιλια μητε υστερον ποτε γενοιτο.

"Tolerabile si Ædificia nostra diruerent Ædificandi capaces."

London:

Printed for R. and J. Dodsley, in Pall Mall.

1759.

12°.

This Inquiry was first published in April, 1759, in a duodecimo volume of 200 pages, price 2s. 6d., sewed. "The second edition, revised and corrected," as the title-page sets forth, appeared in July, 1774, three months after Goldsmith's death. It was printed for J. Dodsley.

The text of this reprint is that of the second edition compared with the first. All the omitted passages, and many of the original readings of the amended paragraphs I have preserved in notes, for the purpose, chiefly, of showing what were Goldsmith's opinions in 1759, when young and unknown, contrasted with his maturer notions, when the world was more with him than it had been, fifteen years before.

CONTENTS.

---

[1] In the second edition (1774) erroneously described as Chapters VII. and VIII.
[2] Chapter VII. of the first edition (1759); omitted in the second (1774).

AN INQUIRY

THE PRESENT STATE OF POLITE LEARNING IN EUROPE.

CHAPTER I.

INTRODUCTION.

IT has been so long the practice to represent literature as declining, that every renewal of this complaint now comes with diminished influence. The public has been so often excited by a false alarm, that at present the nearer we approach the threatened period of decay, the more our security increases.

It will now probably be said that taking the decay of genius for granted, as I do, argues either resentment or partiality. The writer, possessed of fame, it may be asserted, is willing to enjoy it without a rival, by lessening every competitor; or, if unsuccessful, he is desirous to turn upon others the contempt which is levelled at himself; and being convicted at the bar of literary justice, hopes for pardon by accusing every brother of the same profession.

Sensible of this, I am at a loss where to find an apology for persisting to arraign the merit of the age; for joining in a cry which the judicious have long since left to be kept up by the vulgar; and for adopting the sentiments of the multitude, in a performance that at best can please only a few.

Complaints of our degeneracy in literature as well as in morals, I own, have been frequently exhibited of late; but

seem to be enforced more with the ardor of devious declamation than the calmness of deliberate inquiry. The dullest
critic who strives at a reputation for delicacy, by showing he
cannot be pleased may pathetically assure us that our taste is
upon the decline; may consign every modern performance
to oblivion, and bequeath nothing to posterity except the labors of our ancestors, or his own. Such general invective,
however, conveys no instruction; all it teaches is, that the
writer dislikes an age by which he is probably disregarded.
The manner of being useful on the subject would be to
point out the symptoms, to investigate the causes, and direct
to the remedies of the approaching decay. This is a subject
hitherto unattempted in criticism; perhaps it is the only subject in which criticism can be useful.[1]

How far the writer is equal to such an undertaking the
reader must determine; yet perhaps[2] his observations may be
just, though his manner of expressing them should only serve
as an example of the errors he undertakes to reprove.[3]

---

[1] Here, in the first edition, occurs: "To mark out, therefore, the corruptions
that have found way into the republic of letters, to attempt the rescuing of genius from the shackles of pedantry and criticism, to distinguish the decay naturally consequent on an age like ours, grown old in literature, from every erroneous
innovation which admits a remedy, to take a view of those societies which profess the advancement of polite learning, and by a mutual opposition of their excellencies and defects, to attempt the improvement of each, is the design of this
essay."

[2] Instead of "yet perhaps," the first edition has: "But this may be asserted,
without the imputation of vanity, that he enters the lists with no disappointments
to bias his judgment, nor will he ever reprove but with a desire to reform. The
defects of his execution may be compensated by the usefulness of his design; and
his," etc.

[3] Here, in the first edition, we read, commencing a new sentence: "If the present Inquiry were a topic of speculative curiosity, calculated to fill up a few vacant moments in literary indolence, I should think my labor ill-bestowed. To
rank in the same despicable class with the dissertations, enigmas, problems, and
other periodical compilations with which even idleness is dosed at present, is by
no means my ambition. True learning and morality are closely connected; to
improve the head will sensibly influence the heart; a deficiency of taste and a corruption of manners are sometimes found mutually to produce each other.

"Dissenting from received opinions may frequently render this essay liable to
correction, yet the reader may be assured that a passion for singularity never
gives rise to the error. Novelty is not permitted."

Novelty, however, is not permitted to usurp the place of reason; it may attend, but shall not conduct, the inquiry. But it should be observed that the more original any performance is, the more it is liable to deviate; for cautious stupidity is always in the right.[1]

CHAPTER II.

THE CAUSES WHICH CONTRIBUTE TO THE DECLINE OF LEARNING.

IF we consider the revolutions which have happened in the commonwealth of letters, survey the rapid progress of learning in one period of antiquity, or its amazing decline in another, we shall be almost induced to accuse nature of partiality; as if she had exhausted all her efforts in adorning one age, while she left the succeeding entirely neglected. It is not to nature, however, but to ourselves alone that this partiality must be ascribed; the seeds of excellence are sown in every age, and it is wholly owing to a wrong direction in the passions or pursuits of mankind that they have not received the proper cultivation.[2]

As in the best regulated societies the very laws which at first give the government solidity may in the end contribute to its dissolution, so the efforts which might have promoted learning in its feeble commencement may, if continued, retard its progress. The paths of science, which were at first intricate because untrodden, may at last grow toilsome because too much frequented. As learning advances, the candidates for its honors become more numerous, and the ac-

---

[1] The first edition adds: "In literature as in commerce, the value of the acquisition is generally proportioned to the hazard of the adventure. I shall think, therefore, with freedom, and bear correction with candor. It is but just that he who dissents from others should not be displeased if others differ from him. The applause of a few, a very few, will satisfy ambition; and even ill-nature must confess that I have been willing to advance the reputation of the age at the hazard of my own."

[2] Here the first edition adds: "It is not nature that is fatigued with producing her wonders, so much as we that are satiated with admiration."

quisition of fame more uncertain : the modest may despair of attaining it, and the opulent think it too precarious to pursue. Thus the task of supporting the honor of the times may at last devolve on indigence and effrontery, while learning must partake of the contempt of its professors.

To illustrate these assertions, it may be proper to take a slight review of the decline of ancient learning; to consider how far its depravation was owing to the impossibility of supporting continued perfection; in what respects it proceeded from voluntary corruption; and how far it was hastened on by accident. If modern learning be compared with ancient in these different lights, a parallel between both, which has hitherto produced only vain dispute, may contribute to amusement, perhaps to instruction. We shall thus be enabled to perceive what period of antiquity the present age most resembles; whether we are making advances towards excellence, or retiring again to primeval obscurity; we shall thus be taught to acquiesce in those defects which it is impossible to prevent; and reject all faulty innovations, though offered under the specious titles of improvement.[1]

Learning, when planted in any country, is transient and fading, nor does it flourish till slow gradations of improvement have naturalized it to the soil. It makes feeble advances, begins among the vulgar, and rises into reputation among the great. It cannot be established in a state at once, by introducing the learned of other countries; these may grace a court, but seldom enlighten a kingdom. Ptolemy Philadelphus, Constantine Porphyrogeneta, Alfred, or Charlemagne, might have invited learned foreigners into their do-

---

[1] Here the first edition adds: "In early ages, when man was employed in acquiring necessary subsistence or in defending his acquisitions, when without laws or society he led a precarious life, while even the savage rivalled him in the dominion of the forest; in such times of fatigue and darkness we must not look for the origin of arts or learning, which are the offspring of security, opulence, and ease. When experience taught the advantages, when native freedom was exchanged for social security, when man began to feel the benefit of laws, and the mind had leisure for the contemplation of nature and itself, then, probably, the sciences might have been cultivated to add strength to the rising community, and the polite arts introduced to promote its enjoyment."

minions, but could not establish learning. While in the radiance of royal favor, every art and science seemed to flourish; but when that was withdrawn, they quickly felt the rigors of a strange climate, and, with exotic constitutions, perished by neglect.

As the arts and sciences are slow in coming to maturity, it is requisite, in order to their perfection, that the state should be permanent which gives them reception. There are numberless attempts without success, and experiments without conclusion, between the first rudiments of an art and its utmost perfection; between the outlines of a shadow and the picture of an Apelles. Leisure is required to go through the tedious interval, to join the experience of predecessors to our own, or enlarge our views, by building on the ruined attempts of former adventurers. All this may be performed in a society of long continuance; but if the kingdom be but of short duration, as was the case of Arabia, learning seems coeval, sympathizes with its political struggles, and is annihilated in its dissolution.

But permanence in a state is not alone sufficient; it is requisite also for this end that it should be free. Naturalists assure us that all animals are sagacious in proportion as they are removed from the tyranny of others. In native liberty, the elephant is a citizen, and the beaver an architect; but, whenever the tyrant man intrudes upon their community, their spirit is broken, they seem anxious only for safety, and their intellects suffer an equal diminution with their prosperity. The parallel will hold with regard to mankind; fear naturally represses invention; benevolence, ambition; for in a nation of slaves, as in the despotic governments of the East, to labor after fame is to be a candidate for danger.

To attain literary excellence also, it is requisite that the soil and climate should, as much as possible, conduce to happiness. The earth must supply man with the necessaries of life, before he has leisure or inclination to pursue more refined enjoyments. The climate, also, must be equally indulgent; for in too warm a region the mind is relaxed into languor, and by the opposite excess is chilled into torpid inactivity.

II.—2

These are the principal advantages which tend to the improvement of learning,[1] and all these were united in the states of Greece and Rome.

We must now examine what hastens or prevents its decline.

Those who behold the phenomena of nature, and content themselves with the view without inquiring into their causes, are perhaps wiser than is generally imagined. In this manner our rude ancestors were acquainted with facts; and poetry, which helped the imagination and the memory, was thought the most proper vehicle for conveying their knowledge to posterity. It was the poet who harmonized the ungrateful accents of his native dialect; who lifted it above common conversation, and shaped its rude combinations into order. From him the orator formed a style; and though poetry first rose out of prose, in turn it gave birth to every prosaic excellence. Musical period, concise expression, and delicacy of sentiment were all excellencies derived from the poet; in short, he not only preceded, but formed the orator, philosopher, and historian.

When the observations of past ages were collected, Philosophy next began to examine their causes. She had numberless facts from which to draw proper inferences, and Poetry had taught her the strongest expression to enforce[2] them. Thus the Greek philosophers, for instance, exerted all their happy talents in the investigation of truth, and the production of beauty.[3] They saw that there was more excellence in captivating the judgment than in raising a momentary astonishment: in their arts, they imitated only such parts of nature as might please in the representation; in the sciences, they cultivated such parts of knowledge as it was every man's

---

[1] After "learning," the first edition reads: "Encouragement from the great is useful in preventing its decline." And the next paragraph commences: "Those who behold," etc.

[2] "The Greeks (for we know little of the Egyptian learning) now exerted," etc. —*First Edition.*

[3] Here the first edition adds: "Before this, the works of art were remarkable only for their vastness of design, and seemed the productions of giants, not of ordinary men; learning was another name for magic, or, to give it its real appellation, imposture. But these improvers saw that," etc.

duty to know.[1] Thus learning was encouraged, protected, honored, and in its turn it adorned, strengthened, and harmonized the community.[2]

But as the mind is vigorous and active, and experiment[3] is dilatory and painful,[4] the spirit of philosophy being excited, the reasoner, when destitute of experiment, had recourse to theory, and gave up what was useful for refinement.

Critics, sophists, grammarians, rhetoricians, and commentators now began to figure in the literary commonwealth. In the dawn of science, such are generally modest, and not entirely useless; their performances serve to mark the progress of learning, though they seldom contribute to its improvement. But as nothing but speculation was required in making proficients in their respective departments, so neither the satire nor the contempt of the wise, though Socrates was of the number, nor the laws levelled at them by the state, though Cato was in the legislature, could prevent their approaches. Possessed of all the advantages of unfeeling dulness, laborious, insensible, and persevering, they still proceeded mending, and mending every work of genius, or, to speak without irony, undermining all that was polite and useful. Libraries were loaded but not enriched with their labors,

---

[1] Here the first edition adds: "Unity, variety, and proportion charmed in all their design; liberty, patriotism, and a subjection to the laws were what all their true philosophers strove to inculcate. Thus learning," etc.

[2] Here the first edition adds: "From being the disciple of Greece, Rome soon became its rival, and was as much esteemed for its improvements in the arts of peace, as feared for its achievements in those of war. The Romans understood, perhaps better than their masters, the manner of blending art and science for their mutual improvement. By this means their philosophy acquired more grace, and their poetry more sentiment. They entirely banished that magical obscurity which the Greeks first borrowed from other nations, and some part of which their most admired writers thought proper still to retain. The learning of the Romans might justly be styled the truest refinement on common-sense; it was, therefore, a proper instrument in the hands of ambition. Their most powerful men not only encouraged, but became themselves the finest models of literary perfection. Thus the arts and sciences went on together, and reasoning proceeded no farther than where experiment pointed out the way."

[3] "But as the operations of body are slow, those of the mind vigorous and active, as experiment," etc.—*First Edition.*

[4] The first edition adds: "Speculation, quick and amusing."

while the fatigues of reading their explanatory comments was tenfold that which might suffice for understanding the original, and their works effectually increased our application, by professing to remove it.

Against so obstinate and irrefragable an enemy, what could avail the unsupported sallies of genius, or the opposition of transitory resentment? In short, they conquered by persevering, claimed the right of dictating upon every work of taste, sentiment, or genius, and at last, when destitute of other employment, like the supernumerary domestics of the great, made work for each other.

They now took upon them to teach poetry to those who wanted genius; and the power of disputing to those who knew nothing of the subject in debate. It was observed how some of the most admired poets had copied nature. From these they collected dry rules, dignified with long names, and such were obtruded upon the public for their improvement. Common-sense would be apt to suggest that the art might be studied to more advantage, rather by imitation than precept. It might suggest that those rules were collected, not from nature, but a copy of nature, and would consequently give us still fainter resemblances of original beauty. It might still suggest that explained wit makes but a feeble impression; that the observations of others are soon forgotten, those made by ourselves are permanent and useful. But, it seems, understandings of every size were to be mechanically instructed in poetry. If the reader was too dull to relish the beauties of Virgil, the comment of Servius was ready to brighten his imagination; if Terence could not raise him to a smile, Evantius was at hand, with a long-winded scholium to increase his titillation. Such rules are calculated to make blockheads talk; but all the lemmata of the Lyceum are unable to give him feeling.[1]

---

[1] Here the first edition adds: "Their logical disputations seemed even to be the apotheosis of folly. In these the opponent had a right to affirm whatever absurdity he thought proper. The defendant, though he saw the falsehood almost by intuition, was not allowed to use his reason, but his art, in the debate. It was his business only to measure the assertion by one of his artificial instruments, and as

But it would be endless to recount all the absurdities[1] which were hatched in the schools of those specious idlers; be it sufficient to say, that they increased as learning improved, but swarmed on its decline. It was then that every work of taste was buried in long comments; every useful subject in morals was distinguished away into casuistry, and doubt and subtlety characterized the learning of the age. Metrodorus, Valerius Probus, Aulus Gellius, Pedianus, Boethius, and a hundred others, to be acquainted with whom might show much reading and but little judgment; these, I say, made choice each of an author, and delivered all their load of learning on his back. Shame to our ancestors! many of their works have reached our times entire, while Tacitus himself has suffered mutilation.

In a word, the commonwealth of literature was at last wholly overrun by these studious triflers. Men of real genius were lost in the multitude, or, as in a world of fools it were folly to aim at being an only exception, obliged to conform to every prevailing absurdity of the times. Original productions seldom appeared, and learning, as if grown superannuated, bestowed all its panegyric upon the vigor of its youth, and turned encomiast upon its former achievements.

It is to these, then, that the depravation of ancient polite learning is principally to be ascribed. By them it was separated from common-sense, and made the proper employment of speculative idlers. Men bred up among books, and seeing nature only by reflection, could do little except hunt after perplexity and confusion. The public, therefore, with reason rejected learning, when thus rendered barren though voluminous; for we may be assured that the generality of mankind never lose a passion for letters while they continue to be either amusing or useful.

It was such writers as these that rendered learning unfit for uniting and strengthening civil society, or for promoting the

---

it happened to accord or disagree, he found himself qualified to support, or obliged to discontinue, his defence ; which seldom, however, happened till fatigue or anger terminated the inquiry."

[1] "Insect-like absurdities."—*First Edition.*

views of ambition. True philosophy had kept the Grecian states cemented into one effective body more than any law for that purpose; and the Etrurian philosophy, which prevailed in the first ages of Rome, inspired those patriot virtues which paved the way to universal empire. But by the labors of commentators, when philosophy became abstruse or triflingly minute, when doubt was presented instead of knowledge, when the orator was taught to charm the multitude with the music of his periods, and pronounced a declamation that might be sung as well as spoken, and often upon subjects wholly fictitious; in such circumstances learning was entirely unsuited to all the purposes of government or the designs of the ambitious. As long as the sciences could influence the state, and its politics were strengthened by them, so long did the community give them countenance and protection. But the wiser part of mankind would not be imposed upon by unintelligible jargon, nor, like the knight in Pantagruel, swallow a chimera for a breakfast, though even cooked by Aristotle. As the philosopher grew useless in the state, he also became contemptible. In the times of Lucian he was chiefly remarkable for his avarice, his impudence, and his beard.

Under the auspicious influence of genius, arts and sciences grew up together, and mutually illustrated each other. But when once pedants became law-givers, the sciences began to want grace and the polite arts solidity; these grew crabbed and sour, those meretricious and gaudy; the philosopher became disgustingly precise, and the poet, ever straining after grace, caught only finery.

These men also contributed to obstruct the progress of wisdom by addicting their readers to one particular sect or some favorite science. They generally carried on a petty traffic in some little creek; within that they busily plied about and drove an insignificant trade; but never ventured out into the great ocean of knowledge, nor went beyond the bounds that chance, conceit, or laziness had first prescribed their inquiries. Their disciples, instead of aiming at being originals themselves, became imitators of that merit alone which was constantly proposed for their admiration. In exercises of this kind, the most stupid are generally most successful; for there is not in nature a more imitative animal than a dunce.

Hence ancient learning may be distinguished into three periods—its commencement, or the age of poets; its maturity, or the age of philosophers; and its decline, or the age of critics. In the poetical age commentators were very few, but might have in some respects been useful. In its philosophical, their assistance must necessarily become obnoxious, yet, as if the nearer we approached perfection the more we stood in need of their directions, in this period they began to grow numerous. But when polite learning was no more, then it was those literary law-givers made the most formidable appearance. "Corruptissima republica, plurimæ leges."

But let us take a more distinct view of those ages of ignorance in which false refinement had involved mankind, and see how far they resemble our own.[1]

CHAPTER III.

A VIEW OF THE OBSCURE AGES.

WHATEVER the skill of any country may be in the sciences, it is from its excellence in polite learning alone that it must expect a character from posterity. The poet and the historian are they who diffuse a lustre upon the age; and the philosopher scarcely acquires any applause, unless his character be introduced to the vulgar by their mediation.

The obscure ages, which succeeded the decline of the Roman Empire, are a striking instance of the truth of this assertion. Whatever period of those ill-fated times we happen to turn to, we shall perceive more skill in the sciences among the professors of them, more abstruse and deeper inquiry into every philosophical subject, and a greater show of subtlety and close reasoning, than in the most enlightened ages of all antiquity. But their writings were mere speculative amuse-

---

[1] This concluding paragraph is not in the first edition.

ments and all their researches exhausted upon trifles. Unskilled in the arts of adorning their knowledge, or adapting it to common-sense, their voluminous productions rest peacefully in our libraries, or at best are inquired after from motives of curiosity, not by the scholar, but the virtuoso.

I am not insensible that several late French historians have exhibited the obscure ages in a very different light. They have represented them as utterly ignorant both of arts and sciences, buried in the profoundest darkness, or only illuminated with a feeble gleam, which, like an expiring taper, rose and sunk by intervals. Such assertions, however, though they serve to help out the declaimer, should be cautiously admitted by the historian. For instance, the tenth century is particularly distinguished by posterity with the appellation of obscure. Yet even in this, the reader's memory may possibly suggest the names of some whose works, still preserved, discover a most extensive erudition, though rendered almost useless by affectation and obscurity. A few of their names and writings may be mentioned, which will serve at once to confirm what I assert, and give the reader an idea of what kind of learning an age declining into obscurity chiefly chooses to cultivate.

About the tenth century flourished Leo the philosopher. We have seven volumes folio of his collections of laws, published at Paris, 1647. He wrote upon the art military, and understood also astronomy and judicial astrology. He was seven times more voluminous than Plato.

Solomon the German wrote a most elegant dictionary of the Latin tongue, still preserved in the university of Louvain; Pantaleon, in the lives of his illustrious countrymen, speaks of it in the warmest strains of rapture. Dictionary writing was at that time much in fashion.

Constantine Porphyrogeneta was a man universally skilled in the sciences. His tracts on the administration of an empire, on tactics, and on laws, were published, some years since, at Leyden. His court, for he was Emperor of the East, was resorted to by the learned from all parts of the world.

Luitprandus was a most voluminous historian, and particularly famous for the history of his own times.[1] The compliments paid him as a writer are said to exceed even his own voluminous productions. I cannot pass over one of a latter date made him by a German : " Luitprandus nunquam Luitprando dissimilis."[2]

Alfric composed several grammars and dictionaries, still preserved among the curious.

Pope Sylvester the Eleventh wrote a treatise on the sphere, on arithmetic and geometry, published some years since at Paris.

Michael Psellus lived in this age, whose books in the sciences, I will not scruple to assert, contain more learning than those of any one of the earlier ages; his erudition was indeed amazing, and he was as voluminous as he was learned. The character given him by Allatius has, perhaps, more truth in it than will be granted by those who have seen none of his productions. " There was," says he, " no science with which he was unacquainted, none which he did not write something upon, and none which he did not leave better than he found it." To mention his works would be endless. His commentaries on Aristotle alone amount to three folios.

Bertholdus Teutonicus, a very voluminous historian, was a politician, and wrote against the government under which he lived ; but most of his writings, though not all, are lost.

Constantinus Afer was a philosopher and physician. We have remaining but two volumes folio of his philological performances. However, the historian, who prefixes the life of the author to his works, says that he wrote many more, as he kept on writing during the course of a long life.[3]

Lambertus published a universal history about this time, which has been printed at Frankfort, in folio. A universal history in one folio ! If he had consulted with his book-

---

[1] " In this he shows himself a perfect *matter-of-fact man ;* but, like some moderns, who only value themselves on the same qualification, he was a most notorious fabulist.—*First Edition.*

[2] " In English, 'None but himself can be his parallel.' "—*First Edition.*

[3] " And when he had thus compiled more than any man that ever went before him, he fell asleep : *In domino obdormivit.*"—*First Edition.*

seller, he would have spun it out to ten at least; but Lambertus might have had too much modesty.[1]

By this time the reader perceives the spirit of learning which at that time prevailed. The ignorance of the age was not owing to a dislike of knowledge; but a false standard of taste was erected, and a wrong direction given to philosophical inquiry. It was the fashion of the day to write dictionaries, commentaries, and compilations,[2] and to evaporate in a folio the spirit that could scarcely have sufficed for an epigram. The most barbarous times had men of learning, if commentators, compilers, polemic divines, and intricate metaphysicians deserved the title.

I have mentioned but a very inconsiderable number of the writers in this age of obscurity. The multiplicity of their publications will at least equal those of any similar period of the most polite antiquity. As, therefore, the writers of those times are almost entirely forgotten, we may infer that the number of publications alone will never secure any age whatsoever from oblivion. Nor can printing, contrary to what M. Beaumelle has remarked, prevent literary decline for the future, since it only increases the number of books, without advancing their intrinsic merit.[3]

---

[1] The first edition adds: "Olympiodorus published commentaries upon Plato. Doctor Foster, in his late edition of the select dialogues of that philosopher, has often taken occasion to quote him, and mentions him with honor."

[2] Instead of "to write dictionaries, commentaries, and compilations," the first edition reads, "to consult books, not nature."

[3] Here followed, in the first edition:

"CHAPTER IV.

"A PARALLEL BETWEEN THE RISE AND DECLINE OF ANCIENT AND MODERN LEARNING.

"Few subjects have been more frequently and warmly debated than the comparative superiority of the ancients and moderns. It is unaccountable how a dispute so trifling could be contested with so much virulence. A dispute of this nature could have no other consequences, if decided, but to teach young writers to despise the one side or the other. A dispute, therefore, which, if determined, might tend rather to prejudice our taste than improve it, should have been argued with good-nature, as it could not with success. For mere critics to be guilty of such scholastic rage, is not uncommon, but for men of the first rank of fame to be delinquent also, is, I own, surprising.

CHAPTER IV.

OF THE PRESENT STATE OF POLITE LEARNING IN ITALY.

From ancient we are now come to modern times, and in running over Europe, we shall find that, wherever learning has been cultivated, it has flourished by the same advantages as in Greece and Rome; and that, wherever it has declined, it sinks by the same causes of decay.[1]

Dante, who wrote in the thirteenth century, was the first who attempted to bring learning from the cloister into the community, and paint human nature in a language adapted to modern manners. He addressed a barbarous people in a method suited to their apprehensions; united purgatory and the river Styx, St. Peter and Virgil, heaven and hell together, and shows a strange mixture of good-sense and absurdity.

" The reflecting reader need scarcely be informed that this contested excellence can be decided in favor of neither. They have both copied from different originals, described the manners of different ages; have exhibited nature as they found her, and both are excellent in separate imitations. Homer describes his gods as his countrymen believed them. Virgil, in a more enlightened age, describes his with a greater degree of respect; and Milton still rises infinitely above either. The machinery of Homer is best adapted to an unenlightened idolater; that of the Roman poet to a more refined heathen; and that of Milton to a reader illuminated by revelation. Had Homer wrote like Milton, his countrymen would have despised him; had Milton adopted the theology of the ancient bard, he had been truly ridiculous. Again, should I depreciate Plautus for not enlivening his pieces with the characters of a coquet, or a marquis, so humorous in modern comedy? or Molière, for not introducing a legal bawd, or a parasitical boaster, so highly finished in the Roman poet? My censure, in either case, would be as absurd as his who should dislike a geographer for not introducing more rivers or promontories into a country than nature had given it; or the natural historian for not enlivening his description of a dead landscape with a torrent, a cataract, or a volcano.

" The parallel between antiquity and ourselves can, therefore, be managed to advantage only by comparing the rise and progress of ancient and modern learning together, so that, being apprised of the causes of corruption in one, we may be upon our guard against any similar depravations in the other."

[1] This paragraph is not in the first edition.

The truth is, he owes most of his reputation to the obscurity
of the times in which he lived. As in the land of Benin a
man may pass for a prodigy of parts who can read, so in an
age of barbarity a small degree of excellence insures success.
But it was great merit in him[1] to have lifted up the standard of nature, in spite of all the opposition and the persecution he received from contemporary criticism. To this standard every succeeding genius resorted; the germ of every art
and science began to unfold; and to imitate nature was found
to be the surest way of imitating antiquity. In a century or
two after, modern Italy might justly boast of rivalling ancient
Rome; equal in some branches of polite learning, and not far
surpassed in others.

They soon, however, fell from emulating the wonders of
antiquity into simple admiration. As if the word had been
given when Vida and Tasso wrote on the arts of poetry, the
whole swarm of critics was up. The Speronis of the age attempted to be awkwardly merry; and the Virtuosi and the
Nascotti sat upon the merits of every contemporary performance. After the age of Clement VII. the Italians seemed to
think that there was more merit in praising or censuring well
than in writing well; almost every subsequent performance
being designed rather to show the excellence of the critic's
taste than his genius.[2] One or two poets, indeed, seem at
present born to redeem the honor of their country. Metastasio has restored nature in all her simplicity,[3] and Maffei is
the first that has introduced a tragedy among his countrymen without a love-plot. Perhaps the Samson of Milton and
the Athalia of Racine might have been his guides in such an
attempt.[4] But two poets in an age are not sufficient to revive

---

[1] "Be it his greatest merit, therefore, to," etc.—*First Edition*.

[2] Here the first edition adds, commencing a new paragraph: "But, while I describe Italy as then fallen from her former excellence, I cannot restrain the pleasure of mentioning one or two poets who seem born to redeem," etc.

[3] Here the first edition adds: "No poet ever painted more conformably to truth,
nor is there any whose characters speak a more heartfelt passion. His language,
also, if a foreigner may be allowed to determine, excels even that of Tasso; the
scenery is infinitely superior. Maffei," etc.

[4] Here the first edition adds: "Yet he seems as much inferior to either as a

the splendor of decaying genius; nor should we consider them as the standard by which to characterize a nation. Our measures of literary reputation must be taken rather from that numerous class of men who, placed above the vulgar, are yet beneath the great, and who confer fame on others without receiving any portion of it themselves.

In Italy, then, we shall nowhere find a stronger passion for the arts of taste, yet no country making more feeble efforts to promote either. The Virtuosi and Filosofi seem to have divided the Encyclopædia between each other, both inviolably attached to their respective pursuits; and from an opposition of character, each holding the other in the most sovereign contempt. The Virtuosi, professed critics of beauty in the works of art, judge of medals by the smell, and pictures by feeling: in statuary, hang over a fragment with the most ardent gaze of admiration; though wanting the head and the other extremities, if dug from a ruin, the Torso becomes inestimable. An unintelligible monument of Etruscan barbarity cannot be sufficiently prized; and anything from Herculaneum excites rapture. When the intellectual taste is thus decayed, its relishes become false, and, like that of sense, nothing will satisfy but what is best suited to feed[1] the disease.

Poetry is no longer among them an imitation of what we see, but of what a visionary might wish. The zephyr breathes the most exquisite perfume, the trees wear eternal verdure; fauns, and dryads, and hamadryads, stand ready to fan the sultry shepherdess, who has forgot, indeed, the prettinesses with which Guarini's[2] shepherdesses have been reproached, but is so simple and innocent as often to have no meaning. Happy country, where the pastoral age begins to revive! where the wits even of Rome are united into a rural group of nymphs and swains, under the appellation of modern Arcadians! where, in the midst of porticos, processions, and caval-

---

poet, as the subject of his Merope is more happily chosen. Two poets, however, in an age," etc.

[1] "To palliate or feed."—*First Edition.*

[2] "Former Italian."—*First Edition.*

cades, abbés turn shepherds, and shepherdesses, without sheep, indulge their innocent *divertimenti!*[1]

The Filosofi are entirely different from the former. As those pretend to have got their knowledge from conversing with the living and polite, so these boast of having theirs from books and study. Bred up all their lives in colleges, they have there learned to think in track, servilely to follow the leader of their sect, and only to adopt such opinions as their universities or the inquisition are pleased to allow. By these means they are behind the rest of Europe in several modern improvements; afraid to think for themselves; and their universities seldom admit opinions as true till universally received among the rest of mankind. In short, were I to personize my ideas of learning in this country, I would represent it in the tawdry habits of the stage, or else in the more homely guise of bearded school philosophy.

CHAPTER V.

ON POLITE LEARNING IN GERMANY.

IF we examine the state of learning in Germany, we shall find that the Germans early discovered a passion for polite literature; but unhappily, like conquerors, who invading the dominions of others, leave their own to desolation, instead of studying the German tongue, they continue to write in Latin. Thus, while they cultivated an obsolete language, and vainly labored to apply it to modern manners, they neglected their own.

---

[1] Here the first edition adds: "Perhaps, while I am writing, a shepherdess of threescore is listening to the pastoral tale of a French abbé; a warm imagination might paint her in all the splendor of ripened beauty, reclining on a pasteboard rock; might fancy her lover, with looks inexpressibly tender, ravishing a kiss from the snowy softness of one of her hands, while the other holds a crook according to pastoral decorum. Amid such frippery as this, there was no place for friendless Metastasio; he has left Italy, and the genius of nature seems to have left it with him."

At the same time, also, they began at the wrong end, I mean by being commentators; and though they have given many instances of their industry, they have scarcely afforded any of genius. If criticism could have improved the taste of a people, the Germans would have been the most polite nation alive. We shall nowhere behold the learned wear a more important appearance than here; nowhere more dignified with professorships, or dressed out in the fopperies of scholastic finery. However, they seem to earn all the honors of this kind which they enjoy. Their assiduity is unparalleled; and did they[1] employ half those hours on study which they bestow on reading, we might be induced to pity as well as praise their painful pre-eminence. But, guilty of a fault too common to great readers, they write through volumes, while they do not think through a page. Never fatigued themselves, they think the reader can never be weary ; so they drone on, saying all that can be said on the subject, not selecting what may be advanced to the purpose. Were angels to write books, they never would write folios.

But let the Germans have their due ; if they are dull, no nation alive assumes a more laudable solemnity, or better understands all the decorums of stupidity. Let the discourse of a professor run on never so heavily, it cannot be irksome to his dozing pupils, who frequently lend him sympathetic nods of approbation. I have sometimes attended their disputes at gradation. On this occasion they often dispense with their gravity, and seem really all alive. The disputes are managed between the followers of Cartesius, whose exploded system they continue to call the new philosophy, and those of Aristotle. Though both parties are in the wrong, they argue with an obstinacy worthy the cause of truth ; Nego, Probo, and Distinguo grow loud ; the disputants become warm, the moderator cannot be heard, the audience take part in the debate, till at last the whole hall buzzes with sophistry and error.[2]

There are, it is true, several societies in this country which

---

[1] "The learned of this country."—*First Edition.*
[2] "Erroneous philosophy."—*First Edition.*

are chiefly calculated to promote knowledge.[1] His late majesty, as Elector of Hanover,[2] has established one at Gottingen, at an expense of not less than a hundred thousand pounds. This university has already pickled monsters and dissected live puppies without number. Their transactions have been published in the learned world at proper intervals since their institution; and will, it is hoped, one day give them just reputation. But had the fourth part of the immense sum above mentioned been given in proper rewards to genius, in some neighboring countries, it would have rendered the name of the donor immortal, and added to the real interests of society.[3]

Yet it ought to be observed that, of late, learning has been patronized here by a prince, who, in the humblest station, would have been the first of mankind. The society established by the King of Prussia, at Berlin, is one of the finest literary institutions that any age or nation has produced. This academy comprehends all the sciences under four different classes; and although the object of each is different, and admits of being separately treated, yet these classes mutually influence the progress of each other, and concur in the same general design. Experimental philosophy, mathematics, metaphysics, and polite literature are here carried on together.[4] The members are not collected from among the students of some obscure seminary, or the wits of a metropolis, but chosen from all the literati of Europe, supported by the bounty, and ornamented by the productions of their royal founder. We can easily discern how much such an institution excels any other now subsisting. One fundamental error among societies of this kind is their addicting themselves to one branch of science, or some particular part of polite learning. Thus,

---

[1] "Natural knowledge."—*First Edition.*

[2] "The Elector of Hanover."—*First Edition.*

[3] "But let me cease from censure, since I have here so fine an opportunity of praise. Even in the midst of Germany, true learning has found an asylum, and taste and genius have been patronized by a prince, who," etc.—*First Edition.*

[4] "And mutually illustrate and strengthen and adorn each other."—*First Edition.*

in Germany, there are nowhere so many establishments of this nature; but as they generally profess the promotion of natural or medical knowledge, he who reads their Acta will only find an obscure farrago of experiment, most frequently terminated by no resulting phenomena. To make experiments is, I own, the only way to promote natural knowledge; but to treasure up every unsuccessful inquiry into nature, or to communicate every experiment without conclusion, is not to promote science, but oppress it.[1] Had the members of these societies enlarged their plans, and taken in art as well as science, one part of knowledge would have repressed any faulty luxuriance in the other, and all would have mutually assisted each other's promotion. Besides, the society which, with a contempt of all collateral assistance, admits of members skilled in one science only, whatever their diligence or labor may be, will lose much time in the discovery of such truths as are well known already to the learned in a different line; consequently, their progress must be slow in gaining a proper eminence from which to view their subject, and their strength will be exhausted in attaining the station whence they should have set out. With regard to the Royal Society of London, the greatest, and perhaps the oldest institution of the kind, had it widened the basis of its institution, though they might not have propagated more discoveries, they would probably have delivered them in a more pleasing and compendious form. They would have been free from the contempt of the ill-natured and the raillery of the wit, for which even candor must allow there is but too much foundation. The Berlin academy is subject to none of all these inconveniences, but every one of its individuals is in a capacity of deriving more from the common stock than he contributes to it, while each academician serves as a check upon the rest of his fellows.

Yet, very probably, even this fine institution will soon decay. As it rose, so it will decline with its great encourager.

---

[1] "But confuse it. Not to lift learning from obscurity, but with additional weight to oppress it."—*First Edition.*

The society, if I may so speak, is artificially supported. The introduction of foreigners of learning was right; but in adopting a foreign language also, I mean the French, in which all the transactions are to be published and questions debated, in this there was an error. As I have already hinted, the language of the natives of every country should be also the language of its polite learning.[1] To figure in polite learning, every country should make their own language from their own manners; nor will they ever succeed by introducing that of another which has been formed from manners which are different. Besides, an academy composed of foreigners must still be recruited from abroad, unless all the natives of the country to which it belongs are in a capacity of becoming candidates for its honors or rewards. While France, therefore, continues to supply Berlin, polite learning will flourish; but when royal favor is withdrawn, learning will return to its natural country.

CHAPTER VI.[2]

OF POLITE LEARNING IN HOLLAND, AND SOME OTHER COUNTRIES OF EUROPE.

HOLLAND, at first view, appears to have some pretensions to polite learning. It may be regarded as the great emporium, not less of literature than of every other commodity. Here, though destitute of what may be properly called a language of their own, all the languages are understood, cultivated, and spoken. All useful inventions in arts, and new discoveries in science, are published here almost as soon as at the places which first produced them. Its individuals have the same faults, however, with the Germans, of making more use of

---

[1] "I may be supposed to carry the thought too far when I say that to figure," etc.—*First Edition.*

[2] This, in the first edition, was part of Chapter IV.

their memory than their judgment. The chief employment of their literati is to criticise, or answer, the new performances which appear elsewhere.

A dearth of wit in France or England naturally produces a scarcity in Holland. What Ovid says of Echo, may be applied here,

—" nec reticere loquenti,
Nec prior ipsa loqui didicit "—

they wait till something new comes out from others; examine its merits, and reject it, or make it reverberate through the rest of Europe.

After all, I know not whether they should be allowed any national character for polite learning. All their taste is derived to them from neighboring nations, and that in a language not their own. They somewhat resemble their brokers, who trade for immense sums without having any capital.

The other countries of Europe may be considered as immersed in ignorance, or making but feeble efforts to rise. Spain has long fallen from amazing Europe with her wit, to amusing them with the greatness of her catholic credulity. Rome considers her as the most favorite of all her children, and school divinity still reigns there in triumph. In spite of all attempts of the Marquis d'Ensenada, who saw with regret the barbarity of his countrymen, and bravely offered to oppose it by introducing new systems of learning, and suppressing the seminaries of monastic ignorance; in spite of the ingenuity of Padré Feyjoo,[1] whose book of vulgar errors so finely exposes the monkish stupidity of the times—the religious have prevailed. Ensenada has been banished, and now lives in exile.[2] Feyjoo has incurred the hatred and contempt of every bigot whose errors he has attempted to oppose, and feels no doubt the unremitting displeasure of the priesthood.

---

[1] Father Feyjoo (called the Spanish Addison) published his speculations in the form of popular essays. He died in 1765. An edition of his works, in 33 vols. 8vo, was published at Madrid in 1780. See Vol. III. p. 56.

[2] The Marquis d'Ensenada was permitted to return to Spain a few months previous to his death, which took place at Madrid in 1762.

Persecution is a tribute the great must ever pay for pre-eminence.

It is a little extraordinary, however, how Spain, whose genius is naturally fine, should be so much behind the rest of Europe in this particular; or why school divinity should hold its ground there for nearly six hundred years. The reason must be, that philosophical opinions, which are otherwise transient, acquire stability in proportion as they are connected with the laws of the country; and philosophy and law have nowhere been so closely united as here.

Sweden has of late made some attempts in polite learning in its own language. Count Tessin's instructions to the prince, his pupil, are no bad beginning.[1] If the Muses can fix their residence so far northward, perhaps no country bids so fair for their reception. They have, I am told, a language rude but energetic; if so, it will bear a polish. They have also a jealous sense of liberty, and that strength of thinking peculiar to northern climates, without its attendant ferocity. They will certainly in time produce somewhat great, if their intestine divisions do not unhappily prevent them.

The history of polite learning in Denmark may be comprised in the life of one single man; it rose and fell with the late famous Baron Holberg.[2] This was, perhaps, one of the most extraordinary personages that has done honor to the present century. His being the son of a private sentinel did not abate the ardor of his ambition, for he learned to read, though without a master. Upon the death of his father, being left entirely destitute, he was involved in all that distress which is common among the poor, and of which the great have scarcely any idea. However, though only a boy of nine years old, he still persisted in pursuing his studies, travelled about from school to school, and begged his learning and his bread. When at the age of seventeen, instead of applying himself to any of the lower occupations, which seem

---

[1] Count Tessin was born at Stockholm in 1695, and died in Sudermania in 1770. A translation into English of his "Letters to a Young Prince from his Governor," appeared in 1759, in 3 vols. 12mo.

[2] Baron Holberg died in 1754, while Goldsmith was at Leyden.

best adapted to such circumstances, he was resolved to travel for improvement from Norway, the place of his birth, to Copenhagen, the capital city of Denmark. He lived there by teaching French, at the same time avoiding no opportunity of improvement that his scanty funds could permit. But his ambition was not to be restrained, or his thirst of knowledge satisfied, until he had seen the world. Without money, recommendations, or friends, he undertook to set out upon his travels, and make the tour of Europe on foot. A good voice, and a trifling skill in music, were the only finances he had to support an undertaking so extensive; so he travelled by day, and at night sung at the doors of peasants' houses to get himself a lodging. In this manner, while yet very young, Holberg passed through France, Germany, and Holland; and coming over to England, took up his residence for two years in the University of Oxford. Here he subsisted by teaching French and music, and wrote his " Universal History," his earliest but worst performance. Furnished with all the learning of Europe, he at last thought proper to return to Copenhagen, where his ingenious productions quickly gained him that favor he deserved. He composed not less than eighteen comedies. Those in his own language are said to excel, and those which are translated into French have peculiar merit. He was honored with nobility, and enriched by the bounty of the king; so that a life begun in contempt and penury ended in opulence and esteem.

Thus we see in what a low state polite learning is in the countries I have mentioned; either past its prime, or not yet arrived at maturity. And though the sketch I have drawn be general, yet it was for the most part taken on the spot. I am sensible, however, of the impropriety of national reflection; and did not truth bias me more than inclination in this particular, I should, instead of the account already given, have presented the reader with a panegyric on many of the individuals of every country, whose merits deserve the warmest strains of praise. Apostol Zeno, Algarotti, Goldoni, Muratori, and Stay, in Italy; Haller, Klopstock, and Rabner, in Germany; Muschenbrook and Gaubius, in Holland—all deserve the highest applause.[1] Men like these, united by one bond, pursuing one design, spend their labor and their lives in making their fellow-creatures happy, and in repairing the breaches caused by ambition. In this light, the meanest philosopher, though all his possessions are his lamp or his cell, is more truly valuable than he whose name echoes to the shout of the million, and who stands in all the glare of admiration. In this light, though poverty and contemptuous neglect are all the wages of his good-will from mankind, yet the rectitude of his intention is an ample recompense; and self-applause for the present, and the alluring prospect of fame for futurity, reward his labors. The perspective of life brightens upon us when terminated by an object so charming. Every intermediate image of want, banishment, or sorrow receives a lustre from its distant influence. With this in view, the patriot, philosopher, and poet have often looked with calmness on disgrace and famine, and rested on their straw with cheerful serenity. Even the last terrors of departing nature abate of their severity, and look kindly on him who considers his sufferings as a passport to immortality, and lays his sorrows on the bed of fame.

CHAPTER VII.[2]

OF POLITE LEARNING IN FRANCE.

WE have hitherto seen that, wherever the poet was permitted to begin by improving his native language, polite learn-

---

[1] "But it was my design rather to give an idea of the spirit of learning in those countries, than a dry catalogue of authors' names and writings. But let me cease a moment from considering this worthy, however erroneous, part of mankind, on that side alone in which they are exposed to censure, and survey them as the friends of man; while the great and the avaricious of this world are contriving means to aggravate national hatred—and, perhaps, fonder of satisfying vanity than justice, are willing to make the world uneasy, because themselves are so—these harmless instruments of peace united by one bond," etc.—*First Edition.*

[2] This was originally Chapter VIII. Chapter VII. of the first edition was omitted by Goldsmith, and is in this edition printed in an Appendix. *See p. 79.*

ing flourished; but where the critic undertook the same task, it has never risen to any degree of perfection. Let us now examine the merits of modern learning in France and England; where, though it may be on the decline, yet it is still capable of retrieving much of its former splendor. In other places learning has not yet been planted, or has suffered a total decay. To attempt amendment there would be only like the application of remedies to an insensible or a mortified part; but here there is still life, and there is hope. And, indeed, the French themselves are so far from giving in to any despondence of this kind, that, on the contrary, they admire the progress they are daily making in every science.[1] That levity for which we are apt to despise this nation is probably the principal source of their happiness. An agreeable oblivion of past pleasures, a freedom from solicitude about future ones, and a poignant zest of every present enjoyment, if they be not philosophy, are at least excellent substitutes. By this they are taught to regard the period in which they live with admiration. The present manners and the present conversation surpass all that preceded.[2] A similar enthusiasm as strongly tinctures their learning and their taste. While we, with a despondence characteristic of our nature, are for removing back British excellence to the reign of Queen Elizabeth, our more happy rivals of the Continent cry up the writers of the present times with rapture, and regard the age of Louis XV. as the true Augustan age of France.

The truth is, their present writers have not fallen so far short of the merits of their ancestors as ours have done. That self-sufficiency now mentioned may have been of service to them in this particular. By fancying themselves superior to their ancestors, they have been encouraged to enter the lists with confidence; and by not being dazzled at the splendor of another's reputation, have sometimes had sagacity to mark out an unbeaten path to fame for themselves.

---

[1] The passages preceding *figure* 1 are not in the first edition.

[2] Here the first edition adds: "A Frenchman is as little displeased with everything about him as with his own person or existence. This agreeable enthusiasm tinctures not only their manners, but their learning and taste."

Other causes also may be assigned, that their second growth of genius is still more vigorous than ours. Their encouragements to merit are more skilfully directed; the link of patronage and learning still continues unbroken. The French nobility have certainly a most pleasing way of satisfying the vanity of an author, without indulging his avarice. A man of literary merit is sure of being caressed by the great, though seldom enriched. His pension from the crown just supplies half a competence, and the sale of his labors make some small addition to his circumstances. Thus the author leads a life of splendid poverty, and seldom becomes wealthy or indolent enough to discontinue an exertion of those abilities by which he rose. With the English it is different. Our writers of rising merit are generally neglected, while the few of an established reputation are overpaid by luxurious affluence. The young encounter every hardship which generally attends upon aspiring indigence; the old enjoy the vulgar, and perhaps the more prudent satisfaction, of putting riches in competition with fame. Those are often seen to spend their youth in want and obscurity; these are sometimes found to lead an old age of indolence and avarice. But such treatment must naturally be expected from Englishmen, whose national character it is to be slow and cautious in making friends, but violent in friendships once contracted. The English nobility, in short, are often known to give greater rewards to genius than the French, who, however, are much more judicious in the application of their empty favors.

The fair sex in France have also not a little contributed to prevent the decline of taste and literature, by expecting such qualifications in their admirers. A man of fashion at Paris, however contemptible we may think him here, must be acquainted with the reigning modes of philosophy as well as of dress, to be able to entertain his mistress agreeably. The sprightly pedants are not to be caught by dumb show,[1] by the squeeze of the hand, or the ogling of a broad eye; but

---

[1] "The charming pedants are not to be caught, like some damsels to be seen in Holland, by dumb show."—*First Edition.*

must be pursued at once, through all the labyrinths of the Newtonian system, or the metaphysics of Locke.[1] I have seen as bright a circle of beauty at the chemical lectures of Rouelle,[2] as gracing the court of Versailles. And, indeed, wisdom never appears so charming as when graced and protected by beauty.

To these advantages may be added the reception of their language in the different courts of Europe. An author who excels is sure of having all the polite for admirers, and is encouraged to write by the pleasing expectation of universal fame. Add to this that those countries who can make nothing good from their own language have lately begun to write in this, some of whose productions contribute to support the present literary reputation of France.[3]

There are, therefore, many among the French who do honor to the present age, and whose writings will be transmitted to posterity with an ample share of fame. Some of the most celebrated are as follow :

Voltaire, whose voluminous yet spirited productions are too well known to require a eulogy. Does he not resemble the champion mentioned by Xenophon, of great reputation in all the gymnastic exercises united, but inferior to each champion singly, who excels only in one ?

Montesquieu, a name equally deserving fame with the former. The " Spirit of Laws " is an instance how much genius is able to lead learning. His system has been adopted by the literati ; and yet, is it not possible for opinions equally plausible to be formed upon opposite principles, if a genius like his could be found to attempt such an undertaking ? He seems more a poet than a philosopher.

Rousseau, of Geneva, a professed man-hater, or more proper-

---

[1] " And still more the variations of female inclination."—*First Edition.*

[2] " An eminent chemist, born in 1703, at Matthieu, near Caen, in Normandy ; died at Paris in 1770.

[3] Here, in the first edition, this paragraph occurs : " The age of Louis XIV., notwithstanding these advantages, is still superior. It is, indeed, a misfortune for a fine writer to be born in a period so enlightened as ours. The harvest of wit is gathered in, and little is left for him, except to glean what others have thought unworthy their bringing away. Yet there are still some among the French," etc.

ly speaking, a philosopher enraged with one-half of mankind, because they unavoidably make the other half unhappy. Such sentiments are generally the result of much good-nature and little experience.

Piron, an author possessed of as much wit as any man alive, yet with as little prudence to turn it to his own advantage. A comedy of his, called "La Métromanie," is the best theatrical production that has appeared of late in Europe. But I know not whether I should most commend his genius, or censure his obscenity. His "Ode à Priape" has justly excluded him from a place in the Academy of Belles-lettres. However, the good-natured Montesquieu, by his interest, procured the starving bard a trifling pension. His own epitaph was all the revenge he took upon the Academy for being repulsed.

> "Cy-git Piron, qui ne fut jamais rien :
> Pas même Academicien."

Crébillon, junior, a writer of real merit, but guilty of the same indelicate faults with the former. Wit employed in dressing up obscenity is like the art used in painting a corpse; it may be thus rendered tolerable to one sense, but fails not quickly to offend some other.

Gresset, agreeable and easy. His comedy called the "Méchant," and a humorous poem entitled "Ver-vert," have original merit.[1] He was bred a Jesuit; but his wit procured his dismission from the society. This last work particularly could expect no pardon from the convent, being a satire against nunneries.

D'Alembert has united an extensive skill in scientifical

---

[1] "'Le Méchant,' of Gresset, is one of the most elegant productions of the comic muse, and presents an ingenious satire upon Parisian manners as they existed previously to the Revolution. The poetry is excellent, and there is no play of which so many lines have become proverbial, except, perhaps, 'La Métromanie.'"—*Quart. Rev.* vol. xii. p. 131.

"I must again and again repeat that it is on account of the exquisite skill and humor and pleasantry of the use made of the machinery of the sylphs, that Pope's 'Rape of the Lock' has exceeded all the heroi-comic poems in all languages. The 'Ver-vert' of Gresset, in point of delicate satire, is perhaps next to it."—JOSEPH WARTON.

learning with the most refined taste for the polite arts. His excellence in both has procured him a seat in each Academy.

Diderot is an elegant writer and subtile reasoner. He is the supposed author of the famous Thesis which the Abbé Prade sustained before the doctors of the Sorbonne. It was levelled against Christianity, and the Sorbonne too hastily gave it their sanction. They perceived its purport, however, when it was too late. The college was brought into some contempt, and the abbé obliged to take refuge at the court of Berlin.

The Marquis d'Argens attempts to add the character of a philosopher to the vices of a debauchee.

The catalogue might be increased with several other authors of merit, such as Marivaux, Le Franc, Saint Foix, Destouches, and Modonville; but let it suffice to say that by these the character of the present age is tolerably supported. Though their poets seldom rise to fine enthusiasm, they never sink into absurdity; though they fail to astonish, they are generally possessed of talents to please.

The age of Louis XIV., notwithstanding these respectable names, is still vastly superior. For, beside the general tendency of critical corruption, which shall be spoken of by-and-by, there are other symptoms which indicate a decline.[1] There is, for instance, a fondness of scepticism which runs through the works of some of their most applauded writers, and which the numerous class of their imitators have contributed to diffuse. Nothing can be a more certain sign that genius is in the wane, than its being obliged to fly to paradox for support, and attempting to be erroneously agreeable. A man who, with all the impotence of wit and all the eager desires of infidelity, writes against the religion of his country, may raise doubts, but will never give conviction; all he can do is to render society less happy than he found it. It was a good manner which the father of the late poet Saint Foix took to reclaim his son from this juvenile error. The young

---

[1] The preceding passage stands thus in the first edition: " But although taste is still cultivated there with assiduity, I must not conceal those symptoms which seem manifestly tending to promote its decline. There is," etc.

poet had shut himself up for some time in his study; and his
father, willing to know what had engaged his attention so
closely, upon entering found him busied in drawing up a new
system of religion, and endeavoring to show the absurdity of
that already established. The old man knew by experience
that it was useless to endeavor to convince a vain young man
by right reason, so only desired his company up-stairs. When
come into the father's apartment, he takes his son by the
hand, and drawing back a curtain at one end of the room,
discovered a crucifix exquisitely painted. "My son," says he,
"you desire to change the religion of your country—behold
the fate of a reformer."[1] The truth is, vanity is more apt
to misguide men than false reasoning. As some would rather be conspicuous in a mob than unnoticed even in a privy
council, so others choose rather to be foremost in the retinue
of error than follow in the train of truth.[2] What influence
the conduct of such writers may have on the morals of a people, is not my business here to determine. Certain I am, that
it has a manifest tendency to subvert the literary merits of
the country in view. The change of religion in every nation
has hitherto produced barbarism and ignorance; and such
will be probably its consequences in every future period.
For when the laws and opinions of society are made to clash,
harmony is dissolved, and all the parts of peace unavoidably
crushed in the encounter.

The writers of this country have also of late fallen into a
method of considering every part of art and science as arising
from simple principles. The success of Montesquieu, and one
or two more, has induced all the subordinate ranks of genius
into vicious imitation. To this end they turn to our view
that side of the subject which contributes to support their
hypothesis, while the objections are generally passed over in
silence. Thus a universal system rises from a partial representation of the question; a whole is concluded from a part;
a book appears entirely new, and the fancy-built fabric is

---

[1] "Of an innovator."—*First Edition.*

[2] The first edition adds: "And prefer the applause of great stupidity to that approbation which virtue ever pays itself."

styled for a short time very ingenious. In this manner we
have seen of late almost every subject in morals, natural history, politics, economy, and commerce treated. Subjects naturally proceeding on many principles, and some even opposite
to each other, are all taught to proceed along the line of sys-
tematic simplicity, and continue, like other agreeable falsehoods, extremely pleasing till they are detected.

I must still add another fault, of a nature somewhat similar
to the former. As those above mentioned are for contract-
ing a single science into system, so those I am going to speak
of are for drawing up a system of all the sciences united.
Such undertakings as these are carried on by different writers,
cemented into one body, and concurring in the same design
by the mediation of a bookseller. From these inauspicious
combinations proceed those monsters of learning, the Trevoux,
Encyclopédies, and Bibliothèques of the age. In making
these, men of every rank in literature are employed, wits and
dunces contribute their share, and Diderot, as well as Des-
maretz, are candidates for oblivion. The genius of the first
supplies the gale of favor, and the latter adds the useful bal-
last of stupidity. By such means the enormous mass heavily
makes its way among the public, and, to borrow a bookseller's
phrase, "the whole impression moves off." These great collections of learning may serve to make us inwardly repine
at our own ignorance; may serve, when gilt and lettered, to
adorn the lower shelves of a regular library; but woe to the
reader who, not daunted at the immense distance between one
great pasteboard and the other, opens the volume, and ex-
plores his way through a region so extensive, but barren of
entertainment! No unexpected landscape there to delight
the imagination! no diversity of prospect to cheat the painful journey! He sees the wide-extended desert lie before
him; what is past only increases his terror of what is to come.
His course is not half finished: he looks behind him with affright, and forward with despair. Perseverance is at last
overcome, and a night of oblivion lends its friendly aid to
terminate the perplexity.

CHAPTER VIII.

OF LEARNING IN GREAT BRITAIN.

To acquire a character for learning among the English at present it is necessary to know much more than is either important or useful.[1] It seems the spirit of the times for men here to exhaust their natural sagacity in exploring the intricacies of another man's thought, and thus never to have leisure to think for themselves. Others have carried on learning from that stage where the good-sense of our ancestors have thought it too minute or too speculative to instruct or amuse. By the industry of such, the sciences, which in themselves are easy of access, affright the learner with the severity of their appearance. He sees them surrounded with speculation and subtlety, placed there by their professors as if with a view of deterring his approach. Hence it happens that the generality of readers fly from the scholar to the compiler, who offers them a more safe and speedy conveyance.

From this fault also arises that mutual contempt between the scholar and the man of the world, of which every day's experience furnisheth instances.

The man of taste, however, stands neutral in this controversy. He seems placed in a middle station, between the world and the cell, between learning and common-sense. He teaches the vulgar on what part of a character to lay the emphasis of praise, and the scholar where to point his application so as to deserve it. By his means even the philosopher acquires popular applause, and all that are truly great the admiration of posterity. By means of polite learning alone, the patriot and the hero, the man who praiseth virtue and he who practises it, who fights successfully for his country, or

---

[1] The first edition adds: "The absurd passion of being deemed profound has done more injury to all kinds of science than is generally imagined. Some thus exhaust," etc.

who dies in its defence, becomes immortal.[1] But this taste now seems cultivated with less ardor than formerly, and consequently the public must one day expect to see the advantages arising from it, and the exquisite pleasures it affords our leisure, entirely annihilated. For if, as it should seem, the rewards of genius are improperly directed; if those who are capable of supporting the honor of the times by their writings prefer opulence to fame; if the stage should be shut to writers of merit, and open only to interest or intrigue; if such should happen to be the vile complexion of the times (and that it is nearly so we shall shortly see), the very virtue of the age will be forgotten by posterity, and nothing remembered except our filling a chasm in the registers of time, or having served to continue the species.

CHAPTER IX.

OF REWARDING GENIUS IN ENGLAND.

THERE is nothing authors are more apt to lament than want of encouragement from the age. Whatever their differences in other respects, they are all ready to unite in this complaint, and each indirectly offers himself as an instance of the truth of his assertion.

The beneficed divine, whose wants are only imaginary, expostulates as bitterly as the poorest author.[2] Should interest or good-fortune advance the divine to a bishopric, or the poor son of Parnassus into that place which the other has resigned, both are authors no longer; the one goes to prayers once a

---

[1] Here the first edition adds, commencing a new paragraph : " Let none affect to despise future fame; the actions of even the lowest part of mankind testify a desire of this kind. Wealth, titles, and several paltry advantages are secured for posterity, who can only give their applause in return. If all ranks, therefore, are inspired with this passion, how great should his encouragement be who is capable of conferring it not only upon the most deserving, but even upon the age in which he lives. Yet the honest ambition of being admired by posterity cannot be gratified without continual efforts in the present age to deserve it," etc.

[2] " That ever snuffed his candle with finger and thumb."—*First Edition.*

day, kneels upon cushions of velvet, and thanks gracious Heaven for having made the circumstances of all mankind so extremely happy; the other battens on all the delicacies of life, enjoys his wife and his easy-chair, and sometimes, for the sake of conversation, deplores the luxury of these degenerate days.

All encouragements to merit are, therefore, misapplied which make the author too rich to continue his profession. There can be nothing more just than the old observation, that authors, like running horses, should be fed, but not fattened. If we would continue them in our service, we should reward them with a little money and a great deal of praise, still keeping their avarice subservient to their ambition. Not that I think a writer incapable of filling an employment with dignity; I would only insinuate that, when made a bishop or statesman, he will continue to please us as a writer no longer; as, to resume a former allusion, the running horse, when fattened, will still be fit for very useful purposes, though unqualified for a courser.

No nation gives greater encouragements to learning than we do; yet, at the same time, none are so injudicious in the application. We seem to confer them with the same view that statesmen have been known to grant employments at court, rather as bribes to silence than incentives to emulation. Upon this principle, all our magnificent endowments of colleges are erroneous; and at best, more frequently enrich the prudent than reward the ingenious. A lad whose passions are not strong enough in youth to mislead him from that path of science which his tutors, and not his inclinations, have chalked out, by four or five years' perseverance may probably obtain every advantage and honor his college can bestow. I forget whether the simile has been used before, but I would compare the man whose youth has been thus passed in the tranquillity of dispassionate prudence, to liquors which never ferment, and consequently continue always muddy.[1] Pas-

---

[1] "His career might have been compared to that fermentation in liquors, which grow muddy before they brighten; but it must also be confessed that those liquors which never ferment are seldom clear."—GOLDSMITH, *Life of Bolingbroke*.

sions may raise a commotion in the youthful breast, but they disturb only to refine it. However this be, mean talents are often rewarded in colleges with an easy subsistence. The candidates or preferments of this kind often regard their admission as a patent for future indolence;[1] so that a life begun in studious labor is often continued in luxurious indolence.[2]

Among the universities abroad, I have ever observed their riches and their learning in a reciprocal proportion, their stupidity and pride increasing with their opulence. Happening once, in conversation with Gaubius of Leyden, to mention the college of Edinburgh, he began by complaining that all the English students which formerly came to his university now went entirely there; and the fact surprised him more, as Leyden was now as well as ever furnished with masters excellent in their respective professions. He concluded by asking if the professors of Edinburgh were rich? I replied that the salary of a professor there seldom amounted to more than thirty pounds a year. "Poor men," says he, "I heartily wish they were better provided for; until they become rich, we can have no expectation of English students at Leyden."

Premiums also proposed for literary excellence, when given as encouragements to boys, may be useful; but when designed as rewards to men, are certainly misapplied. We have seldom seen a performance of any great merit in consequence of rewards proposed in this manner. Who has ever observed a writer of any eminence a candidate in so precarious a contest? The man who knows the real value of his own genius will no more venture it upon an uncertainty, than he who knows the true use of a guinea will stake it with a sharper.[3]

Every encouragement given to stupidity, when known to be such, is also a negative insult upon genius. This appears in nothing more evident than the undistinguished success of those who solicit subscriptions. When first brought into fashion, subscriptions were conferred upon the ingenious alone, or

---

[1] "Laziness."—*First Edition.* [2] "Affluence."—*First Edition.*
[3] The first edition adds: "By throwing a main."

II.—4

those who were reputed such. But at present we see them made a resource of indigence, and requested not as rewards of merit, but as a relief of distress. If tradesmen happen to want skill in conducting their own business, yet they are able to write a book: if mechanics want money, or ladies shame, they write books and solicit subscriptions. Scarcely a morning passes that proposals of this nature are not thrust into the half-opening doors of the rich, with perhaps a paltry petition, showing the author's wants, but not his merits. I would not. willingly prevent that pity which is due to indigence; but while the streams of liberality are thus diffused, they must, in the end, become proportionably shallow.

What, then, are the proper encouragements of genius? I answer, subsistence and respect; for these are rewards congenial to its nature. Every animal has an aliment peculiarly suited to its constitution. The heavy ox seeks nourishment from earth; the light chameleon has been supposed to exist on air; a sparer diet even than this will satisfy the man of true genius, for he makes a luxurious banquet upon empty applause. It is this alone which has inspired all that ever was truly great and noble among us. It is, as Cicero finely calls it, the echo of virtue. Avarice is the passion of inferior natures; money the pay of the common herd. The author who draws his quill merely to take a purse, no more deserves success than he who presents a pistol.[1]

---

[1] " It requires a good deal of art and temper [in an author] to write consistently against the dictates of his own heart. Thus, notwithstanding our author talks so familiarly of *us*, the great, and affects to be thought to stand in the rank of patrons, we cannot help thinking that in more places than one he has betrayed, in himself, the man he so severely condemns for drawing his quill to take a purse. We are even so firmly convinced of this, that we dare put the question home to his conscience, whether he never experienced the unhappy situation he so feelingly describes in that of a literary understrapper ? His remarking him as coming down from his garret to rummage the bookseller's shop for materials to work upon, and the knowledge he displays of his minutest labors, give great reason to suspect he may himself have had concerns in the *bad trade* of book-making. *Fronti nulla fides.* We have heard of many a writer who, 'patronized only by his bookseller,' has, nevertheless, affected the gentleman in print, and talked full as cavalierly as our author himself. We have even known one hardy enough publicly to stigmatize men of the first rank in literature for their immoralities, while conscious him-

When the link between patronage and learning was entire, then all who deserved fame were in a capacity of attaining it. When the great Somers was at the helm, patronage was fashionable among our nobility. The middle ranks of mankind, who generally imitate the great, then followed their example, and applauded from fashion, if not from feeling. I have heard an old poet[1] of that glorious age say that a dinner with his lordship has procured him invitations for the whole week following; that an airing in his patron's chariot has supplied him with a citizen's coach on every future occasion. For who would not be proud to entertain a man who kept so much good company?

But this link now seems entirely broken. Since the days of a certain prime-minister of inglorious memory,[2] the learned have been kept pretty much at a distance. A jockey, or a laced player, supplies the place of the scholar, poet, or the man of virtue. Those conversations, once the result of wisdom, wit, and innocence, are now turned to humbler topics, little more being expected from a companion than a laced coat, a pliant bow, and an immoderate friendship for—a well-served table.

---

self of laboring under the infamy of having, by the vilest and meanest actions, forfeited all pretensions to honor and honesty. If such men as these, boasting a liberal education, and pretending to genius, practise at the same time those arts which bring the sharper to the cart's tail or the pillory, need our author wonder that 'learning partakes the contempt of its professors.' If characters of this stamp are to be found among the learned, need any one be surprised that the great prefer the society of fiddlers, gamesters, and buffoons?"—*Kenrick's Notice of the Present State, etc.* (*Monthly Review for November,* 1759.)

An apology was made for this "undesigned" offence in the *Monthly Review* for June, 1762. Goldsmith had been a writer in the very *Review* in which this offensive attack upon him was permitted to appear. But he had attacked booksellers; had been indebted, and was perhaps still indebted, to Griffiths, the publisher and proprietor of the *Monthly Review;* and was, when the criticism on his "Inquiry" appeared, actually a writer for the *Critical Review.*

[1] Said to be Dr. Young, with whom Goldsmith might have had an opportunity of conversing while reader in the office of Richardson, the printer and novelist.

[2] Sir Robert Walpole. "The severity of a poet gave Walpole very little uneasiness. A man whose schemes, like this minister's, seldom extended beyond the exigency of the year, but little regarded the contempt of posterity."—GOLDSMITH, *On Poetry a Rhapsody,* by Swift.

Wit, when neglected by the great, is generally despised by the vulgar. Those who are unacquainted with the world are apt to fancy the man of wit as leading a very agreeable life. They conclude, perhaps, that he is attended to with silent admiration, and dictates to the rest of mankind with all the eloquence of conscious superiority. Very different is his present situation. He is called an author, and all know that an author is a thing only to be laughed at. His person, not his jest, becomes the mirth of the company. At his approach, the most fat, unthinking face brightens into malicious meaning. Even aldermen laugh, and revenge on him the ridicule which was lavished on their forefathers:

> "Etiam victis redit in præcordia virtus,
>   Victoresque cadunt."

It is, indeed, a reflection somewhat mortifying to the author who breaks his ranks, and singles out for public favor, to think that he must combat contempt before he can arrive at glory: that he must expect to have all the fools of society united against him before he can hope for the applause of the judicious. For this, however, he must prepare beforehand; as those who have no idea of the difficulty of his employment will be apt to regard his inactivity as idleness; and, not having a notion of the pangs of uncomplying thought in themselves, it is not to be expected they should have any desire of rewarding it in others.

Voltaire has finely described the hardships a man must encounter who writes for the public. I need make no apology for the length of the quotation:

"Your fate, my dear Le Fevre, is too strongly marked to permit your retiring. The bee must toil in making honey, the silk-worm must spin, the philosopher must dissect them, and you are born to sing of their labors. You must be a poet and a scholar, even though your inclinations should resist; nature is too strong for inclination. But hope not, my friend, to find tranquillity in the employment you are going to pursue. The route of genius is not less obstructed with disappointment than that of ambition.

" If you have the misfortune not to excel in your profession as a poet, repentance must tincture all your future enjoyments; if you succeed, you make enemies. You tread a narrow path : contempt on one side, and hatred on the other, are ready to seize you upon the slightest deviation.

" But why must I be hated ? you will perhaps reply ; why must I be persecuted for having written a pleasing poem, for having produced an applauded tragedy, or for otherwise instructing or amusing mankind or myself ?

" My dear friend, these very successes shall render you miserable for life. Let me suppose your performance has merit; let me suppose you have surmounted the teasing employments of printing and publishing; how will you be able to lull the critics, who, like Cerberus, are posted at all the avenues of literature, and who settle the merits of every new performance ? How, I say, will you be able to make them open in your favor ? There are always three or four literary journals in France, as many in Holland, each supporting opposite interests. The booksellers who guide these periodical compilations find their account in being severe ; the authors employed by them have wretchedness to add to their natural malignity. The majority may be in your favor, but you may depend on being torn by the rest. Loaded with unmerited scurrility, perhaps you reply ; they rejoin ; both plead at the bar of the public, and both are condemned to ridicule.

" But if you write for the stage, your case is still more worthy compassion. You are there to be judged by men whom the custom of the times has rendered contemptible. Irritated by their own inferiority, they exert all their little tyranny upon you, revenging upon the author the insults they receive from the public. From such men, then, you are to expect your sentence. Suppose your piece admitted, acted ; one single ill-natured jest from the pit is sufficient to cancel all your labors. But allowing that it succeeds. There are a hundred squibs flying all abroad to prove that it should not have succeeded. You shall find your brightest scenes burlesqued by the ignorant; and the learned, who know a little Greek, and nothing of their native language, affect to despise you.

" But perhaps, with a panting heart, you carry your piece before a woman of quality. She gives the labors of your brain to her maid to be cut into shreds for curling her hair ; while the laced footman, who carries the gaudy livery of luxury, insults your appearance, who bear the livery of indigence.

" But granting your excellence has at last forced envy to confess that your works have some merit ; this then is all the reward you can expect while living. However; for this tribute of applause you must expect persecution. You will be reputed the author of scandal which you have never seen, of verses you despise, and of sentiments directly contrary to your own. In short, you must embark in some one party, or all parties will be against you.

" There are among us a number of learned societies, where a lady presides, whose wit begins to twinkle when the splendor of her beauty begins to decline. One or two men of learning compose her ministers of state. These must be flattered, or made enemies by being neglected. Thus, though you had the merit of all antiquity united in your person, you grow old in misery and disgrace. Every place designed for men of letters is filled up by men of intrigue. Some nobleman's private tutor, some court flatterer, shall bear away the prize, and leave you to anguish and to disappointment."

Yet it were well if none but the dunces of society were combined to render the profession of an author ridiculous or unhappy. Men of the first eminence are often found to indulge this illiberal vein of raillery. Two contending writers often, by the opposition of their wit, render their profession contemptible in the eyes of ignorant persons, who should have been taught to admire. And yet, whatever the reader may think of himself, it is at least two to one but he is a greater blockhead than the most scribbling dunce he affects to despise.

The poet's poverty is a standing topic of contempt. His writing for bread is an unpardonable offence. Perhaps of all mankind an author in these times is used most hardly. We keep him poor, and yet revile his poverty. Like angry parents who correct their children till they cry, and then correct them for crying, we reproach him for living by his wit, and yet allow him no other means to live.

His taking refuge in garrets and cellars[1] has of late been violently objected to him, and that by men who I dare hope are more apt to pity than insult his distress.[2] Is poverty the writer's fault ?   No doubt he knows how to prefer a bottle of champagne to the nectar of the neighboring ale-house, or a venison pasty to a plate of potatoes.   Want of delicacy is not in him, but in us, who deny him the opportunity of making an elegant choice.

Wit certainly is the property of those who have it, nor should we be displeased if it is the only property a man sometimes has.   We must not underrate him who uses it for subsistence, and flies from the ingratitude of the age even to a bookseller for redress.   If the profession of an author is to be laughed at by the stupid, it is certainly better to be con- temptibly rich than contemptibly poor.   For all the wit that ever adorned the human mind will at present no more shield the author's poverty from ridicule, than his high-topped gloves conceal the unavoidable omissions of his laundress.

To be more serious, new fashions, follies, and vices make new monitors necessary in every age.   An author may be considered as a merciful substitute to the legislature.   He acts not by punishing crimes, but preventing them.   How- ever virtuous the present age, there may be still growing em- ployment for ridicule or reproof, for persuasion or satire.   If the author be, therefore, still so necessary among us, let us treat him with proper consideration as a child of the public, not a rent-charge on the community.[3]   And, indeed, a child of the public he is in all respects; for while so well able to

---

[1] The first edition adds : " And living among vermin."

[2] "The great topic of his [Pope's] ridicule is poverty; the crimes with which he reproaches his antagonists are their debts, their habitation in the Mint, and their want of a dinner."—JOHNSON's *Life of Pope.*

[3] Goldsmith had Dryden's lines to Congreve in his mind :

" Unprofitably kept at Heaven's expense,
   I live a rent-charge on his providence."

direct others, how incapable is he frequently found of guiding
himself! His simplicity exposes him to all the insidious approaches of cunning; his sensibility, to the slightest invasions
of contempt. Though possessed of fortitude to stand unmoved the expected bursts of an earthquake, yet of feelings
so exquisitely poignant as to agonize under the slightest disappointment. Broken rest, tasteless meals, and causeless anxiety shorten his life, or render it unfit for active employment;
prolonged vigils and intense application still further contract
his span, and make his time glide insensibly away. Let us
not, then, aggravate those natural inconveniences by neglect;
we have had sufficient instances of this kind already. Sale
and Moore[1] will suffice for one age at least.[2] But they are
dead, and their sorrows are over. The neglected author of
the "Persian Eclogues,"[3] which, however inaccurate, excel
any in our language, is still alive: happy, if *insensible* of our
neglect, not *raging* at our ingratitude! It is enough that the
age has already produced instances of men pressing foremost
in the lists of fame, and worthy of better times; schooled by
continued adversity into a hatred of their kind, flying from
thought to drunkenness, yielding to the united pressure of
labor, penury, and sorrow, sinking unheeded, without one
friend to drop a tear on their unattended obsequies, and indebted to charity for a grave.[4]

The author, when unpatronized by the great, has naturally

---

[1] "Sale, *Savage, Amhurst*, Moore."—*First Edition.*   George Sale, the translator
of the "Koran," and one of the authors of the "Universal History" and the "General Dictionary," died 1736.   Edward Moore, author of "Fables for the Female
Sex," and projector of the periodical work entitled *The World.*   He died in 1757,
while the last number, in which he details the imaginary death of the author, was
passing through the press.   Richard Savage, the poet, died in 1743, and was buried
at the expense of the keeper of the jail in which he died.   Nicholas Amhurst, the
editor of *The Craftsman*, died in 1742, wholly neglected by the party he had
served, and was buried at the expense of his printer.   Their names (Sale excepted)
occur again in *The Bee*, No. 8, "An Account of the Augustan Age of England."

[2] "It is enough for one age to have neglected Mr. Cowley and starved Mr. Butler."—DRYDEN, *Letter to Hyde, Lord Rochester.*

[3] William Collins the poet.   This was said in April, 1759, and on the following
12th of June Collins died—mad.

[4] The first edition adds: "Among the dregs of mankind."

recourse to the bookseller. There cannot perhaps be imagined a combination more prejudicial to taste than this. It is
the interest of the one to allow as little for writing, and of
the other to write as much as possible. Accordingly, tedious
compilations and periodical magazines are the result of their
joint endeavors. In these circumstances, the author bids
adieu to fame; writes for bread, and for that only imagination is seldom called in. He sits down to address the venal
muse with the most phlegmatic apathy; and, as we are told
of the Russian, courts his mistress by falling asleep in her
lap. His reputation never spreads in a wider circle than that
of "the trade," who generally value him, not for the fineness
of his compositions, but the quantity he works off in a given
time.

A long habit of writing for bread thus turns the ambition
of every author at last into avarice. He finds that he has
written many years, that the public are scarcely acquainted
even with his name; he despairs of applause, and turns to
profit, which invites him. He finds that money procures all
those advantages, that respect, and that ease which he vainly
expected from fame. Thus the man who, under the protection of the great, might have done honor to humanity, when
only patronized by the bookseller, becomes a thing little superior to the fellow who works at the press.[1]

CHAPTER X.[2]

OF THE MARKS OF LITERARY DECAY IN FRANCE AND ENGLAND.

THE faults already mentioned are such as learning is often
found to flourish under; but there is one of a much more
dangerous nature, which has begun to fix itself among us. I
mean criticism; which may properly be called the natural

---

[1] The first edition adds: "Sint Mæcenates, non deerunt, Flacce, Marones."
[2] This is made up of Chapters VI. and XI. of the first edition.

destroyer of polite learning. We have seen that critics, or
those whose only business is to write books upon other books,
are always more numerous as learning is more diffused; and
experience has shown that, instead of promoting its interest,
which they profess to do, they generally injure it. This decay which criticism produces may be deplored, but can scarcely be remedied; as the man who writes against the critics is
obliged to add himself to the number. Other depravations
in the republic of letters, such as affectation in some popular
writer leading others into vicious imitation; political struggles in the state; a depravity of morals among the people;
ill-directed encouragement, or no encouragement from the
great—these have been often found to co-operate in the decline of literature; and it has sometimes declined, as in modern Italy, without them; but an increase of criticism has always portended a decay. Of all misfortunes, therefore, in
the commonwealth of letters, this of judging from rule, and
not from feeling, is the most severe. At such a tribunal no
work of original merit can please. Sublimity, if carried to
an exalted height, approaches burlesque, and humor sinks
into vulgarity. The person who cannot feel may ridicule
both as such, and bring rules to corroborate his assertion.
There is, in short, no excellence in writing that such judges
may not place among the neighboring defects. Rules render
the reader more difficult to be pleased, and abridge the author's power of pleasing.

If we turn to either country, we shall perceive evident
symptoms of this natural decay beginning to appear. Upon
a moderate calculation, there seems to be as many volumes
of criticism published in those countries as of all other kinds
of polite erudition united. Paris sends forth not less than
four literary journals every month—the "Année Littéraire"
and the "Feuille," by Fréron; the "Journal Etrangère," by
the Chevalier d'Arc, and "Le Mercure," by Marmontel. We
have two literary reviews in London,[1] with critical newspapers and magazines without number. The compilers of these

---

[1] The *Monthly Review*, established in 1749, and the *Critical*, in 1756.

resemble the commoners of Rome; they are all for levelling property, not by increasing their own, but by diminishing that of others.   The man who has any good-nature in his disposition must, however, be somewhat displeased to see distinguished reputations often the sport of ignorance—to see by one false pleasantry the future peace of a worthy man's life disturbed, and this only because he has unsuccessfully attempted to instruct or amuse us.   Though ill-nature is far from being wit, yet it is generally laughed at as such.   The critic enjoys the triumph, and ascribes to his parts what is only due to his effrontery.[1]   I fire with indignation when I see persons wholly destitute of education and genius indent to the Press, and thus turn book-makers, adding to the sin of criticism the sin of ignorance also; whose trade is a bad one, and who are bad workmen in the trade.

When I consider those industrious men as indebted to the works of others for a precarious subsistence; when I see them coming down at stated intervals to rummage the bookseller's counter for materials to work upon, it raises a smile, though mixed with pity.   It reminds me of an animal called by naturalists the soldier.   "This little creature," says the historian, "is passionately fond of a shell; but, not being supplied with one by nature, has recourse to the deserted shell of some other.   I have seen these harmless reptiles," continues he, "come down once a year from the mountains, rank and file, cover the whole shore, and ply busily about, each in request of a shell to please it.   Nothing can be more amusing than their industry upon this occasion.   One shell is too big, another too little: they enter and keep possession sometimes for a good while, until one is at last found entirely to please.   When all are thus properly equipped, they march up again to

---

[1] What follows stands thus in the first edition (p. 79): "If there be any, however, among these writers, who, being bred gentlemen and scholars, are obliged to have recourse to such an employment for subsistence, I wish them one more suited to their inclinations; but for such who, wholly destitute of education and genius, indent to the Press, and turn mere book-makers, they deserve the severest censure.   These add to the sin of criticism the sin of ignorance also.   Their trade is a bad one, and they are bad workmen in the trade."

the mountains, and live in their new acquisition till under a necessity of changing."

There is, indeed, scarcely an error of which our present writers are guilty,[1] that does not arise from their opposing systems; there is scarcely an error that criticism cannot be brought to excuse. From this proceeds the affected security of our odes, the tuneless flow of our blank verse, the pompous epithet, labored diction, and every other deviation from common-sense which procures the poet the applause of the month:[2] he is praised by all, read by a few, and soon forgotten.

There never was an unbeaten path trodden by the poet that the critic did not endeavor to reclaim him by calling his attempt innovation. This might be instanced in Dante, who first followed nature, and was persecuted by the critics as long as he lived. Thus novelty, one of the greatest beauties in poetry, must be avoided, or the connoisseur be displeased. It is one of the chief privileges, however, of genius, to fly from the herd of imitators by some happy singularity; for should he stand still, his heavy pursuers will at length certainly come up, and fairly dispute the victory.

The ingenious Mr. Hogarth used to assert that every one except the connoisseur was a judge of painting. The same may be asserted of writing: the public in general set the whole piece in the proper point of view; the critic lays his eye close to all its minuteness, and condemns or approves in detail. And this may be the reason why so many writers at present are apt to appeal from the tribunal of criticism to that of the people.

---

[1] Chapter XI. of the first edition opens thus: "But there are still some men, whom fortune has blessed with affluence, to whom the Muse pays her morning visit, not like a creditor, but a friend; to this happy few, who have leisure to polish what they write, and liberty to choose their own subjects, I would direct my advice, which consists in a few words: *write what you think, regardless of the critics.* To persuade to this was the chief design of this essay. To break, or at least to loosen those bonds, first put on by caprice, and afterward drawn hard by fashion, is my wish. I have assumed the critic only to dissuade from criticism.

"There is scarce an error of which our present writers are guilty," etc.

[2] "Connoisseur."—*First Edition.*

From a desire in the critic, of grafting the spirit of ancient languages upon the English, have proceeded of late several disagreeable instances of pedantry. Among the number I think we may reckon blank verse.[1] Nothing but the greatest sublimity of subject can render such a measure pleasing; however, we now see it used upon the most trivial occasions. It has particularly found its way into our didactic poetry,[2] and is likely to bring that species of composition into disrepute, for which the English are deservedly famous.

Those who are acquainted with writing know that our language runs almost naturally into blank verse. The writers of our novels, romances, and all of this class who have no notion of style, naturally hobble into this unharmonious measure. If rhymes, therefore, be more difficult, for that very reason I would have our poets write in rhyme. Such a restriction upon the thought of a good poet often lifts and increases the vehemence of every sentiment; for fancy, like a fountain, plays highest by diminishing the aperture. But rhymes, it will be said, are a remnant of monkish stupidity, an innovation upon the poetry of the ancients. They are but indifferently acquainted with antiquity who make the assertion. Rhymes are probably of older date than either the Greek or Latin dactyl and spondee. The Celtic, which

---

[1] "Yet, however this art [poetry] may be neglected by the powerful, it is still in great danger from the mistaken efforts of the learned to improve it. What criticisms have we not heard of late in favor of blank verse, and Pindaric odes, choruses, anapests, and iambics, alliterative care, and happy negligence! Every absurdity has now a champion to defend it : and as he is generally much in the wrong, so he has always much to say; for error is ever talkative. . . .

"What reception a poem may find which has neither abuse, party, nor blank verse to support it, I cannot tell, nor am I solicitous to know."—GOLDSMITH, *Dedication to The Traveller*, 1765.

[2] Goldsmith alludes to Akenside's "Pleasures of Imagination" (1744); Armstrong's "Art of Preserving Health" (1744); Dyer's "Fleece" (1757). "A poem frigidly didactic without rhyme is so near to prose, that the reader only scorns it for pretending to be verse."—JOHNSON's *Life of Roscommon*. "Contending angels may shake the regions of heaven in blank verse ; but the flow of equal measures, and the embellishment of rhyme, must recommend to our attention the art of ingrafting, and decide the merit of the red-streak and pearmain."—JOHNSON's *Life of J. Philips*.

is allowed to be the first language spoken in Europe, has ever preserved them, as we may find in the Edda of Iceland, and the Irish carols, still sung among the original inhabitants of that island. Olaus Wormius gives us some of the Teutonic poetry in this way; and Pontoppidan, Bishop of Bergen, some of the Norwegian. In short, this jingle of sounds is almost natural to mankind, at least it is so to our language, if we may judge from many unsuccessful attempts to throw it off.

I should not have employed so much time in opposing this erroneous innovation, if it were not apt to introduce another in its train; I mean, a disgusting solemnity of manner into our poetry; and, as the prose writer has been ever found to follow the poet, it must consequently banish in both all that agreeable trifling which, if I may so express it, often deceives us into instruction.[1] The finest sentiment and the most weighty truth may put on a pleasant face; and it is even virtuous to jest when serious advice must be disgusting. But instead of this, the most trifling performance among us now assumes all the didactic stiffness of wisdom. The most diminutive son of fame or of famine has his *we* and his *us*, his *firstlies* and his *secondlies*, as methodical as if bound in cowhide and closed with clasps of brass. Were these monthly reviews and magazines frothy, pert, or absurd, they might find some pardon; but to be dull and dronish is an encroachment on the prerogative of a folio. These things should be considered as pills to purge melancholy; they should be made up in our splenetic climate to be taken as physic, and not so as to be used when we take it.[2]

However, by the power of one single monosyllable, our critics have almost got the victory over humor among us.

---

[1] Here the first edition adds: "Dry reasoning and dull morality have no force with the wild, fantastic libertine. He must be met with smiles, and courted with the allurements of gayety; he must be taught to believe that he is in pursuit of pleasure, and be surprised into reformation."

[2] Here the first edition adds: "Some such law should be enacted in the republic of letters as we find takes place in the House of Commons. As no man there can show his wisdom unless first qualified by three hundred pounds a year, so none here should possess gravity unless his work amounted to three hundred pages."

Does the poet paint the absurdities of the vulgar, then he is *low;* does he exaggerate the features of folly to render it more thoroughly ridiculous, he is then very *low*.   In short, they have proscribed the comic or satirical muse from every walk but high life; which, though abounding in fools as well as the humblest station, is by no means so fruitful in absurdity.   Among well-bred fools we may despise much, but have little to laugh at; nature seems to present us with a universal blank of silk, ribbons, smiles, and whispers.   Absurdity is the poet's game, and good-breeding is the nice concealment of absurdities.   The truth is, the critic generally mistakes humor for wit, which is a very different excellence.   Wit raises human nature above its level; humor acts a contrary part, and equally depresses it.   To expect exalted humor is a contradiction in terms; and the critic, by demanding an impossibility from the comic poet, has, in effect, banished new comedy from the stage.   But to put the same thought in a different light.

When an unexpected similitude in two objects strikes the imagination—in other words, when a thing is wittily expressed—all our pleasure turns into admiration of the artist who had fancy enough to draw the picture.   When a thing is humorously described, our burst of laughter proceeds from a very different cause; we compare the absurdity of the character represented with our own, and triumph in our conscious superiority.   No natural defect can be a cause of laughter; because it is a misfortune to which ourselves are liable.   A defect of this kind changes the passion into pity or horror.   We only laugh at those instances of moral absurdity to which we are conscious we ourselves are not liable.   For instance, should I describe a man as wanting his nose, there is no humor in this, as it is an accident to which human nature is subject, and may be any man's case; but should I represent this man without his nose as extremely curious in the choice of his snuffbox, we here see him guilty of an absurdity of which we imagine it impossible for ourselves to be guilty, and therefore applaud our own good-sense on the comparison.   Thus, then, the pleasure we receive from wit turns on the admiration of another; that which we feel from humor centres in the admiration of ourselves. The poet, therefore, must place the object he would have the subject of humor in a state of inferiority; in other words, the subject of humor must be low.

The solemnity worn by many of our modern writers is, I fear, often the mask of dulness; for certain it is, it seems to fit every author who pleases to put it on. By the complexion of many of our late publications one might be apt to cry out with Cicero, "Civem, mehercule! non puto esse qui his temporibus ridere possit." On my conscience, I believe we have all forgot to laugh in these days. Such writers probably make no distinction between what is praised and what is pleasing; between those commendations which the reader pays his own discernment and those which are the genuine result of his sensations.

It were to be wished, therefore, that we no longer found pleasure with the inflated style[1] that has for some years been looked upon as fine writing, and which every young writer is now obliged to adopt, if he chooses to be read. We should now dispense with loaded epithet and dressing up trifles with dignity; for, to use an obvious instance, it is not those who make the greatest noise with their wares in the streets that have most to sell. Let us, instead of writing finely, try to write naturally; not hunt after lofty expressions to deliver mean ideas, nor be forever gaping, when we only mean to deliver a whisper.

---

[1] In the first edition: "As our gentlemen writers have it, therefore, so much in their power to lead the taste of the times, they may now part with the inflated style," etc.

CHAPTER XI.[1]

OF THE STAGE.

Our theatre has been generally confessed to share in this general decline, though partaking of the show and decoration of the Italian opera, with the propriety and declamation of French performance. The stage, also, is more magnificent with us than any other in Europe, and the people in general fonder of theatrical entertainment. Yet still, as our pleasures, as well as more important concerns, are generally managed by party, the stage has felt its influence. The managers, and all who espouse their side, are for decoration and ornament; the critic, and all who have studied French decorum, are for regularity and declamation. Thus it is almost impossible to please both parties; and the poet, by attempting it, finds himself often incapable of pleasing either. If he introduces stage pomp, the critic consigns his performance to the vulgar; if he indulges in recital and simplicity, it is accused of insipidity, or dry affectation.

From the nature, therefore, of our theatre, and the genius of our country, it is extremely difficult for a dramatic poet to please his audience. But happy would he be were these the only difficulties he had to encounter: there are many other more dangerous combinations against the little wit of the age. Our poet's performance must undergo a process truly chemical, before it is presented to the public. It must be tried in the manager's fire, strained through a licenser,[1] suffer from re-

---

[1] "And purified in the review or the newspaper of the day. At the rate, before it can come to a private table it may probably be a mere *caput mortuum*, and only proper entertainment for the licenser, manager, or critic himself. But it may be answered, that we have a sufficient number of plays upon our theatres already, and, therefore, there is no need of new ones. But are they sufficiently good? And is the credit of our age nothing? Must our present times pass away unnoticed by posterity? We are desirous of leaving them liberty, wealth, and titles, and we can have no recompense but their applause. The title of 'learned' given

peated corrections, till it may be a mere *caput mortuum* when it arrives before the public.

The success, however, of pieces upon the stage would be of little moment, did it not influence the success of the same piece in the closet. Nay, I think it would be more for the interests of virtue, if stage performances were read, not acted; made rather our companions in the cabinet[1] than on the theatre. While we are readers, every moral sentiment strikes us in all its beauty, but the love scenes are frigid, tawdry, and disgusting. When we are spectators, all the persuasives to vice receive an additional lustre. The love scene is aggravated, the obscenity heightened; the best actors figure in the most debauched characters, while the parts of morality, as they are called, are thrown to some mouthing machine, who puts even virtue out of countenance by his wretched imitation.[2]

---

to an age is the most glorious applause, and shall this be disregarded? Our reputation among foreigners will quickly be discontinued when we discontinue our efforts to deserve it, and shall we despise their praise? Are our new absurdities, with which no nation more abounds, to be left unnoticed? Is the pleasure such performances give upon the perusal to be entirely given up? If these are all matters of indifference, it then signifies nothing, whether we are to be entertained with the actor or the poet, with fine sentiments, or painted canvas, or whether the dancer, or the carpenter, be constituted master of the ceremonies.

"But they are not matters of indifference. Every age produces new follies and new vices, and one absurdity is often displaced in order to make room for another. The dramatic poet, however, who should be, and has often been, a firm champion in the cause of virtue, detects all the new machinations of vice, levels his satire at the rising structures of folly, or drives her from behind the retrenchments of fashion. Thus far, then, the poet is useful; but how far the actor, that dear favorite of the public, may be so, is a question next to be determined.

"As the poet's merit is often not sufficient to introduce his performance among the public with proper dignity, he is often obliged to call in the assistance of decoration and dress to contribute to this effect. By this means a performance which pleases on the stage often instructs in the closet, and for one who has seen it acted hundreds will be readers. The actor, then, is useful, by introducing the works of the poet to the public with becoming splendor; but when these have once become popular, I must confess myself so much a sceptic as to think it would be more for the interests of virtue," etc.—*First Edition.*

[1] "Closet."—*First Edition.*

[2] Here the first edition adds: "The principal performers find their interest in choosing such parts as tend to promote, not the benefit of society, but their own

But whatever be the incentives to vice which are found at the theatre, public pleasures are generally less guilty than solitary ones.   To make our solitary satisfaction truly innocent, the actor is useful, as by his means the poet's work makes its way from the stage to the closet; for all must allow that the reader receives more benefit by perusing a well-written play than by seeing it acted.[1]

But how is this rule inverted on our theatres at present! Old pieces are revived, and scarcely any new ones admitted. The actor is ever in our eye, and the poet seldom permitted to appear; the public are again obliged to ruminate over those hashes of absurdity, which were disgusting to our ancestors even in an age of ignorance; and the stage, instead of serving the people, is made subservient to the interests of avarice.[2]

We seem to be pretty much in the situation of travellers at a Scotch inn; vile entertainment is served up, complained of, and sent down; up comes worse, and that also is changed; and every change makes our wretched cheer more unsavory. What must be done? only sit down contented, cry up all that

---

reputation; and in using arts which inspire emotions very different from those of morality.   How many young men go to the playhouse speculatively in love with the rule of right, but return home actually enamored of an actress.   I have often attended to the reflections of the company upon leaving the theatre; one actor had the finest pipe, but the other the most melodious voice; one was a bewitching creature, another a charming devil; and such are generally our acquisitions at the playhouse: it brings to my remembrance an old lady, who, being passionately fond of a famous preacher, went every Sunday to church, but, struck only with his graceful manner of delivery, disregarded and forgot the truths of his discourse."

[1] In the first edition: "But it is needless to mention the incentives to vice which are to be found at the theatre, or the immorality of some of the performers. Such impeachments, though true, would be regarded as cant, while their exhibitions continue to amuse.   I would only infer from hence that an actor is chiefly useful in introducing new performances upon the stage, since the reader receives more benefit by perusing a well-written play in his closet than by seeing it acted. I would also infer that to the poet is to be ascribed all the good that attends seeing plays, and to the actor all the harm."

[2] The first edition adds: "We must now see the literary honors of our country suppressed that an actor may dine with elegance; we must tamely sit and see the celestial Muse made a slave to the histrionic Demon."

comes before us, and admire even the absurdities of Shakspeare.

Let the reader suspend his censure. I admire the beauties of this great father of our stage as much as they deserve, but could wish, for the honor of our country, and for his honor too, that many of his scenes were forgotten. A man blind of one eye should always be painted in profile. Let the spectator who assists at any of these newly-revived pieces only ask himself whether he would approve such a performance if written by a modern poet? I fear he will find that much of his applause proceeds merely from the sound of a name, and an empty veneration for antiquity. In fact, the revival of those pieces of forced humor, far-fetched conceit, and unnatural hyperbole, which have been ascribed to Shakspeare, is rather gibbeting than raising a statue to his memory; it is rather a trick of the actor, who thinks it safest acting in exaggerated characters, and who, by outstepping nature, chooses to exhibit the ridiculous *outré* of a harlequin under the sanction of that venerable name.

What strange vamped comedies, farcical tragedies, or what shall I call them, speaking pantomimes, have we not of late seen! No matter what the play may be, it is the actor who draws an audience. He throws life into all; all are in spirits and merry, in at one door and out at another; the spectator, in a fool's paradise, knows not what all this means, till the last act concludes in matrimony. The piece pleases our critics, because it talks old English; and it pleases the galleries, because it has ribaldry. True taste, or even common-sense, are out of the question.

But great art must be sometimes used before they can thus impose upon the public. To this purpose, a prologue written with some spirit generally precedes the piece, to inform us that it was composed by Shakspeare, or old Ben, or somebody else who took them for his model. A face of iron could not have the assurance to avow dislike; the theatre has its partisans who understand the force of combinations, trained up to vociferation, clapping of hands, and clattering of sticks; and though a man might have strength sufficient to overcome a lion in single combat, he may run the risk of being devoured by an army *of ants*.[1]

I am not insensible that *third nights*[2] are disagreeable drawbacks upon the annual profits of the stage. I am confident it is much more to the manager's advantage to furbish up all the lumber which the good-sense of our ancestors, but for his care, had consigned to oblivion. It is not with him, therefore, but with the public I would expostulate; they have a right to demand respect, and surely those newly-revived plays are no instances of the manager's deference.

I have been informed that no new play can be admitted upon our theatres unless the author chooses to wait some years, or, to use the phrase in fashion, till it comes to be played in turn.[3] A poet thus can never expect to contract a fa-

---

[1] The first edition reads: "An army even of mice; he may run the risk of being eaten up, marrow-bones and all."

[2] Third nights were given to the author after the expenses of the house for the night were paid. Thus we read in Pope of "*thin* third nights," and "*warm* third nights." Some successful poets with successful plays enjoyed a sixth and even a ninth night. The poet's third night was, like the actor's annual benefit night, his principal produce from the stage. Managers generally looked coldly upon *third nights*, though they liked the run of a new piece.

[3] "The first knowledge Mr. Garrick had of his [Goldsmith's] abilities was from an attack upon him by Goldsmith, when he was but a very young author, in a book called 'The Present State of Learning.' Among other abuses (for the Doctor loved to dwell upon grievances) he took notice of the behavior of managers to authors; this must surely have proceeded from the most generous principles of reforming what was amiss for the benefit of others, for the Doctor at that time had not the most distant views of commencing dramatic author.

"Little did Goldsmith imagine he should one day be obliged to ask a favor from the director of a playhouse; however, when the office of Secretary to the Society of Arts became vacant, the Doctor was persuaded to offer himself a candidate. He was told that Mr. Garrick was a leading member of that learned body, and his interest and recommendation would be of consequence to enforce his pretensions.

"He waited upon the manager, and, in few words, requested his vote and interest. Mr. Garrick could not avoid observing to him that it was impossible he could lay claim to any recommendation from him, as he had taken pains to deprive himself of his assistance by an unprovoked attack upon his management of the theatre, in his 'State of Learning.' Goldsmith, instead of making an apology for his conduct, either from misinformation or misconception, bluntly replied, 'In truth he had spoken his mind, and believed what he said was very right.' The manager dismissed him with civility; and Goldsmith lost the office by a very great majority, who voted in favor of Dr. Templeman."—DAVIES's *Life of Garrick*, ii. 143. Ed. 1780.

miliarity with the stage, by which alone he can hope to succeed; nor can the most signal success relieve immediate want. Our Saxon ancestors had but one name for a wit and a witch. I will not dispute the propriety of uniting those characters then; but the man who, under the present discouragements, ventures to write for the stage, whatever claim he may have to the appellation of a wit, at least he has no right to be called a conjurer.[1]

---

[1] Here the first edition adds: "Yet getting a play on, even in three or four years, is a privilege reserved only for the happy few who have the arts of courting the manager as well as the muse; who have adulation to please his vanity, powerful patrons to support their merit, or money to indemnify disappointment. The poet must act like our beggars at Christmas, who lay the first shilling on the plate for themselves. Thus all wit is banished from the stage, except it be supported by friends or fortune; and poets are seldom overburdened with either.

"I am not at present writing for a party, but above theatrical connections in every sense of the expression; I have no particular spleen against the fellow who sweeps the stage with the besom, or the hero who brushes it with his train. It were a matter of indifference to me, whether our heroines are in keeping, or our candle-snuffers burn their fingers, did not such make a great part of public care and polite conversation. It is not these, but the age I would reproach; the vile complexion of the times, when those employ our most serious thoughts, and separate us into parties, whose business is only to amuse our idlest hours. I cannot help reproaching our meanness in this respect; for our stupidity and our folly will be remembered, when even the attitudes and eyebrows of a favorite actor shall be forgotten.

"In the times of Addison and Steele, players were held in greater contempt than, perhaps, they deserved. Honest Estcourt, Verbruggen, and Underhill were extremely poor, and assumed no airs of insolence. They were contented with being merry at a city feast, with promoting the mirth of a set of cheerful companions, and gave their jest for their reckoning. At that time it was kind to say something in defence of the poor, good-natured creatures, if it were only to keep them in good-humor; but at present such encouragements are unnecessary. Our actors assume all that state off the stage which they do on it; and, to use an expression borrowed from the greenroom, every one is *up* in his part. I am sorry to say it, they seem to forget their real characters; more provoking still, the public seems to forget them too.

"Macrobius has preserved a prologue spoken and written by the poet Laberius, a Roman knight, whom Cæsar forced upon the stage, written with great elegance and spirit, which shows what opinion the Romans in general entertained of the profession of an actor:

"'Necessitas cujus cursus transversi impetum,' etc."

Here followed the prologue printed in Vol. I. p. 105.

From all that has been said upon the state of our theatre, we may easily foresee whether it is likely to improve or decline; and whether the free-born muse can bear to submit to those restrictions which avarice or power would impose. For the future it is somewhat unlikely that he whose labors are valuable, or who knows their value, will turn to the stage for either fame or subsistence, when he must at once flatter an actor and please an audience.[1]

CHAPTER XII.

ON UNIVERSITIES.

INSTEAD of losing myself in a subject of such extent, I shall only offer a few thoughts as they occur, and leave their connection to the reader.

We seem divided, whether an education formed by travelling or by a sedentary life be preferable. We see more of the world by travel, but more of human nature by remaining at home; as in an infirmary, the student who only attends to the disorders of a few patients is more likely to understand his profession than he who indiscriminately examines them all.

A youth just landed at the Brille resembles a clown at a puppet-show; carries his amazement from one miracle to another; from this cabinet of curiosities to that collection of pictures; but wondering is not the way to grow wise.

Whatever resolutions we set ourselves not to keep company with our countrymen abroad, we shall find them broken when

---

[1] The first edition adds : ": Let no manager impute this to spleen or disappointment. I only assert the claims of the public, and endeavor to vindicate a profession which has hitherto wanted a defender. A mean or mercenary conduct may continue for some time to triumph over opposition, but it is possible the public will at last be taught to vindicate their privileges. Perhaps there may come a time when the poet will be at liberty to increase the entertainments of the people; but such a period may possibly not arise till our discouragements have banished poetry from the stage."

once we leave home. Among strangers we consider ourselves as in a solitude, and it is but natural to desire society.

In all the great towns of Europe there are to be found Englishmen residing either from interest or choice. These generally lead a life of continued debauchery. Such are the countrymen a traveller is likely to meet with.

This may be the reason why Englishmen are all thought to be mad or melancholy by the vulgar abroad. Their money is giddily and merrily spent among sharpers of their own country; and when that is gone, of all nations the English bear worst that disorder called the *maladie de poche*.

Countries wear very different appearances to travellers of different circumstances. A man who is whirled through Europe in a post-chaise, and the pilgrim who walks the grand tour on foot, will form very different conclusions.[1]

To see Europe with advantage, a man should appear in various circumstances of fortune; but the experiment would be too dangerous for young men.

There are many things relative to other countries which can be learned to more advantage at home; their laws and policies are among the number.

The greatest advantages which result to youth from travel, are an easy address, the shaking off national prejudices, and the finding nothing ridiculous in national peculiarities.

The time spent in these acquisitions could have been more usefully employed at home. An education in a college seems therefore preferable.[2]

We attribute to universities either too much or too little. Some assert that they are the only proper places to advance learning; while others deny even their utility in forming an education. Both are erroneous.

Learning is most advanced in popular cities, where chance often conspires with industry to promote it; where the mem-

---

[1] "Haud inexpertus loquor."—*First Edition.*

[2] The first edition adds: "It has lately been disputed whether the arts and sciences do most benefit or injury to mankind. Mere speculative trifling! Ask the housebreaker or highwayman in what university they were bred. They will answer—in none."

bers of this large university, if I may so call it, catch manners as they rise, study life not logic, and have the world for correspondents.

The greatest number of universities have ever been founded in times of the greatest ignorance.

New improvements in learning are seldom adopted in colleges until admitted everywhere else. And this is right; we should always be cautious of teaching the rising generation uncertainties for truth. Thus, though the professors in universities have been too frequently found to oppose the advancement of learning, yet when once established, they are the properest persons to diffuse it.[1]

There is more knowledge to be acquired from one page of the volume of mankind, if the scholar only knows how to read, than in volumes of antiquity. We grow learned, not wise, by too long a continuance at college.

This points out the time in which we should leave the university. Perhaps the age of twenty-one, when at our universities the first degree is generally taken, is the proper period.

The universities of Europe may be divided into three classes. Those upon the old scholastic establishment, where the pupils are immured, talk nothing but Latin, and support every day syllogistical disputations in school philosophy. Would not one be apt to imagine this was the proper education to make a man a fool? Such are the universities of Prague, Louvain, and Padua. The second is where the pupils are under few restrictions, where all scholastic jargon is banished, where they take a degree when they think proper, and live not in the college but the city. Such are Edinburgh, Leyden, Göttingen, Geneva. The third is a mixture of the two former, where the pupils are restrained, but not confined; where many, though not all, of the absurdities of scholastic philosophy are suppressed, and where the first degree is taken after four years' matriculation. Such are Oxford, Cambridge, and Dublin.

---

[1] The first edition adds: "The rudiments of learning are best implanted in a college, the cultivation of it is best promoted in the world."

As for the first class, their absurdities are too apparent to admit of a parallel. It is disputed which of the two last are more conducive to national improvement.

Skill in the professions is acquired more by practice than study; two or three years may be sufficient for learning their rudiments. The universities of Edinburgh, etc., grant a license for practising them when the student thinks proper, which our universities refuse till after a residence of several years.

The dignity of the professions may be supported by this dilatory proceeding; but many men of learning are thus too long excluded from the lucrative advantages which superior skill has a right to expect.

Those universities must certainly be most frequented which promise to give in two years the advantages which others will not under twelve.

The man who has studied a profession for three years, and practised it for nine more, will certainly know more of his business than he who has only studied it for twelve.

The universities of Edinburgh, etc., must certainly be most proper for the study of those professions in which men choose to turn their learning to profit as soon as possible.

The universities of Oxford, etc., are improper for this, since they keep the student from the world, which, after a certain time, is the only true school of improvement.

When a degree in the professions can be taken only by men of independent fortunes, the number of candidates in learning is lessened, and consequently the advancement of learning retarded.

This slowness of conferring degrees is a remnant of scholastic barbarity. Paris, Louvain, and those universities which still retain their ancient institutions, confer the doctor's degree slower even than we.

The statutes of every university should be considered as adapted to the laws of its respective government. Those should alter as these happen to fluctuate.

Four years spent in the arts (as they are called in colleges), is perhaps laying too laborious a foundation. Entering a profession without any previous acquisitions of this kind, is building too bold a superstructure.

Teaching by lecture, as at Edinburgh, may make men scholars, if they think proper; but instructing by examination, as at Oxford, will make them so, often against their inclination.

Edinburgh only disposes the student to receive learning; Oxford often makes him actually learned.

In a word, were I poor, I should send my son to Leyden or Edinburgh, though the annual expense in each, particularly in the first, is very great. Were I rich, I would send him to one of our own universities. By an education received in the first, he has the best likelihood of living; by that received in the latter, he has the best chance of becoming great.

We have of late heard much of the necessity of studying oratory. Vespasian was the first who paid professors of rhetoric for publicly instructing youth at Rome. However, those pedants never made an orator.

The best orations that ever were spoken were pronounced in the parliaments of King Charles the First. These men never studied the rules of oratory.

Mathematics are, perhaps, too much studied at our universities. This seems a science to which the meanest intellects are equal. I forget who it is that says, "All men might understand mathematics if they would."

The most methodical manner of lecturing, whether on morals or nature, is first rationally to explain, and then produce the experiment. The most instructive method is to show the experiment first; curiosity is then excited, and attention awakened to every subsequent deduction. Hence it is evident that, in a well-formed education, a course of history should ever precede a course of ethics.

The sons of our nobility are permitted to enjoy greater liberties in our universities than those of private men. I should blush to ask the men of learning and virtue who preside in our seminaries the reason of such a prejudicial distinction. Our youth should there be inspired with a love of philosophy; and the first maxim among philosophers is—that merit only makes distinction.

Whence has proceeded the vain magnificence of expensive architecture in our colleges? Is it that men study to more advantage in a palace than in a cell? One single performance of taste or genius confers more real honors on its parent university than all the labors of the chisel.

Surely pride itself has dictated to the fellows of our colleges the absurd passion of being attended at meals, and on other public occasions, by those poor men who, willing to be scholars, come in upon some charitable foundation. It implies a contradiction, for men to be at once learning the *liberal* arts, and at the same time treated as *slaves;* at once studying freedom, and practising servitude.

CHAPTER XIII.

THE CONCLUSION.

EVERY subject acquires an adventitious importance to him who considers it with application. He finds it more closely connected with human happiness than the rest of mankind are apt to allow; he sees consequences resulting from it which do not strike others with equal conviction; and still pursuing speculation beyond the bounds of reason, too frequently becomes ridiculously earnest in trifles or absurdity.

It will, perhaps, be incurring this imputation to deduce a universal degeneracy of manners from so slight an origin as the depravation of taste—to assert that, as a nation grows dull, it sinks into debauchery. Yet such probably may be the consequence of literary decay; or, not to stretch the thought beyond what it will bear, vice and stupidity are always mutually productive of each other.

Life, at the greatest and best, has been compared to a froward child, that must be humored and played with till it falls asleep, and then all the care is over. Our few years are labored away in varying its pleasures; new amusements are pursued with studious attention; the most childish vanities are dignified with titles of importance ; and the proudest boast of the most aspiring philosopher is no more than that he provides his little playfellows the greatest pastime with the greatest innocence.

Thus the mind, ever wandering after amusement, when abridged of happiness on one part, endeavors to find it on another ; when intellectual pleasures are disagreeable, those of sense will take the lead.   The man who in this age is enamored of the tranquil joys of study and retirement, may in the next, should learning be fashionable no longer, feel an ambition of being foremost at a horse-course ; or, if such could be the absurdity of the times, of being himself a jockey. Reason and appetite are, therefore, masters of our revels in turn ; and, as we incline to the one or pursue the other, we rival angels or imitate the brutes.   In the pursuit of intellectual pleasure lies every virtue ; of sensual, every vice.

It is this difference of pursuit which marks the morals and characters of mankind ; which lays the line between the enlightened philosopher and the half-taught citizen ; between the civil citizen and illiterate peasant ; between the law-obeying peasant and the wandering savage of Africa, an animal less mischievous, indeed, than the tiger, because endued with fewer powers of doing mischief.   The man, the nation, must therefore be good, whose chiefest luxuries consist in the refinement of reason ; and reason can never be universally cultivated unless guided by taste, which may be considered as the link between science and common-sense, the medium through which learning should ever be seen by society.

Taste will, therefore, often be a proper standard, when others fail, to judge of a nation's improvement or degeneracy in morals.   We have often no permanent characteristics by which to compare the virtues or the vices of our ancestors with our own.   A generation may rise and pass away without leaving any traces of what it really was ; and all complaints of our deterioration may be only topics of declamation or the cavillings of disappointment ; but in taste we have standing evidence ; we can with precision compare the literary performances of our fathers with our own, and from their excellence or defects determine the moral, as well as the literary, merits of either.

If, then, there ever comes a time when taste is so far depraved among us, that critics shall load every work of genius with unnecessary comment, and quarter their empty performances with the substantial merits of an author, both for subsistence and applause; if there comes a time when censure shall speak in storms, but praise be whispered in the breeze, while real excellence often finds shipwreck in either; if there be a time when the muse shall seldom be heard, except in plaintive elegy, as if she wept her own decline, while lazy compilations supply the place of original thinking; should there ever be such a time, may succeeding critics, both for the honor of our morals as well as our learning, say that such a period bears no resemblance to the present age!

APPENDIX.

THE POLITE LEARNING OF ENGLAND AND FRANCE INCAPABLE OF COMPARISON.[1]

WHATEVER preference the vulgar of every nation may think due to their own in particular, the learned, who look beyond the bounds of national prejudice and are citizens of the world, seem unanimous in regarding the English and French as the principal literary supporters of the present age. Their emulation in learning, as well as in power, have divided the wits not less than the armies of Europe. "A niuno è nascosto," says a modern writer, " come la Francia e l'Inghilterra sono rivali nella politica, nel commercio, nella gloria delle arme delle lettere."

This acknowledged superiority was, however, no easy conquest over that national pride with which every country is more or less tinctured. Every part of Europe was at one time or another candidates for this pre-eminence, which though they had not the good fortune to obtain, their attempts served in a subordinate degree to assist and refine the taste of their contemporaries. Thus Spain exhibited fine examples of humor; Italy of delicacy; and Holland of freedom in inquiry. But to blend these excellences, and arrive at perfection, seemed reserved for the poets and philosophers of England and France in the illustrious reigns of Queen Anne and Louis XIV. The writers of that period not only did honor to their respective countries, but even to human nature. Like stars lost in each other's brightness, though no single writer attracts our attention alone, yet their conjunction diffuses such brightness upon the age as will give the minutest actions of those two reigns an importance which the revolutions of empire will want that were transacted in greater obscurity.

Yet that excellence which now excites the admiration of Europe served, at that period of which I am speaking, only to promote envy in the respective writers of those two countries. They both took every method to depreciate the merit of each other; the French sel-

---

[1] Chapter VII. of the first edition; omitted in the second. See p. 38.

dom mentioned the English but with disrespect, put themselves foremost in every literary contest, and, to leave the English no color of competition, placed the Italians in the second rank. The English, on the other hand, regarded the French as triflers, accused the flimsy texture of their style, and the false brilliancy of their sentiments. Yet, while each thus loaded the other with contempt, it seemed as if done with a view of having their mutual plagiarism pass with less suspicion. In works of entertainment, we borrowed from the French unsparingly; and they plundered our serious performances with as little compunction. Europe, however, regarded the contest with impartiality, and the debate seemed at last determined. Their writings are allowed to have more taste, ours more truth. We are allowed the honor of striking out sentiments, they of dressing them in the most pleasing form. If we have produced reasoners who have refined mankind, it is by means of French translations and abstracts that they are generally known in Europe. Their language has prevailed, and our philosophy.

And this, indeed, is all the English had a right to expect in a contest of this nature, nor have they any just reason to regret not being chosen supreme in taste as well as truth; for if we only consider how different our manners are from those of every other nation on the Continent; how little we are visited by travellers of discernment; how ignorant our neighbors are of our various absurdities and humors; if we consider this, it cannot be expected that our works of taste, which imitate our peculiar manners, can please those that are unacquainted with the originals themselves. Though our descriptions and characters are drawn from nature, yet they may appear exaggerated, or faintly copied, to those who, unacquainted with the peculiarities of our island, have no standard by which to make the comparison.

The French are much more fortunate than we in this particular. A universal sameness of character appears to spread itself over the whole Continent; particularly, the fools and coxcombs of every country abroad seem almost cast in the same mould. The battered beau, who affects the boy at threescore, or the petit-maître, who would be a man at fifteen, are characters which may be seen at every coffee-house out of England. The French pictures, therefore, of life and manners are immediately allowed to be just, because foreigners are acquainted with the models from whence they are copied. The Marquis of Molière strikes all Europe. Sir John Falstaff, with all the merry men of Eastcheap, are entirely of England, and please the English alone.

Let us, then, be satisfied the world has allowed us superiority in the strength and justness of our sentiments, for it hath truth as a standard by which to compare them; we are placed inferior in regard to taste, for in this there is no standard to judge of our desert, our manners being unknown. Truth is a positive, taste a relative excellence. We may justly appeal from the sentence of our judges; though we must do them the justice to own that their verdict has been impartial.

But it may be objected that this is setting up a particular standard of taste in every country; this is removing that universal one which has hitherto united the armies and enforced the commands of criticism; by this reasoning the critics of one country will not be proper guides to the writers of another; Grecian or Roman rules will not be generally binding in France or England; but the laws designed to improve our taste, by this reasoning, must be adapted to the genius of every people, as much as those enacted to promote morality.

What I propose as objections are really the sentiments I mean to prove, not to obviate. I must own it as my opinion, that if criticism be at all requisite to promote the interests of learning, its rules should be taken from among the inhabitants, and adapted to the genius and temper of the country it attempts to refine. I must own it, though, perhaps, by this opinion's prevailing, many a scholium of the ancients and many a folio of criticism translated from the French, now in repute among us, would infallibly sink into oblivion. English taste, like English liberty, should be restrained only by laws of its own promoting.

But to use argument as well as assertion, let us take a nearer view of what is called taste, examine its standard, see if foreign critics are just in setting up theirs as a model to us, or whether we be right in adopting their proffered improvements. As the disquisition, however, is dry, I shall study conciseness.

All objects affect us with pleasure one of these two ways, either by immediately gratifying the senses with pleasing sensations, or by being thought in a secondary manner capable of making other objects contribute to this effect. The pleasures of immediate sensation are coeval with our senses, and, perhaps, most vivid in infancy; the secondary source of pleasure results from experience only, from considering the analogy of nature, or the capacity a part has to unite to a whole. The pleasures of the first sort are derived from the beauty of the object; those of the second from a consideration of its use. The first are natural; no art can increase them without mending the organ

II.—6

which was to give them admission. The second are artificial, and continually altering, as whim, climate, or seasons direct. To illustrate my meaning. The beauty of a guinea, for instance, its regular figure and shining color, are equally obvious to the senses in every country and climate; these qualities please the wildest savage as much as the most polished European: as far as it affects the senses, the pleasure a guinea gives is, therefore, in every country the same.

But the consideration of the uses it can be turned to is another source of pleasure, which is different in different countries. A native of Madagascar prefers to it a glass bead; a native of Holland prefers it to everything else. The pleasure, then, of its sensible qualities are everywhere the same; those of its secondary qualities everywhere different. He whom nature has furnished with the most vivid perceptions of beauty, and to whom experience has suggested the greatest number of uses, in the contemplation of any object, may be said to receive the greatest pleasure that object is capable of affording. Thus the barbarian finds some small pleasure in the contemplation of a guinea; the enlightened European, who is acquainted with its uses, still more than him; the chemist, who, besides this, knows the peculiar fixedness and malleability of the metal, most of all. This capacity of receiving pleasure may be called Taste in the objects of nature. The polite arts, in all their variety, are only an imitation of nature. He, then, must excel in them who is capable of inspiring us at once with the most vivid perceptions of beauty, and with the greatest number of experimental uses in any object described. But as the artist, to give vivid perceptions, must be perspicuous and concise, and yet to exhibit usefulness requires minuteness; here are two opposite qualities required in the writer—in one of which his imagination, in the other his reasoning faculty, is every moment liable to offend; what has he in this case to guide him? Taste is, perhaps, his only director. *Taste in writing is the exhibition of the greatest quantity of beauty and of use that may be admitted into any description without counteracting each other.*

The perfection of taste, therefore, proceeds from a knowledge of what is beautiful and useful. Criticism professes to increase our taste. But our taste cannot be increased with regard to beauty; because, as has been shown, our perceptions of this kind cannot be increased, but are most vivid in infancy. Criticism, then, can only improve our taste in the useful. But this, as was observed, is different in every climate and country—what is useful in one climate being óften noxious in another; therefore, criticism must understand the nature of the climate and country, etc., before it gives rules to direct taste. In other words, every country should have a national system of criticism.

In fact, nothing can be more absurd than rules to direct the taste of one country drawn from the manners of another. There may be some general marks in nature by which all writers are to proceed; these, however, are obvious, and might as well have never been pointed out; but to trace the sources of our passions, to mark the evanescent boundaries between satiety and disgust, and how far elegance differs from finery, requires a thorough knowledge of the people to whom the criticism is directed.

If, for instance, the English be a people who look upon death as an incident no way terrible, but sometimes fly to it for refuge from the calamities of life, why should a Frenchman be disgusted at our bloody stage? There is nothing hideous in the representation to one of us, whatever there might be to him.

We have long been characterized as a nation of spleen, and our rivals on the Continent as a land of levity. Ought they to be offended at the melancholy air which many of our modern poets assume, or ought we to be displeased with them for all their harmless trifling upon pin-cushions, parrots, and pretty faces? What is rational with us becomes with them formality; and what is fancy at Paris is at London fantastical. Critics should, therefore, imitate physicians, and consider every country as having a peculiar constitution, and consequently requiring a peculiar regimen.

THE CITIZEN OF THE WORLD;

OR,

LETTERS FROM A CHINESE PHILOSOPHER RESIDING IN LONDON TO HIS FRIENDS IN THE EAST.

London:

Printed for J. Newbery, at the Bible and Sun,
in St. Paul's Church-yard.

MDCCLXII.[1]

[2 vols. 12°.]

---

[1] Copies of this edition exist with a different title page to each volume; viz.—

London :
Printed for the Author ;
and
Sold by J. Newbery and W. Bristow, in St.
Paul's Church-yard ; J. Leake and W. Frederick
at Bath ; B. Collins at Salisbury ; and A. M. Smart & Co.
at Reading.
MDCCLXXII.

In every other respect the editions are identically the same. The first edition of
"The Vicar of Wakefield" was printed in 1766, for B. Collins, at Salisbury.

These letters (one hundred and twenty-three in number) were written for *The Public Ledger*, a London newspaper so called, started by John Newbery, a publisher, bookseller, and seller of medicines, living at the sign of "The Bible and Sun," afterwards known as No. 65, St. Paul's Church-yard. The first number of *The Public Ledger* appeared on the 12th of January, 1760; and the first letter of "The Citizen of the World" on the 24th of the same month.

Goldsmith's remuneration appears to have been at the rate of *a guinea* a Letter (Prior, i. 356).

The celebrated "Turkish Spy," the once celebrated "Persian Tales" ("turned" by Ambrose Philips), De Foe's "Tour through England" (written as a foreigner), and Walpole's Letter "from Xo Ho, a Chinese Philosopher at London, to his friend Lien Chi, at Peking," 1757, fol., had prepared the public for the ready reception of the "Chinese Letters." They were at once popular; and between the period of their publication in the columns of a newspaper and the year of Goldsmith's death, 1760–1774, went through three separate editions. The vagaries of Sir William Chambers, the architect (admirably ridiculed by Mason), added to their temporary popularity; but their present reputation rests entirely on their own excellences, independent of any other assistance.

I may add that Goldsmith remembered a quotation from Voltaire made by himself in *The Monthly Review* for August, 1757:—"The success of the 'Persian Letters' arose from the delicacy of their satire. That satire which, in the mouth of an Asiatic, is poignant, would lose all its force when coming from an European."

The text of this reprint has been derived from a collation with the three editions which Goldsmith saw through the press, the third and last appearing in 1774, with this imprint:—"London: printed for T. Carnan and F. Newbery, junior, at Number 65 in St. Paul's Churchyard, 1774." 2 vols., 12°.

CONTENTS.

In the editions of " The Citizen of the World" published in Goldsmith's lifetime there are apparently, by the numbers, only 119 letters; but there are 123 letters in all. The error arises from three wrong numberings, viz., two of 25, two of 57, and two of 116.

EDITOR'S PREFACE.[1]

THE schoolmen had formerly a very exact way of computing the abilities of their saints or authors. Escobar,[2] for instance, was said to have learning as five, genius as four, and gravity as seven. Caramuel[3] was greater than he. His learning was as eight, his genius as six, and his gravity as thirteen. Were I to estimate the merits of our Chinese philosopher by the same scale, I would not hesitate to state his genius still higher; but as to his learning and gravity, these, I think, might safely be marked as nine hundred and ninety-nine, within one degree of absolute frigidity.

Yet, upon his first appearance here, many were angry not to find him as ignorant as a Tripoline ambassador, or an envoy from Mujac. They were surprised to find a man born so far from London, that school of prudence and wisdom, endued even with a moderate capacity. They expressed the same surprise at his knowledge that the Chinese do at ours. "How comes it," said they, "that the Europeans, so remote from China, think with so much justice and precision? They have never read our books, they scarcely know even our letters, and

---

[1] That is, Goldsmith's.

[2] A famous casuist, born 1588, of a noble family of Seville, died 1669. His polemical and other writings occupy twenty-three folio volumes.

[3] A Cistercian monk, born at Madrid in 1606, died 1682. He wrote many works of controversial theology, and a system of divinity, in seven volumes folio.

yet they talk and reason just as we do."[1] The truth is, the Chinese and we are pretty much alike. Different degrees of refinement, and not of distance, mark the distinctions among mankind. Savages of the most opposite climates have all but one character of improvidence and rapacity; and tutored nations, however separate, make use of the very same methods to procure refined enjoyment.

The distinctions of polite nations are few; but such as are peculiar to the Chinese appear in every page of the following correspondence. The metaphors and allusions are all drawn from the East. Their formality our author carefully preserves. Many of their favorite tenets in morals are illustrated. The Chinese are always concise, so is he. Simple, so is he. The Chinese are grave and sententious, so is he. But in one particular the resemblance is peculiarly striking: the Chinese are often dull, and so is he. Nor has my assistance been wanting. We are told in an old romance of a certain knight-errant and his horse who contracted an intimate friendship. The horse most usually bore the knight; but in cases of extraordinary despatch the knight returned the favor, and carried his horse. Thus in the intimacy between my author and me, he has usually given me a lift of his Eastern sublimity, and I have sometimes given him a return of my colloquial ease.

Yet it appears strange, in this season of panegyric, when scarcely an author passes unpraised either by his friends or

---

[1] Le Comte, vol. i. p. 210.—GOLDSMITH. The author, a Jesuit of Bordeaux, was one of the six missionaries sent to China in 1685, by command of the King of France; he died in 1729. The work referred to by Goldsmith ("Nouveaux Mémoires sur la Chine") gave great offence to the faculty of divinity at Paris, on account of the author's prejudices in favor of the Chinese, whom he placed on a level with the Jews; and, by a decree of the parliament of Paris, passed in 1762, it was ordered to be burnt.

himself, that such merit as our philosopher's should be forgotten. While the epithets of ingenious, copious, elaborate, and refined are lavished among the mob, like medals at a coronation, the lucky prizes fall on every side, but not one on him. I could on this occasion make myself melancholy by considering the capriciousness of public taste, or the mutability of fortune; but during this fit of morality, lest my reader should sleep, I'll take a nap myself, and when I awake tell him my dream.

I imagined the Thames was frozen over, and I stood by its side. Several booths were erected upon the ice, and I was told by one of the spectators that Fashion Fair was going to begin. He added that every author who would carry his works there might probably find a very good reception. I was resolved, however, to observe the humors of the place in safety from the shore, sensible that ice was at best precarious, and having been always a little cowardly in my sleep.

Several of my acquaintance seemed much more hardy than I, and went over the ice with intrepidity. Some carried their works to the fair on sledges, some on carts, and those which were more voluminous were conveyed in wagons. Their temerity astonished me. I knew their cargoes were heavy, and expected every moment they would have gone to the bottom. They all entered the fair, however, in safety, and each soon after returned, to my great surprise, highly satisfied with his entertainment and the bargains he had brought away.

The success of such numbers at last began to operate upon me. If these, cried I, meet with favor and safety, some luck may, perhaps, for once attend the unfortunate. I am resolved to make a new adventure. The furniture, frippery, and fireworks of China have long been fashionably bought up. I'll try the fair with a small cargo of Chinese morality.

If the Chinese have contributed to vitiate our taste, I'll try how far they can help to improve our understanding. But as others have driven into the market in wagons, I'll cautiously begin by venturing with a wheelbarrow. Thus resolved, I baled up my goods and fairly ventured; when, upon just entering the fair, I fancied the ice that had supported a hundred wagons before cracked under me, and wheelbarrow and all went to the bottom.

Upon awaking from my reverie with the fright, I cannot help wishing that the pains taken in giving this correspondence an English dress had been employed in contriving new political systems, or new plots for farces. I might then have taken my station in the world, either as a poet or a philosopher, and made one in those little societies where men club to raise each other's reputation. But at present I belong to no particular class. I resemble one of those animals that has been forced from its forest to gratify human curiosity. My earliest wish was to escape unheeded through life; but I have been set up for half-pence, to fret and scamper at the end of my chain. Though none are injured by my rage, I am naturally too savage to court any friends by fawning, too obstinate to be taught new tricks, and too improvident to mind what may happen. I am appeased, though not contented. Too indolent for intrigue, and too timid to push for favor, I am—but what signifies what am I.

Ἐλπὶς καὶ σὺ τύχη μέγα χαίρετε · τὸν λιμέν εὗρον.
Οὐδὲν ἐμοὶ χ᾽ ὑμῖν · παίζετε τούς μετ᾽ ἐμε.

LETTERS

OF

A CITIZEN OF THE WORLD.

LETTER I.

INTRODUCTION.—A CHARACTER OF THE CHINESE PHILOSOPHER.[1]

To Mr. ——, Merchant in London.

Amsterdam.

SIR,—Yours of the 13th instant, covering two bills—one on Messrs. R. and D., value 478*l*. 10*s*., and the other on Mr. ——, value 285*l*.—duly came to hand; the former of which met with honor, but the other has been trifled with, and I am afraid will be returned protested.

The bearer of this is my friend, therefore let him be yours. He is a native of Honan, in China, and one who did me signal services, when he was a mandarin, and I a factor at Canton. By frequently conversing with the English there, he has learned the language, though entirely a stranger to their manners and customs. I am told he is a philosopher; I am sure he is an honest man; that to you will be his best recommendation, next to the consideration of his being the friend of, sir, yours, etc.

---

[1] The "Contents" of the several Letters were not, in Goldsmith's lifetime, prefixed to the Letters themselves, but added at the end of each volume by way of index. I have retained the useful transfer to the heading of each letter made by former editors.

II.—7

LETTER II.

From Lien Chi Altangi to ——, Merchant in Amsterdam.

London.

FRIEND OF MY HEART,—May the wings of peace rest upon thy dwelling, and the shield of conscience preserve thee from vice and misery! For all thy favors accept my gratitude and esteem, the only tributes a poor philosophic wanderer can return. Sure, Fortune is resolved to make me unhappy, when she gives others a power of testifying their friendship by actions, and leaves me only words to express the sincerity of mine.

I am perfectly sensible of the delicacy with which you endeavor to lessen your own merit and my obligations. By calling your late instances of friendship only a return for former favors, you would induce me to impute to your justice what I owe to your generosity.

The services I did you at Canton, justice, humanity, and my office bade me perform; those you have done me since my arrival at Amsterdam, no laws obliged you to, no justice required; even half your favors would have been greater than my most sanguine expectations.

The sum of money, therefore, which you privately conveyed into my baggage, when I was leaving Holland, and which I was ignorant of till my arrival in London, I must beg leave to return. You have been bred a merchant, and I a scholar; you consequently love money better than I. You can find pleasure in superfluity; I am perfectly content with what is sufficient; take, therefore, what is yours; it may give you some pleasure, even though you have no occasion to use it; my happiness it cannot improve, for I have already all that I want.

My passage by sea from Rotterdam to England was more painful to me than all the journeys I ever made on land. I have traversed the immeasurable wilds of Mogul Tartary; felt all the rigors of Siberian skies; I have had my repose a hundred times disturbed by invading savages, and have seen, without shrinking, the desert sands rise like a troubled ocean all around me; against these calamities I was armed with resolution; but in my passage to England, though nothing occurred that gave the mariners any uneasiness, to one who was never at sea before, all was a subject of astonishment and terror. To find the land disappear, to see our ship mount the waves swift as an arrow from the Tartar bow, to hear the wind howling through the cordage, to feel a sickness which depresses even the spirits of the brave; these were unexpected distresses, and consequently assaulted me unprepared to receive them!

You men of Europe think nothing of a voyage by sea. With us of China, a man who has been from sight of land is regarded upon his return with admiration. I have known some provinces where there is not even a name for the ocean. What a strange people, therefore, am I got among, who have founded an empire on this unstable element, who build cities upon billows that rise higher than the mountains of Tipartala, and make the deep more formidable than the wildest tempest!

Such accounts as these, I must confess, were my first motives for seeing England. These induced me to undertake a journey of seven hundred painful days, in order to examine its opulence, buildings, sciences, arts, and manufactures on the spot. Judge, then, my disappointment on entering London to see no signs of that opulence so much talked of abroad: wherever I turn, I am presented with a gloomy solemnity in the houses, the streets, and the inhabitants; none of that beautiful gilding which makes a principal ornament in Chinese architecture.[1] The streets of Nankin are sometimes strewed with gold-leaf; very different are those of London:

---

[1] "The beauty of the ornamental gate-ways in the middle of Chinese streets arises wholly from the painting and gilding, and not from the proportions, which are weak and flimsy."—Davis, *Chinese*, ii. 320.

in the midst of their pavements a great lazy puddle moves muddily along; heavy-laden machines, with wheels of unwieldy thickness, crowd up every passage; so that a stranger, instead of finding time for observation, is often happy if he has time to escape from being crushed to pieces.

The houses borrow very few ornaments from architecture; their chief decoration seems to be a paltry piece of painting hung out at their doors or windows, at once a proof of their indigence and vanity: their vanity, in each having one of those pictures exposed to public view; and their indigence, in being unable to get them better painted. In this respect, the fancy of their painters is also deplorable. Could you believe it? I have seen five black lions and three blue boars in less than the circuit of half a mile; and yet you know that animals of these colors are nowhere to be found except in the wild imaginations of Europe.[1]

From these circumstances in their buildings, and from the dismal looks of the inhabitants, I am induced to conclude that the nation is actually poor; and that, like the Persians, they make a splendid figure everywhere but at home. The proverb of Xixofou is, that a man's riches may be seen in his eyes; if we judge of the English by this rule, there is not a poorer nation under the sun.

I have been here but two days, so will not be hasty in my decisions; such letters as I shall write to Fipsihi in Moscow, I beg you'll endeavor to forward with all diligence; I shall send them open, in order that you may take copies or translations, as you are equally versed in the Dutch and Chinese languages. Dear friend, think of my absence with regret, as I sincerely regret yours; even while I write, I lament our separation. Farewell.

---

[1] "Our streets are filled with blue boars, black swans, and red lions; not to mention flying pigs, and hogs in armor. Strange! that one who has all the birds and beasts in nature to choose out of, should live at the sign of an *Ens Rationis*." —Addison. The house or door signs of London were taken down in 1766, and numbers and names substituted in their stead. The removal diminished considerably the picturesque character of the streets. See Letter LXXVII.

LETTER III.

THE DESCRIPTION OF LONDON CONTINUED.—THE LUXURY OF THE
ENGLISH, ITS BENEFITS.—THE FINE GENTLEMAN.—THE FINE
LADY.

*From Lien Chi Altangi, to the care of Fipsihi, resident in Moscow ; to be forwarded
by the Russian caravan to Fum Hoam, first President of the Ceremonial Academy
at Pekin, in China.*

THINK not, O thou guide of my youth, that absence can
impair my respect, or interposing trackless deserts blot your
reverend figure from my memory. The farther I travel I
feel the pain of separation with stronger force; those ties
that bind me to my native country and you, are still unbroken. By every remove, I only drag a greater length of
chain.[1]

Could I find aught worth transmitting from so remote a
region as this to which I have wandered, I should gladly send
it; but, instead of this, you must be contented with a renewal of my former professions, and an imperfect account of a
people with whom I am as yet but superficially acquainted.
The remarks of a man who has been but three days in the
country can only be those obvious circumstances which force
themselves upon the imagination. I consider myself here as
a newly created being introduced into a new world; every
object strikes with wonder and surprise. The imagination,
still unsated, seems the only active principle of the mind.
The most trifling occurrences give pleasure till the gloss of
novelty is worn away. When I have ceased to wonder, I
may possible grow wise ;[2] I may then call the reasoning principle to my aid, and compare those objects with each other,
which were before examined without reflection.

---

[1] "And drags at each remove a lengthening chain."—*The Traveller*, 1765.
[2] "But wondering is not the way to grow wise."—*Inquiry into Polite Learning.*

Behold me, then, in London, gazing at the strangers, and they at me; it seems they find somewhat absurd in my figure; and had I been never from home, it is possible I might find an infinite fund of ridicule in theirs; but by long travelling I am taught to laugh at folly alone, and to find nothing truly ridiculous but villany and vice.

When I had just quitted my native country, and crossed the Chinese wall, I fancied every deviation from the customs and manners of China was a departing from nature; I smiled at the blue lips and red foreheads of the Tonguese; and could hardly contain when I saw the Daures dress their heads with horns. The Ostiacs powdered with red earth; and the Calmuck beauties, tricked out in all the finery of sheep-skin, appeared highly ridiculous; but I soon perceived that the ridicule lay not in them, but in me; that I falsely condemned others of absurdity, because they happened to differ from a standard originally founded in prejudice or partiality.

I find no pleasure, therefore, in taxing the English with departing from nature in their external appearance, which is all I yet know of their character; it is possible they only endeavor to improve her simple plan, since every extravagance in dress proceeds from a desire of becoming more beautiful than nature made us; and this is so harmless a vanity, that I not only pardon but approve it. A desire to be more excellent than others is what actually makes us so, and as thousands find a livelihood in society by such appetites, none but the ignorant inveigh against them.

You are not insensible, most reverend Fum Hoam, what numberless trades, even among the Chinese, subsist by the harmless pride of each other. Your nose-borers, feet-swathers, tooth-stainers, eyebrow pluckers would all want bread should their neighbors want vanity. These vanities, however, employ much fewer hands in China than in England; and a fine gentleman, or a fine lady, here dressed up to the fashion, seems scarcely to have a single limb that does not suffer some distortions from art.

To make a fine gentleman, several trades are required, but chiefly a barber. You have undoubtedly heard of the Jewish

champion whose strength lay in his hair; one would think
that the English were for placing all wisdom there: to appear wise, nothing more is requisite here than for a man to
borrow hair from the heads of all his neighbors, and clap it
like a bush on his own; the distributors of law and physic
stick on such quantities, that it is almost impossible, even in
idea, to distinguish between the head and the hair.

Those whom I have now been describing affect the gravity
of the lion; those I am going to describe, more resemble the
pert vivacity of smaller animal. The barber, who is still master of the ceremonies, cuts their hair close to the crown; and
then with a composition of meal and hog's lard plasters the
whole in such a manner, as to make it impossible to distinguish whether the patient wears a cap or a plaster; but, to
make the picture more perfectly striking, conceive the tail of
some beast—a greyhound's tail, or a pig's tail, for instance—
appended to the back of the head, and reaching down to that
place where tails in other animals are generally seen to begin; thus betailed and bepowdered, the man of taste fancies he improves in beauty, dresses up his hard-featured
face in smiles, and attempts to look hideously tender. Thus
equipped, he is qualified to make love, and hopes for success,
more from the powder on the outside of his head than the
sentiments within.

Yet when I consider what sort of a creature the fine lady is
to whom he is supposed to pay his addresses, it is not strange
to find him thus equipped in order to please. She is herself
every whit as fond of powder and tails, and hog's lard, as he.
To speak my secret sentiments, most reverend Fum, the ladies
here are horridly ugly; I can hardly endure the sight of them;
they no way resemble the beauties of China; the Europeans
have a quite different idea of beauty from us. When I reflect on the small-footed perfections of an Eastern beauty,
how is it possible I should have eyes for a woman whose feet
are ten inches long? I shall never forget the beauties of my native city of Nangfew. How very broad their faces! how very
short their noses! how very little their eyes! how very thin
their lips! how very black their teeth! the snow on the tops

of Bao is not fairer than their cheeks : and their eyebrows as small as the line by the pencil of Quamsi. Here a lady with such perfections would be frightful ; Dutch and Chinese beauties, indeed, have some resemblance, but English women are entirely different ; red cheeks, big eyes, and teeth of a most odious whiteness are not only seen here, but wished for ; and then they have such masculine feet, as actually serve *some* for walking !

Yet uncivil as Nature has been, they seem resolved to outdo her in unkindness ; they use white powder, blue powder, and black powder for their hair, and a red powder for the face on some particular occasions.

They like to have the face of various colors, as among the Tartars of Koreki, frequently sticking on, with spittle, little black patches on every part of it, except on the tip of the nose, which I have never seen with a patch. You'll have a better idea of their manner of placing these spots, when I have finished a map of an English face patched up to the fashion, which shall shortly be sent to increase your curious collection of paintings, medals, and monsters.

But what surprises more than all the rest is what I have just now been credibly informed by one of this country. "Most ladies here," says he, "have two faces; one face to sleep in, and another to show in company : the first is generally reserved for the husband and family at home ; the other put on to please strangers abroad. The family face is often indifferent enough, but the out-door one looks something better ; this is always made at the toilet, where the looking-glass and toad-eater sit in council, and settle the complexion of the day."

I can't ascertain the truth of this remark ; however, it is actually certain that they wear more clothes within doors than without ; and I have seen a lady, who seemed to shudder at a breeze in her own apartment, appear half-naked in the streets. Farewell.

LETTER IV.

ENGLISH PRIDE.—LIBERTY.—AN INSTANCE OF BOTH.—NEWS-
PAPERS.—POLITENESS.

To the Same.

THE English seem as silent as the Japanese, yet vainer than
the inhabitants of Siam. Upon my arrival I attributed that
reserve to modesty, which I now find has its origin in pride.
Condescend to address them first, and you are sure of their acquaintance; stoop to flattery, and you conciliate their friendship and esteem. They bear hunger, cold, fatigue, and all the
miseries of life without shrinking; danger only calls forth
their fortitude; they even exult in calamity; but contempt is
what they cannot bear. An Englishman fears contempt more
than death; he often flies to death as a refuge from its pressure, and dies when he fancies the world has ceased to esteem
him.

Pride seems the source not only of their national vices, but
of their national virtues also. An Englishman is taught to
love his king as his friend, but to acknowledge no other master than the laws which himself has contributed to enact. He
despises those nations who, that one may be free, are all content to be slaves; who first lift a tyrant into terror, and then
shrink under his power as if delegated from heaven. Liberty
is echoed in all their assemblies; and thousands might be
found ready to offer up their lives for the sound, though perhaps not one of all the number understands its meaning. The
lowest mechanic, however, looks upon it as his duty to be a
watchful guardian of his country's freedom, and often uses a
language that might seem haughty, even in the mouth of the
great emperor who traces his ancestry to the moon.

A few days ago, passing by one of their prisons, I could
not avoid stopping, in order to listen to a dialogue, which I

thought might afford me some entertainment. The conversation was carried on between a debtor through the grate of his prison, a porter who had stopped to rest his burden, and a soldier at the window. The subject was upon a threatened invasion from France, and each seemed extremely anxious to rescue his country from the impending danger. "For my part," cries the prisoner, "the greatest of my apprehensions is for our freedom; if the French should conquer, what would become of English liberty? My dear friends, liberty is the Englishman's prerogative; we must preserve that at the expense of our lives; of that the French shall never deprive us; it is not to be expected that men who are slaves themselves would preserve our freedom should they happen to conquer." "Ay, slaves," cries the porter, "they are all slaves, fit only to carry burdens, every one of them. Before I would stoop to slavery, may this be my poison (and he held the goblet in his hand), may this be my poison[1]—but I would sooner list for a soldier."

The soldier, taking the goblet from his friend, with much awe fervently cried out, "It is not so much our liberties as our religion that would suffer by such a change; ay, our religion, my lads. May the devil sink me into flames" (such was the solemnity of his adjuration), "if the French should come over, but our religion would be utterly undone." So saying, instead of a libation, he applied the goblet to his lips, and confirmed his sentiments with a ceremony of the most persevering devotion.

In short, every man here pretends to be a politician; even the fair sex are sometimes found to mix the severity of national altercation with the blandishments of love, and often become conquerors by more weapons of destruction than their eyes.

This universal passion for politics is gratified by daily

---

[1] A phrase used in the "Adventures of a Strolling Player" (Essay XXI. Vol. III.), in "The Haunch of Venison," Vol. I. p. 69, and in Vol. III. p. 286:

> "And, madam," quoth he, "may this bit be my poison,
> A prettier dinner I never set eyes on."

gazettes, as with us at China.[1]   But as in ours the emperor endeavors to instruct his people, in theirs the people endeavor to instruct the administration.   You must not, however, imagine that they who compile these papers have any actual knowledge of the politics or the government of a state; they only collect their materials from the oracle of some coffeehouse; which oracle has himself gathered them the night before from a beau at a gaming-table, who has pillaged his knowledge from a great man's porter, who has had his information from the great man's gentleman, who has invented the whole story for his own amusement the night preceding.

The English, in general, seem fonder of gaining the esteem than the love of those they converse with.   This gives a formality to their amusements; their gayest conversations have something too wise for innocent relaxation; though in company you are seldom disgusted with the absurdity of a fool, you are seldom lifted into rapture by those strokes of vivacity which give instant though not permanent pleasure.

What they want, however, in gayety, they make up in politeness.   You smile at hearing me praise the English for their politeness; you who have heard very different accounts from the missionaries at Pekin, who have seen such a different behavior in their merchants and seamen at home.   But I must still repeat it, the English seem more polite than any of their neighbors; their great art in this respect lies in endeavoring, while they oblige, to lessen the force of the favor. Other countries are fond of obliging a stranger; but seem desirous that he should be sensible of the obligation.   The English confer their kindness with an appearance of indifference, and give away benefits with an air as if they despised them.

Walking a few days ago, between an English and a French man, into the suburbs of the city, we were overtaken by a

---

[1] When Lord Macartney visited China gazettes were published at Pekin, under the authority of government.   The various appointments throughout the empire, the remission of taxes to districts suffering by dearth, the sovereign's rewards for extraordinary services, remarkable instances of longevity, and even cases of *crim. con.* were regularly recorded.   See MACARTNEY's *Embassy*, ii. 296.

heavy shower of rain. I was unprepared; but they had each
large coats, which defended them from what seemed to me a
perfect inundation. The Englishman seeing me shrink from
the weather, accosted me thus: " Pshaw, man, what dost shrink
at ? here, take this coat; I don't want it; I find it no way useful to me; I had as lief be without it." The Frenchman began to show his politeness in turn. " My dear friend," cries
he, " why won't you oblige me by making use of my coat?
You see how well it defends me from the rain; I should not
choose to part with it to others, but to such a friend as you I
could even part with my skin to do him service."

From such minute instances as these, most reverend Fum
Hoam, I am sensible your sagacity will collect instruction.
The volume of nature is the book of knowledge; and he
becomes most wise who makes the most judicious selection.
Farewell.

LETTER V.

ENGLISH PASSION FOR POLITICS.—A SPECIMEN OF A NEWSPAPER.
    —CHARACTERISTICS OF THE MANNERS OF DIFFERENT COUN-
    TRIES.

To the Same.

I HAVE already informed you of the singular passion of
this nation for politics. An Englishman, not satisfied with
finding, by his own prosperity, the contending powers of
Europe properly balanced, desires also to know the precise
value of every weight in either scale. To gratify this curiosity, a leaf of political instruction is served up every morning
with tea: when our politician has feasted upon this, he repairs to a coffee-house, in order to ruminate upon what he has
read, and increase his collection; from thence he proceeds to
the ordinary, inquires what news, and treasuring up every
acquisition there, hunts about all the evening in quest of
more, and carefully adds it to the rest. Thus at night he retires home, full of the important advices of the day; when
lo! awaking next morning, he finds the instructions of yester-

day a collection of absurdity or palpable falsehood. This one would think a mortifying repulse in the pursuit of wisdom; yet our politician, no way discouraged, hunts on, in order to collect fresh materials, and in order to be again disappointed.

I have often admired the commercial spirit which prevails over Europe; have been surprised to see them carry on a traffic with productions that an Asiatic stranger would deem entirely useless. It is a proverb in China, that a European suffers not even his spittle to be lost; the maxim, however, is not sufficiently strong, since they sell even their lies to great advantage. Every nation drives a considerable trade in this commodity with their neighbors.

An English dealer in this way, for instance, has only to ascend to his workhouse, and manufacture a turbulent speech, averred to be spoken in the senate; or a report supposed to be dropped at court; a piece of scandal that strikes at a popular mandarin; or a secret treaty between two neighboring powers. When finished, these goods are baled up, and consigned to a factor abroad, who sends in return two battles, three sieges, and a shrewd letter filled with dashes ——, blanks   , and stars * * * * of great importance.

Thus you perceive that a single gazette is the joint manufacture of Europe; and he who would peruse it with a philosophical eye might perceive in every paragraph something characteristic of the nation to which it belongs. A map does not exhibit a more distinct view of the boundaries and situation of every country, than its news does a picture of the genius and the morals of its inhabitants. The superstition and erroneous delicacy of Italy, the formality of Spain, the cruelty of Portugal, the fears of Austria, the confidence of Prussia, the levity of France, the avarice of Holland, the pride of England, the absurdity of Ireland, and the national partiality of Scotland are all conspicuous in every page.

But, perhaps, you may find more satisfaction in a real newspaper, than in my description of one; I therefore send a specimen, which may serve to exhibit the manner of their being written, and distinguish the characters of the various nations which are united in its composition.

Naples.—"We have lately dug up here a curious Etruscan monument, broken in two in the raising. The characters are scarce visible; but Nugosi, the learned antiquary, supposes it to have been erected in honor of Picus, a Latin king, as one of the lines may be plainly distinguished to begin with a P. It is hoped this discovery will produce something valuable, as the literati of our twelve academies are deeply engaged in the disquisition."

Pisa.—"Since father Fudgi,[1] prior of St. Gilbert's, has gone to reside at Rome, no miracles have been performed at the shrine of St. Gilbert: the devout begin to grow uneasy, and some begin actually to fear that St. Gilbert has forsaken them with the reverend father."

Lucca.—"The administrators of our serene republic have frequent conferences upon the part they shall take in the present commotions of Europe. Some are for sending a body of their troops, consisting of one company of foot and six horsemen, to make a diversion in favor of the empress-queen; others are as strenuous assertors of the Prussian interest; what turn these debates may take, time only can discover. However, certain it is, we shall be able to bring into the field, at the opening of the next campaign, seventy-five armed men, a commander-in-chief, and two drummers of great experience."

Spain.—"Yesterday the new king showed himself to his subjects, and, after having stayed half an hour in his balcony, retired to the royal apartment. The night concluded on this extraordinary occasion with illuminations, and other demonstrations of joy. The queen is more beautiful than the rising sun, and reckoned one of the first wits in Europe; she had a glorious opportunity of displaying the readiness of her invention, and her skill in repartee, lately at court. The Duke of Lerma, coming up to her with a low bow and a smile, and presenting a nosegay set with diamonds, 'Madam,' cries he, 'I am your most obedient humble servant.' 'Oh, sir,' replies the queen, without any prompter, or the least hesitation, 'I'm

---

[1] Father Fudgi was doubtless the original of *Fudge*, the persevering exclamation of Burchell in "The Vicar of Wakefield."

very proud of the very great honor you do me.'   Upon which
she made a low courtesy, and all the courtiers fell a-laughing
at the readiness and the smartness of her reply."

Lisbon.—"Yesterday we had an *auto-da-fé*, at which were
burnt three young women accused of heresy, one of them
of exquisite beauty, two Jews, and an old woman convicted
of being a witch: one of the friars, who attended this last,
reports that he saw the devil fly out of her, at the stake, in
the shape of a flame of fire.   The populace behaved on this
occasion with great good-humor, joy, and sincere devotion.[1]

"Our merciful sovereign has been for some time past recovered of his fright; though so atrocious an attempt[2] deserved to exterminate half the nation, yet he has been graciously pleased to spare the lives of his subjects, and not above
five hundred have been broken upon the wheel, or otherwise
executed,[3] upon this horrid occasion."

Vienna.—"We have received certain advices that a party
of twenty thousand Austrians, having attacked a much superior body of Prussians, put them all to flight, and took the
rest prisoners of war."

Berlin.—"We have received certain advices that a party
of twenty thousand Prussians, having attacked a much superior body of Austrians, put them to flight, and took a great
number of prisoners, with their military chest, cannon, and
baggage.   Though we have not succeeded this campaign to
our wishes; yet, when we think of him who commands us,

---

[1] "At the *auto-da-fé* at Lisbon, on the 20th September (1761), the number of
criminals amounted to fifty-four, including three in effigy.   Father Malagrida was
the only person burnt at the stake for writing heretical books, and pretending to
the spirit of prophecy and revelations.   This *auto* exceeded all before it in magnificence; the boxes were built round the square *Da Rosico*, and all the regiments
of horse and foot attended upon duty.   The nobility, judges, and great officers of
state were present, and a grand entertainment was given in the convent by the in-
quisitor Nuno de Mello."—*Gentleman's Mag.* for 1761, vol. xxxi. p. 478.

[2] A conspiracy against the life of the King of Portugal, attempted in September, 1758, as he was going at night through the streets of Lisbon.   Many Jesuits,
and several of the noble families of the dukes D'Aveiro and marquises of Tavora,
were put to death for it.

[3] Some of the assassins were burnt alive, and their ashes thrown into the sea.

we rest in security: while we sleep, our king is watchful for our safety."

Paris.—"We shall soon strike a signal blow. We have seventeen flat-bottomed boats at Havre. The people are in excellent spirits, and our ministers make no difficulty in raising the supplies.

"We are all undone; the people are discontented to the last degree; the ministers are obliged to have recourse to the most rigorous methods to raise the expenses of the war.

"Our distresses are great; but Madame Pompadour continues to supply our king, who is now growing old, with a fresh lady every night. His health, thank Heaven! is still pretty well; nor is he in the least unfit, as was reported, for any kind of royal exercitation. He was so frightened at the affair of Damiens,[1] that his physicians were apprehensive lest his reason should suffer, but that wretch's tortures soon composed the kingly terrors of his breast."

England.—"Wanted an usher to an academy. N.B.—He must be able to read, dress hair, and must have had the small-pox."

Dublin.—"We hear that there is a benevolent subscription on foot among the nobility and gentry of this kingdom, who are great patrons of merit, in order to assist Black and All Black in his contest with the Paddereen mare.[2] We hear from Germany that Prince Ferdinand has gained a complete victory, and taken twelve kettle-drums, five standards, and four wagons of ammunition, prisoners of war."

Edinburgh.—"We are positive when we say that Saunders M'Gregor, who was lately executed for horse-stealing, is not a Scotchman, but born in Carrickfergus." Farewell.

---

[1] "Luke's iron crown and Damiens' bed of steel."—*The Traveller.*

[2] A celebrated Irish racer. "There has been more money spent in the encouragement of the Padareen mare there [in Ireland] in one season, than given in rewards to learned men since the times of Usher."—*Goldsmith to Daniel Hodson, Dec.* 27, 1757.

LETTER VI.

HAPPINESS LOST BY SEEKING AFTER REFINEMENT.—THE CHINESE
PHILOSOPHER'S DISGRACES.

*Fum Hoam, first President of the Ceremonial Academy at Pekin, to Lien Chi
Altangi, the discontented Wanderer: by the way of Moscow.*

WHETHER sporting on the flowery banks of the river Irtis,
or scaling the steepy mountains of Douchenour; whether
traversing the black deserts of Kobi, or giving lessons of politeness to the savage inhabitants of Europe; in whatever
country, whatever climate, and whatever circumstances, all
hail! May Tien, the universal soul, take you under his protection, and inspire you with a superior portion of himself!

How long, my friend, shall an enthusiasm for knowledge
continue to obstruct your happiness, and tear you from all
the connections that make life pleasing? How long will you
continue to rove from climate to climate, circled by thousands, and yet without a friend, feeling all the inconveniences
of a crowd, and all the anxiety of being alone?

I know you will reply, that the refined pleasure of growing
every day wiser is a sufficient recompense for every inconvenience. I know you will talk of the vulgar satisfaction of
soliciting happiness from sensual enjoyment only; and probably enlarge upon the exquisite raptures of sentimental bliss.
Yet, believe me, friend, you are deceived; all our pleasures,
though seemingly never so remote from sense, derive their
origin from some one of the senses. The most exquisite
demonstration in mathematics, or the most pleasing disquisition in metaphysics, if it does not ultimately tend to increase
some sensual satisfaction, is delightful only to fools, or to
men who have by long habit contracted a false idea of pleasure; and he who separates sensual and sentimental enjoyments, seeking happiness from mind alone, is, in fact, as
wretched as the naked inhabitant of the forest, who places
II.—8

all happiness in the first, regardless of the latter. There are two extremes in this respect—the savage, who swallows down the draught of pleasure without staying to reflect on his happiness; and the sage, who passeth the cup while he reflects on the conveniences of drinking.

It is with a heart full of sorrow, my dear Altangi, that I must inform you, that what the world calls happiness must now be yours no longer. Our great emperor's displeasure at your leaving China, contrary to the rules of our government and the immemorial custom of the empire, has produced the most terrible effects. Your wife, daughter, and the rest of your family, have been seized by his order, and appropriated to his use; all, except your son, are now the peculiar property of him who possesses all: him I have hidden from the officers employed for this purpose; and even at the hazard of my life I have concealed him. The youth seems obstinately bent on finding you out, wherever you are; he is determined to face every danger that opposes his pursuit. Though yet but fifteen, all his father's virtues and obstinacy sparkle in his eyes, and mark him as one destined to no mediocrity of fortune.

You see, my dearest friend, what imprudence has brought thee to; from opulence, a tender family, surrounding friends, and your master's esteem, it has reduced thee to want, persecution, and, still worse, to our mighty monarch's displeasure. Want of prudence is too frequently the want of virtue; nor is there on earth a more powerful advocate for vice than poverty. As I shall endeavor to guard thee from the one, so guard thyself from the other; and still think of me with affection and esteem. Farewell.

LETTER VII.

THE TIE OF WISDOM ONLY TO MAKE US HAPPY.—THE BENEFITS
OF TRAVELLING UPON THE MORALS OF A PHILOSOPHER.

From Lien Chi Altangi, to Fum Hoam, first President of the Ceremonial Academy
in China.

The Editor thinks proper to acquaint the reader, that the greatest part of the following letter seems to him to be little more than a rhapsody of sentences borrowed from Confucius, the Chinese philosopher.

A WIFE, a daughter, carried into captivity to expiate my
offence, a son scarce yet arrived at maturity, resolving to encounter every danger in the pious pursuit of one who has
undone him—these, indeed, are circumstances of distress;
though my tears were more precious than the gem of Gol-
conda, yet would they fall upon such an occasion.

But I submit to the stroke of Heaven: I hold the volume
of Confucius in my hand, and as I read, grow humble, and
patient, and wise. We should feel sorrow, says he, but not
sink under its oppression. The heart of a wise man should
resemble a mirror, which reflects every object without being
sullied by any. The wheel of fortune turns incessantly
round; and who can say within himself, I shall to-day be up-
permost? We should hold the immutable mean that lies between insensibility and anguish; our attempts should be not
to extinguish nature, but to repress it; not to stand unmoved
at distress, but endeavor to turn every disaster to our own
advantage. Our greatest glory is, not in never falling, but in
rising every time we fall.

I fancy myself at present, O thou reverend disciple of Taou,[1]

---

[1] "Taou appeared nearly simultaneously with Confucius. As far as can be
gathered of the real drift of his doctrines, he seems to have inculcated a contempt
of riches and honors, and all worldly distinctions, and to have aimed, like Epicu-
rus, at subduing every passion that could interfere with personal tranquillity and
self-enjoyment."—DAVIS, vol. ii. p. 114.

more than a match for all that can happen. The chief business of my life has been to procure wisdom, and the chief object of that wisdom was to be happy. My attendance on your lectures, my conferences with the missionaries of Europe, and all my subsequent adventures upon quitting China, were calculated to increase the sphere of my happiness, not my curiosity. Let European travellers cross seas and deserts merely to measure the height of a mountain, to describe the cataract of a river, or tell the commodities which every country may produce: merchants or geographers, perhaps, may find profit by such discoveries, but what advantage can accrue to a philosopher from such accounts, who is desirous of understanding the human heart, who seeks to know the *men* of every country, who desires to discover those differences which result from climate, religion, education, prejudice, and partiality?

I should think my time very ill-bestowed, were the only fruits of my adventures to consist in being able to tell that a tradesman of London lives in a house three times as high as that of our great emperor; that the ladies wear longer clothes than the men; that the priests are dressed in colors which we are taught to detest, and that their soldiers wear scarlet, which is with us the symbol of peace and innocence. How many travellers are there who confine their relations to such minute and useless particulars! For one who enters into the genius of those nations with whom he has conversed, who discloses their morals, their opinions, the ideas which they entertain of religious worship, the intrigues of their ministers, and their skill in sciences, there are twenty who only mention some idle particulars, which can be of no real use to a true philosopher. All their remarks tend neither to make themselves nor others more happy; they no way contribute to control their passions, to bear adversity, to inspire true virtue, or raise a detestation of vice.

Men may be very learned, and yet very miserable; it is easy to be a deep geometrician, or a sublime astronomer, but very difficult to be a good man. I esteem, therefore, the traveller who instructs the heart, but despise him who only indulges the imagination. A man who leaves home to mend himself and others is a philosopher; but he who goes from country to country, guided by the blind impulse of curiosity, is only a vagabond. From Zerdusht[1] down to him of Tyanæa,[2] I honor all those great names who endeavor to unite the world by their travels: such men grew wiser as well as better, the farther they departed from home, and seemed like rivers, whose streams are not only increased, but refined, as they travel from their source.

For my own part, my greatest glory is, that travelling has not more steeled my constitution against all the vicissitudes of climate, and all the depressions of fatigue, than it has my mind against the accidents of fortune, or the accesses of despair. Farewell.

LETTER VIII.

THE CHINESE DECEIVED BY A PROSTITUTE IN THE STREETS OF LONDON.

To the Same.

How insupportable, O thou possessor of heavenly wisdom, would be this separation, this immeasurable distance from my friends, were I not able thus to delineate my heart upon paper, and to send thee daily a map of my mind!

I am every day better reconciled to the people among whom I reside, and begin to fancy that in time I shall find them more opulent, more charitable, and more hospitable than I at first imagined. I begin to learn somewhat of their manners and customs, and to see reasons for several deviations which they make from us, from whom all other nations derive their politeness as well as their original.

In spite of taste, in spite of prejudice, I now begin to think their women tolerable. I can now look on a languishing

---

[1] Zoroaster.

[2] Apollonius of Tyanæa, the celebrated traveller, astrologer, etc., who numbered Vespasian among his dupes.

blue eye without disgust, and pardon a set of teeth even though whiter than ivory. I now begin to fancy there is no universal standard for beauty. The truth is, the manners of the ladies in this city are so very open and so vastly engaging, that I am inclined to pass over the more glaring defects of their persons, since compensated by the more solid, yet latent beauties of the mind. What though they want black teeth, or are deprived of the allurements of feet no bigger than their thumbs, yet still they have souls, my friend; such souls, so free, so pressing, so hospitable, and so engaging! I have received more invitations in the streets of London from the sex in one night, than I have met with at Pekin in twelve revolutions of the moon.

Every evening, as I return home from my usual solitary excursions, I am met by several of those well-disposed daughters of hospitality, at different times, and in different streets, richly dressed, and with minds not less noble than their appearance. You know that nature has indulged me with a person by no means agreeable; yet are they too generous to object to my homely appearance; they feel no repugnance at my broad face and flat nose; they perceive me to be a stranger, and that alone is a sufficient recommendation. They even seem to think it their duty to do the honors of the country by every act of complaisance in their power. One takes me under the arm, and in a manner forces me along; another catches me round the neck, and desires to partake in this office of hospitality; while a third, kinder still, invites me to refresh my spirits with wine. Wine is in England reserved only for the rich; yet here even wine is given away to the stranger!

A few nights ago, one of these generous creatures, dressed all in white, and flaunting like a meteor by my side, forcibly attended me home to my own apartment. She seemed charmed with the elegance of the furniture, and the convenience of my situation: and well indeed she might, for I have hired an apartment for not less than two shillings of their money every week. But her civility did not rest here; for at parting, being desirous to know the hour and perceiving my watch out of order, she kindly took it to be repaired by a relation of her own, which you may imagine will save some expense; and she assures me that it will cost her nothing. I shall have it back in a few days, when mended, and am preparing a proper speech, expressive of my gratitude on the occasion. "Celestial excellence," I intend to say, "happy I am in having found out, after many painful adventures, a land of innocence, and a people of humanity: I may rove into other climes, and converse with nations yet unknown, but where shall I meet a soul of such purity as that which resides in thy breast? Sure thou hast been nurtured by the bill of the Shin Shin, or sucked the breasts of the provident Gin Hiung. The melody of thy voice could rob the Chong Fou of her whelps, or inveigle the Boh that lives in the midst of the waters. Thy servant shall ever retain a sense of thy favors, and one day boast of thy virtue, sincerity, and truth, among the daughters of China." Adieu.

LETTER IX.

THE LICENTIOUSNESS OF THE ENGLISH WITH REGARD TO WOMEN. —A CHARACTER OF A WOMAN'S MAN.

To the Same.

I HAVE been deceived! She whom I fancied a daughter of paradise has proved to be one of the infamous disciples of Han! I have lost a trifle; I have gained the consolation of having discovered a deceiver. I once more, therefore, relax into my former indifference with regard to the English ladies; they once more begin to appear disagreeable in my eyes. Thus is my whole time passed in forming conclusions which the next minute's experience may probably destroy; the present moment becomes a comment on the past, and I improve rather in humility than wisdom.

Their laws and religion forbid the English to keep more than one woman; I therefore concluded that prostitutes were banished from society. I was deceived; every man here keeps as many wives as he can maintain. The laws are cemented with blood, praised, and disregarded. The very Chinese, whose religion allows him two wives, takes not half the liberties of the English in this particular. Their laws may be compared to the books of the Sibyls; they are held in great veneration, but seldom read, or seldomer understood; even those who pretend to be their guardians dispute about the meaning of many of them, and confess their ignorance of others. The law, therefore, which commands them to have but one wife is strictly observed only by those for whom one is more than sufficient, or by such as have not money to buy two. As for the rest, they violate it publicly, and some glory in its violation. They seem to think, like the Persians, that they give evident marks of manhood by increasing their seraglio. A mandarin, therefore, here generally keeps four wives, a gentleman three, and a stage-player two. As for the magistrates, the country justices, and squires, they are employed first in debauching young virgins, and then punishing the transgression.

From such a picture you will be apt to conclude that he who employs four ladies for his amusement has four times as much constitution to spare as he who is contented with one; that a mandarin is much cleverer than a gentleman, and a gentleman than a player; and yet it is quite the reverse: a mandarin is frequently supported on spindle shanks, appears emaciated by luxury, and is obliged to have recourse to variety, merely from the weakness, not the vigor, of his constitution—the number of his wives being the most equivocal symptom of his virility.

Beside the country squire, there is also another set of men whose whole employment consists in corrupting beauty. These the silly part of the fair sex call amiable; the more sensible part of them, however, give them the title of abominable. You will probably demand what are the talents of a man thus caressed by the majority of the opposite sex? what talents, or what beauty is he possessed of superior to the rest of his fellows? To answer you directly, he has neither talents nor beauty, but then he is possessed of impudence and assiduity.   With assiduity and impudence, men of all ages and all figures may commence admirers.   I have even been told of some who made professions of expiring for love, when all the world could perceive they were going to die of old age; and what is more surprising still, such battered beaus are generally most infamously successful.

A fellow of this kind employs three hours every morning in dressing his head, by which is understood only his hair. He is a professed admirer, not of any particular lady, but of the whole sex.   He is to suppose every lady has caught cold every night, which gives him an opportunity of calling to see how she does the next morning.   He is upon all occasions to show himself in very great pain for the ladies: if a lady drops even a pin he is to fly in order to present it.   He never speaks to a lady without advancing his mouth to her ear, by which he frequently addresses more senses than one.   Upon proper occasions he looks excessively tender.   This is performed by laying his hand upon his heart, shutting his eyes, and showing his teeth.   He is excessively fond of dancing a minuet with the ladies, by which is only meant walking round the floor eight or ten times with his hat on, affecting great gravity, and sometimes looking tenderly on his partner.   He never affronts any man himself, and never resents an affront from another.   He has an infinite variety of small talk upon all occasions, and laughs when he has nothing more to say. Such is the killing creature who prostrates himself to the sex till he has undone them ; all whose submissions are the effects of design, and who to please the ladies almost becomes himself a lady.

LETTER X.

THE JOURNEY OF THE CHINESE FROM PEKIN TO MOSCOW.—THE
CUSTOMS OF THE DAURES.

To the Same.

I ʜᴀᴠᴇ hitherto given you no account of my journey from
China to Europe, of my travels through countries where Nature sports in primeval rudeness, where she pours forth her
wonders in solitude; countries from whence the rigorous climate, the sweeping inundation, the drifted desert, the howling forest, and mountains of immeasurable height banish the
husbandman and spread extensive desolation; countries where
the brown Tartar wanders for a precarious subsistence, with
a heart that never felt pity, himself more hideous than the
wilderness he makes.

You will easily conceive the fatigue of crossing vast tracts
of land, either desolate, or still more dangerous by its inhabitants; the retreat of men who seem driven from society in
order to make war upon all the human race; nominally professing a subjection to Muscovy or China, but without any
resemblance to the countries on which they depend.

After I had crossed the great wall, the first objects that
presented themselves were the remains of desolated cities, and
all the magnificence of venerable ruin. There were to be
seen temples of beautiful structure, statues wrought by the
hand of a master, and around, a country of luxuriant plenty;
but not one single inhabitant to reap the bounties of Nature.
These were prospects that might humble the pride of kings,
and repress human vanity. I asked my guide the cause of
such desolation. These countries, says he, were once the
dominions of a Tartar prince; and these ruins the seat of
arts, elegance, and ease. This prince waged an unsuccessful
war with one of the emperors of China; he was conquered,
his cities plundered, and all his subjects carried into captivity.

Such are the effects of the ambition of kings! Ten dervises, says the Indian proverb, shall sleep in peace upon a single carpet, while two kings shall quarrel, though they have kingdoms to divide them. Sure, my friend, the cruelty and the pride of man have made more deserts than Nature ever made! she is kind, but man is ungrateful.

Proceeding in my journey through this pensive scene of desolated beauty, in a few days I arrived among the Daures, a nation still dependent on China. Xaizigar is their principal city, which, compared with those of Europe, scarcely deserves the name. The governors, and other officers, who are sent yearly from Pekin, abuse their authority, and often take the wives and daughters of the inhabitants to themselves. The Daures, accustomed to base submission, feel no resentment at these injuries, or stifle what they feel. Custom and necessity teach even barbarians the same art of dissimulation, that ambition and intrigue inspire in the breasts of the polite. Upon beholding such unlicensed stretches of power, alas! thought I, how little does our wise and good emperor know of these intolerable exactions! these provinces are too distant for complaint, and too insignificant to expect redress. The more distant the government, the honester should be the governor to whom it is intrusted; for hope of impunity is a strong inducement to violation.

The religion of the Daures is more absurd than even that of the sectaries of Fohi. How would you be surprised, O sage disciple and follower of Confucius! you who believe one eternal intelligent cause of all, should you be present at the barbarous ceremonies of this infatuated people! How would you deplore the blindness and folly of mankind! His boasted reason seems only to light him astray, and brutal instinct more regularly points out the path to happiness. Could you think it? they adore a wicked divinity; they fear him and they worship him; they imagine him a malicious being, ready to injure and ready to be appeased. The men and women assemble at midnight in a hut, which serves for a temple. A priest stretches himself on the ground, and all the people pour forth the most horrid cries, while drums and timbrels swell the infernal concert. After this dissonance, miscalled music, has continued about two hours, the priest rises from the ground, assumes an air of inspiration, grows big with the inspiring demon, and pretends to a skill in futurity.

In every country, my friend, the bonzes, the brachmans, and the priests deceive the people: all reformations begin from the laity; the priests point us out the way to heaven with their fingers, but stand still themselves, nor seem to travel toward the country in view.

The customs of this people correspond to their religion. They keep their dead for three days on the same bed where the person died; after which they bury him in a grave moderately deep, but with the head still uncovered. Here for several days they present him different sorts of meats; which when they perceive he does not consume, they fill up the grave, and desist from desiring him to eat for the future. How, how can mankind be guilty of such strange absurdity? to entreat a dead body already putrid to partake of the banquet! Where, I again repeat it, is human reason? not only some men, but whole nations, seem divested of its illumination. Here we observe a whole country adoring a divinity through fear, and attempting to feed the dead. These are their most serious and most religious occupations; are these men rational, or are not the apes of Borneo more wise?

Certain I am, O thou instructor of my youth, that without philosophers, without some few virtuous men, who seem to be of a different nature from the rest of mankind, without such as these the worship of a wicked divinity would surely be established over every part of the earth. Fear guides more to their duty than gratitude: for one man who is virtuous from the love of virtue, from the obligation which he thinks he lies under to the Giver of All, there are ten thousand who are good only from their apprehensions of punishment. Could these last be persuaded, as the Epicureans were, that heaven had no thunders in store for the villain, they would no longer continue to acknowledge subordination, or thank that Being who gave them existence. Adieu.

LETTER XI.

THE BENEFITS OF LUXURY IN MAKING A PEOPLE MORE WISE AND HAPPY.

To the Same.

FROM such a picture of nature in primeval simplicity, tell me, my much respected friend, are you in love with fatigue and solitude? Do you sigh for the severe frugality of the wandering Tartar, or regret being born amid the luxury and dissimulation of the polite? Rather tell me, has not every kind of life vices peculiarly its own? Is it not a truth, that refined countries have more vices, but those not so terrible; barbarous nations few, and they of the most hideous complexion? Perfidy and fraud are the vices of civilized nations, credulity and violence those of the inhabitants of the desert. Does the luxury of the one produce half the evils of the inhumanity of the other? Certainly, those philosophers who declaim against luxury have but little understood its benefits; they seem insensible that to luxury we owe not only the greatest part of our knowledge, but even of our virtues.

It may sound fine in the mouth of a declaimer, when he talks of subduing our appetites, of teaching every sense to be content with a bare sufficiency, and of supplying only the wants of nature; but is there not more satisfaction in indulging those appetites, if with innocence and safety, than in restraining them? Am not I better pleased in enjoyment, than in the sullen satisfaction of thinking that I can live without enjoyment? The more various our artificial necessities, the wider is our circle of pleasure; for all pleasure consists in obviating necessities as they rise; luxury, therefore, as it increases our wants, increases our capacity for happiness.

Examine the history of any country remarkable for opulence and wisdom, you will find they would never have been wise had they not been first luxurious; you will find poets, philosophers, and even patriots marching in luxury's train. The reason is obvious: we then only are curious after knowledge when we find it connected with sensual happiness. The senses ever point out the way, and reflection comments upon the discovery. Inform a native of the desert of Kobi of the exact measure of the parallax of the moon, he finds no satisfaction at all in the information; he wonders how any could take such pains, and lay out such treasure, in order to solve so useless a difficulty; but connect it with his happiness, by showing that it improves navigation, that by such an investigation he may have a warmer coat, a better gun, or a finer knife, and he is instantly in raptures at so great an improvement. In short, we only desire to know what we desire to possess; and whatever we may talk against it, luxury adds the spur to curiosity, and gives us a desire of becoming more wise.

But not our knowledge only, but our virtues are improved by luxury. Observe the brown savage of Thibet, to whom the fruits of the spreading pomegranate supply food, and its branches a habitation. Such a character has few vices, I grant, but those he has are of the most hideous nature; rapine and cruelty are scarce crimes in his eye; neither pity nor tenderness, which ennoble every virtue, has any place in his heart; he hates his enemies, and kills those he subdues. On the other hand, the polite Chinese and civilized European seem even to love their enemies. I have just now seen an instance where the English have succored those enemies whom their own countrymen actually refused to relieve.[1]

The greater the luxuries of every country, the more closely, politically speaking, is that country united. Luxury is the child of society alone; the luxurious man stands in need of a thousand different artists to furnish out his happiness; it is more likely, therefore, that he should be a good citizen who

---

[1] Alluding to a large public subscription then going on in England for the relief of distressed French prisoners of war. The subject occurs again in Letter xxiii.

is connected by motives of self-interest with so many, than the abstemious man who is united to none.

In whatsoever light, therefore, we consider luxury—whether as employing a number of hands naturally too feeble for more laborious employment, as finding a variety of occupation for others who might be totally idle, or as furnishing out new inlets to happiness without encroaching on mutual property—in whatever light we regard it, we shall have reason to stand up in its defence, and the sentiment of Confucius still remains unshaken: "That we should enjoy as many of the luxuries of life as are consistent with our own safety and the prosperity of others; and that he who finds out a new pleasure is one of the most useful members of society."[1]

LETTER XII.

THE FUNERAL SOLEMNITIES OF THE ENGLISH.—THEIR PASSION FOR FLATTERING EPITAPHS.

To the Same.

FROM the funeral solemnities of the Daures, who think themselves the politest people in the world, I must make a

---

[1] "On Tuesday, April 13, 1775, Johnson, Goldsmith, and I dined at General Oglethorpe's. Goldsmith expatiated on the common topic that the race of our people was degenerated, and that this was owing to luxury. JOHNSON: 'Sir, in the first place, I doubt the fact. I believe there are as many tall men in England now as ever there were. But, secondly, supposing the stature of our people to be diminished, that is not owing to luxury; for, sir, consider to how very small a proportion of our people luxury can reach. . . . Luxury, so far as it reaches the poor, will do good to the race of people; it will strengthen and multiply them. . . . Let us take a walk from Charing Cross to Whitechapel, through, I suppose, the greatest series of shops in the world: what is there in any of these shops (if you except gin-shops) that can do any human being any harm?' GOLDSMITH: 'Well, sir, I'll accept your challenge. The very next shop to Northumberland House is a pickle-shop.' JOHNSON: 'Well, sir, do we not know that a maid can in one afternoon make pickles sufficient to serve a whole family for a year? nay, that five pickle-shops can serve all the kingdom? Besides, sir, there is no harm done to anybody by the making of pickles, or the eating of pickles.'"—BOSWELL, by Croker, p. 251.

transition to the funeral solemnities of the English, who think themselves as polite as they. The numberless ceremonies which are used here when a person is sick appear to me so many evident marks of fear and apprehension. Ask an Englishman, however, whether he is afraid of death, and he boldly answers in the negative; but observe his behavior in circumstances of approaching sickness, and you will find his actions give his assertions the lie.

The Chinese are very sincere in this respect; they hate to die, and they confess their terrors;[1] a great part of their life is spent in preparing things proper for their funeral. A poor artisan will spend half his income in providing himself a tomb twenty years before he wants it; and denies himself the necessaries of life, that he may be amply provided for when he shall want them no more.[2]

But people of distinction in England really deserve pity; for they die in circumstances of the most extreme distress. It is an established rule never to let a man know that he is dying; physicians are sent for, the clergy are called, and everything passes in silent solemnity round the sick-bed. The patient is in agonies, looks round for pity; yet not a single creature will say that he is dying. If he is possessed of fortune, his relations entreat him to make his will, as it may restore the tranquillity of his mind. He is desired to undergo the rites of the Church, for decency requires it. His friends take their leave only because they do not care to see him in pain. In short, a hundred stratagems are used to make him do what he might have been induced to perform only by being told, "Sir, you are past all hopes, and had as good think decently of dying."

Besides all this, the chamber is darkened, the whole house echoes to the cries of the wife, the lamentations of the chil-

---

[1] The Chinese seldom mention death except by a circumlocution, as "to become immortal;" that is, in the modified sense of the Buddhists.—DAVIS's *Chinese*, vol. i. p. 299.

[2] Of all the subjects of their care, there are none which the Chinese so religiously attend to as the tombs of their ancestors, conceiving that any neglect is sure to be followed by worldly misfortune.—DAVIS's *Chinese*, vol. i. p. 294.

dren, the grief of the servants, and the sighs of friends. The bed is surrounded with priests and doctors in black, and only flambeaux emit a yellow gloom. Where is the man, how intrepid soever, that would not shrink at such a hideous solemnity? For fear of affrighting their expiring friends, the English practise all that can fill them with terror. Strange effect of human prejudice, thus to torture, merely from mistaken tenderness!

You see, my friend, what contradictions there are in the tempers of those islanders: when prompted by ambition, revenge, or disappointment, they meet death with the utmost resolution; the very man who in his bed would have trembled at the aspect of a doctor, shall go with intrepidity to attack a bastion, or deliberately noose himself up in his garters.

The passion of the Europeans for magnificent interments is equally strong with that of the Chinese. When a tradesman dies, his frightful face is painted up by an undertaker, and placed in a proper situation to receive company; this is called lying in state. To this disagreeable spectacle all the idlers in town flock, and learn to loathe the wretch dead, whom they despised when living. In this manner you see some, who would have refused a shilling to save the life of their dearest friend, bestow thousands on adorning their putrid corpse. I have been told of a fellow who, grown rich by the price of blood, left it in his will that he should lie in state, and thus unknowingly gibbeted himself into infamy, when he might have otherwise quietly retired into oblivion.[1]

When the person is buried, the next care is to make his epitaph; they are generally reckoned best which flatter most; such relations, therefore, as have received most benefits from the defunct discharge this friendly office, and generally flatter in proportion to their joy. When we read those monumental histories of the dead, it may be justly said that " all

---

[1] "*Croaker:* Well, well, it's a good child, so say no more: but come with me, and we shall see something that will give us a great deal of pleasure, I promise you— old Ruggins, the curry-comb maker, lying in state; I am told he makes a very handsome corpse, and becomes his coffin prodigiously."—*The Good-Natured Man,* Act I.

II.—9

men are equal in the dust;" for they all appear equally remarkable for being the most sincere Christians, the most benevolent neighbors, and the honestest men of their time. To
go through a European cemetery, one would be apt to wonder how mankind could have so basely degenerated from
such excellent ancestors. Every tomb pretends to claim your
reverence and regret: some are praised for piety in those inscriptions, who never entered the temple until they were dead ;
some are praised for being excellent poets, who were never
mentioned except for their dulness when living; others for
sublime orators, who were never noted except for their impudence; and others still for military achievements, who were
never in any other skirmishes but with the watch. Some
even make epitaphs for themselves, and bespeak the reader's
good - will. It were, indeed, to be wished that every man
would early learn in this manner to make his own; that he
would draw it up in terms as flattering as possible, and that
he would make it the employment of his whole life to deserve it !

I have not yet been in a place called Westminster Abbey,
but soon intend to visit it. There, I am told, I shall see justice done to deceased merit: none, I am told, are permitted
to be buried there but such as have adorned as well as improved mankind. There no intruders, by the influence of
friends or fortune, presume to mix their unhallowed ashes
with philosophers, heroes, and poets. Nothing but true merit
has a place in that awful sanctuary. The guardianship of
the tombs is committed to several reverend priests, who are
never guilty, for a superior reward, of taking down the names
of good men to make room for others of equivocal character,
nor ever profane the sacred walls with pageants that posterity cannot know, or shall blush to own.

I always was of opinion that sepulchral honors of this
kind should be considered as a national concern, and not
trusted to the care of the priests of any country, how respectable soever; but, from the conduct of the reverend personages whose disinterested patriotism I shall shortly be able to
discover, I am taught to retract my former sentiments. It is

true, the Spartans and the Persians made a fine political use of sepulchral vanity; they permitted none to be thus interred who had not fallen in the vindication of their country. A monument thus became a real mark of distinction; it nerved the hero's arm with tenfold vigor, and he fought without fear who only fought for a grave. Farewell.

LETTER XIII.

A VISIT TO WESTMINSTER ABBEY.

From the Same.

I AM just returned from Westminster Abbey, the place of sepulture for the philosophers, heroes, and kings of England. What a gloom do monumental inscriptions and all the venerable remains of deceased merit inspire! Imagine a temple marked with the hand of antiquity, solemn as religious awe, adorned with all the magnificence of barbarous profusion, dim windows, fretted pillars, long colonnades, and dark ceilings. Think, then, what were my sensations at being introduced to such a scene. I stood in the midst of the temple and threw my eyes round on the walls, filled with the statues, the inscriptions, and the monuments of the dead.

Alas! I said to myself, how does pride attend the puny child of dust even to the grave! Even humble as I am, I possess more consequence in the present scene than the greatest hero of them all; they have toiled for an hour to gain a transient immortality, and are at length retired to the grave where they have no attendant but the worm, none to flatter but the epitaph.

As I was indulging such reflections, a gentleman, dressed in black, perceiving me to be a stranger, came up, entered into conversation, and politely offered to be my instructor and guide through the temple. "If any monument," said he, "should particularly excite your curiosity, I shall endeavor to satisfy your demands." I accepted with thanks the gentleman's offer, adding that "I was come to observe the policy, the wisdom, and the justice of the English, in conferring rewards upon deceased merit. If adulation like this," continued I, "be properly conducted, as it can no ways injure those who are flattered, so it may be a glorious incentive to those who are now capable of enjoying it. It is the duty of every good government to turn this monumental pride to its own advantage; to become strong in the aggregate from the weakness of the individual. If none but the truly great have a place in this awful repository, a temple like this will give the finest lessons of morality, and be a strong incentive to true ambition. I am told that none have a place here but characters of the most distinguished merit." The man in black seemed impatient at my observations; so I discontinued my remarks, and we walked on together to take a view of every particular monument in order as it lay.

As the eye is naturally caught by the finest objects, I could not avoid being particularly curious about one monument, which appeared more beautiful than the rest. "That," said I to my guide, "I take to be the tomb of some very great man. By the peculiar excellence of the workmanship, and the magnificence of the design, this must be a trophy raised to the memory of some king who has saved his country from ruin, or law-giver who has reduced his fellow-citizens from anarchy into just subjection." "It is not requisite," replied my companion, smiling, "to have such qualifications in order to have a very fine monument here. More humble abilities will suffice." "What! I suppose, then, the gaining two or three battles, or the taking half a score towns, is thought a sufficient qualification?" "Gaining battles, or taking towns," replied the man in black, "may be of service; but a gentleman may have a very fine monument here without ever seeing a battle or a siege." "This, then, is the monument of some poet, I presume, of one whose wit has gained him immortality?" "No, sir," replied my guide, "the gentleman who lies here never made verses; and as for wit, he despised it in others because he had none himself." "Pray, tell me then, in a word," said I, peevishly, "what is the great man who lies here particularly remarkable for?" "Remarkable, sir!" said my companion; "why, sir, the gentleman that lies here is remarkable, very remarkable — for a tomb in Westminster Abbey." "But, head of my ancestors! how has he got here? I fancy he could never bribe the guardians of the temple to give him a place. Should he not be ashamed to be seen among company where even moderate merit would look like infamy?" "I suppose," replied the man in black, "the gentleman was rich, and his friends, as is usual in such a case, told him he was great. He readily believed them; the guardians of the temple, as they got by the self-delusion, were ready to believe him too; so he paid his money for a fine monument; and the workman, as you see, has made him one of the most beautiful. Think not, however, that this gentleman is singular in his desire of being buried among the great; there are several others in the temple, who, hated and shunned by the great while alive, have come here, fully resolved to keep them company now they are dead."

As we walked along to a particular part of the temple, "There," says the gentleman, pointing with his finger, "that is the Poets' Corner; there you see the monuments of Shakspeare, and Milton, and Prior, and Drayton." "Drayton!" I replied, "I never heard of him before;[1] but I have been told of one Pope; is he there?" "It is time enough," replied my guide, "these hundred years; he is not long dead; people have not done hating him yet." "Strange," cried I; "can any be found to hate a man whose life was wholly spent in entertaining and instructing his fellow-creatures?" "Yes," says my guide, "they hate him for that very reason. There is a set of men called answerers of books, who take upon them

---

[1] Michael Drayton, author of the "Poly-Olbion" (d. 1631). His monument in Westminster Abbey, erected at the expense of the famous Anne Pembroke, Dorset, and Montgomery, bears the well-known epitaph—

"Do, pious marble, let thy readers know
What they, and what their children owe
To Drayton's name," etc.—

generally attributed to Ben Jonson, though there is reason to believe that it was actually written by Quarles.

to watch the republic of letters, and distribute reputation by the sheet; they somewhat resemble the eunuchs in a seraglio, who are incapable of giving pleasure themselves, and hinder those that would. These answerers have no other employment but to cry out Dunce, and Scribbler; to praise the dead, and revile the living; to grant a man of confessed abilities some small share of merit; to applaud twenty blockheads, in order to gain the reputation of candor; and to revile the moral character of the man whose writings they cannot injure. Such wretches are kept in pay by some mercenary bookseller, or more frequently the bookseller himself[1] takes this dirty work off their hands, as all that is required is to be very abusive and very dull. Every poet of any genius is sure to find such enemies; he feels, though he seems to despise, their malice; they make him miserable here, and, in the pursuit of empty fame, at last he gains solid anxiety.

"Has this been the case with every poet I see here?" cried I. "Yes, with every mother's son of them," replied he, "except he happened to be born a mandarin. If he has much money, he may buy reputation from your book-answerers, as well as a monument from the guardians of the temple."

"But are there not some men of distinguished taste, as in China, who are willing to patronize men of merit, and soften the rancor of malevolent dulness?" "I own there are many," replied the man in black; "but, alas, sir, the book-answerers crowd about them, and call themselves the writers of books; and the patron is too indolent to distinguish; thus poets are kept at a distance, while their enemies eat up all their rewards at the mandarin's table."

Leaving this part of the temple, we made up to an iron gate, through which my companion told me we were to pass, in order to see the monuments of the kings. Accordingly I marched up without further ceremony, and was going to enter, when a person, who held the gate in his hand, told me I must pay first.[2] I was surprised at such a demand, and asked

---

[1] All this is aimed at Griffiths, the publisher and proprietor of the *Monthly Review*, and the review by Kenrick of Goldsmith's "Inquiry" in that publication.

[2] The passage from Poets' Corner to the western door was long a public thor-

the man whether the people of England kept a show? whether the paltry sum he demanded was not a national reproach? whether it was not more to the honor of the country to let their magnificence or their antiquities be openly seen, than thus meanly to tax a curiosity which tended to their own honor? "As for your questions," replied the gate-keeper, "to be sure they may be very right, because I don't understand them; but, as for that there threepence, I farm it from one—who rents it from another—who hires it from a third—who leases it from the guardians of the temple, and we all must live." I expected, upon paying here, to see something extraordinary, since what I had seen for nothing filled me with so much surprise: but in this I was disappointed; there was little more within than black coffins, rusty armor, tattered standards, and some few slovenly figures in wax.[1] I was sorry I had paid, but I comforted myself by considering it would be my last payment. A person attended us, who, without once blushing, told a hundred lies; he talked of a lady who died by pricking her finger;[2] of a king with a golden head,[3] and twenty such pieces of absurdity. "Look ye there, gentlemen," says he, pointing to an old oak chair, "there's a curiosity for ye! in that chair the kings of England were crowned; you see also a stone underneath, and that stone is Jacob's pillow." I could see no curiosity either in the oak chair or the stone; could I, indeed, behold one of the old kings of England seated in this, or Jacob's head laid upon the other, there might be something curious in the sight; but in the present case there was no more reason for my surprise than if I should pick a stone from their streets, and call it a curiosity merely because one of the kings happened to tread upon it as he passed in a procession.

From hence our conductor led us through several dark

---

oughfare. The Chinese had, therefore, seen the monuments in Poets' Corner without payment. This was not always the case.

[1] The Duke of Albemarle, the Duchess of Richmond (La Belle Stuart), etc., long familiarly known as "The Ragged Regiment."

[2] Elizabeth Russell, in the chapel of St. Edmund.

[3] He means with a *silver* head. The head of the effigy of Henry V. was of silver.

walks and winding ways, uttering lies, talking to himself, and
flourishing a wand which he held in his hand. He reminded
me of the black magicians of Kobi. After we had been almost fatigued with a variety of objects, he at last desired me
to consider attentively a certain suit of armor, which seemed
to show nothing remarkable. "This armor," said he, "belonged to General Monk." "Very surprising that a general
should wear armor!" "And pray," added he, "observe this
cap: this is General Monk's cap." "Very strange indeed,
very strange, that a general should have a cap also! Pray,
friend, what might this cap have cost originally?" "That,
sir," says he, "I don't know; but this cap is all the wages I
have for my trouble." "A very small recompense truly,"
said I. "Not so very small," replied he, "for every gentleman puts some money into it, and I spend the money."
"What, more money! still more money!" "Every gentleman gives something, sir." "I'll give thee nothing," returned I;" the guardians of the temple should pay you your
wages, friend, and not permit you to squeeze thus from every
spectator. When we pay our money at the door to see a
show, we never give more as we are going out. Sure, the
guardians of the temple can never think they get enough.
Show me the gate; if I stay longer, I may probably meet
with more of those ecclesiastical beggars."

Thus leaving the temple precipitately, I returned to my
lodgings, in order to ruminate over what was great, and to
despise what was mean, in the occurrences of the day.[1]

---

[1] "JOHNSON: 'I remember once being with Goldsmith in Westminster Abbey.
While we surveyed the Poets' Corner I said to him,

"Forsitan et nostrum nomen miscebitur istis."

When we got to Temple Bar he stopped me, pointed to the heads upon it, and
slyly whispered me,

"Forsitan et nostrum nomen miscebitur istis."' "

BOSWELL, by Croker, p. 258.

LETTER XIV.

THE RECEPTION OF THE CHINESE FROM A LADY OF DISTINCTION.

From the Same.

I was some days ago agreeably surprised by a message from a lady of distinction, who sent me word that she most passionately desired the pleasure of my acquaintance; and, with the utmost impatience, expected an interview. I will not deny, my dear Fum Hoam, but that my vanity was raised at such an invitation. I flattered myself that she had seen me in some public place, and had conceived an affection for my person, which thus induced her to deviate from the usual decorums of the sex. My imagination painted her in all the bloom of youth and beauty. I fancied her attended by the loves and graces; and I set out with the most pleasing expectations of seeing the conquest I had made.

When I was introduced into her apartment my expectations were quickly at an end; I perceived a little shrivelled figure indolently reclined on a sofa, who nodded by way of approbation at my approach. This, as I was afterwards informed, was the lady herself, a woman equally distinguished for rank, politeness, taste, and understanding. As I was dressed after the fashion of Europe, she had taken me for an Englishman, and consequently saluted me in her ordinary manner; but when the footman informed her Grace that I was the gentleman from China, she instantly lifted herself from the couch, while her eyes sparkled with unusual vivacity. "Bless me! can this be the gentleman that was born so far from home? What an unusual share of *somethingness* in his whole appearance! Lord, how I am charmed with the outlandish cut of his face! how bewitching the exotic breadth of his forehead! I would give the world to see him in his own country dress. Pray turn about, sir, and let me see you

behind.   There! there's a travelled air for you. You that
attend there, bring up a plate of beef cut into small pieces :
I have a violent passion to see him eat.   Pray, sir, have you
got your chopsticks about you ?[1]   It will be so pretty to see
the meat carried to the mouth with a jerk.   Pray speak a
little Chinese : I have learned some of the language myself.
Lord! have you nothing pretty from China about you ; something that one does not know what to do with ?   I have got
twenty things from China that are of no use in the world.
Look at those jars, they are of the right pea-green ; these are
the furniture."   "Dear madam," said I, "these, though they
may appear fine in your eyes, are but paltry to a Chinese ;
but, as they are useful utensils, it is proper they should have
a place in every apartment."   "Useful, sir!" replied the lady ;
"sure you mistake ; they are of no use in the world."—"What!
are they not filled with an infusion of tea as in China ?" replied I.   "Quite empty and useless, upon my honor, sir."
"Then they are the most cumbrous and clumsy furniture in
the world, as nothing is truly elegant but what unites use with
beauty."   "I protest," says the lady, "I shall begin to suspect
thee of being an actual barbarian.   I suppose you hold my
two beautiful pagods in contempt ?"   "What!" cried I, "has
Fohi spread his gross superstitions here also ?   Pagods of all
kinds are my aversion."   "A Chinese, a traveller, and want
taste! it surprises me.   Pray, sir, examine the beauties of that
Chinese temple which you see at the end of the garden.   Is
there anything in China more beautiful ?"   "Where I stand
I see nothing, madam, at the end of the garden, that may not
as well be called an Egyptian pyramid as a Chinese temple ;
for that little building in view is as like the one as t'other."
"What, sir! is not that a Chinese temple ? you must surely
be mistaken.   Mr. Freeze, who designed it, calls it one, and
nobody disputes his pretensions to taste."   I now found it
vain to contradict the lady in anything she thought fit to advance ; so was resolved rather to act the disciple than the in-

---

[1] Two slender sticks, or porcupine quills, by the means of which, placed between
the thumb and the two first fingers of the right hand, the Chinese throw their food,
with great expedition, into their mouths.

structor. She took me through several rooms all furnished, as she told me, in the Chinese manner; sprawling dragons, squatting pagods, and clumsy mandarins were stuck upon every shelf: in turning round, one must have used caution not to demolish a part of the precarious furniture.

In a house like this, thought I, one must live continually upon the watch; the inhabitant must resemble a knight in an enchanted castle, who expects to meet an adventure at every turning. "But, madam," said I, "do no accidents ever happen to all this finery?" "Man, sir," replied the lady, "is born to misfortunes, and it is but fit I should have a share. Three weeks ago, a careless servant snapped off the head of a favorite mandarin. I had scarce done grieving for that, when a monkey broke a beautiful jar; this I took the more to heart, as the injury was done me by a friend. However, I survived the calamity—when yesterday crash went half a dozen dragons upon the marble hearth-stone; and yet I live; I survive it all: you can't conceive what comfort I find under afflictions from philosophy. There is Seneca, and Bolingbroke, and some others, who guide me through life, and teach me to support its calamities." I could not but smile at a woman who makes her own misfortunes, and then deplores the miseries of her situation. Wherefore, tired of acting with dissimulation, and willing to indulge my meditations in solitude, I took leave just as the servant was bringing in a plate of beef, pursuant to the directions of his mistress. Adieu.

LETTER XV.

AGAINST CRUELTY TO ANIMALS.—A STORY FROM THE ZEND-
AVESTA OF ZOROASTER.

From the Same.

THE better sort here pretend to the utmost compassion for animals of every kind: to hear them speak, a stranger would be apt to imagine they could hardly hurt the gnat that stung them; they seem so tender, and so full of pity, that one would

take them for the harmless friends of the whole creation, the
protectors of the meanest insect or reptile that was privileged
with existence.   And yet (would you believe it?) I have seen
the very men who have thus boasted of their tenderness at
the same time devouring the flesh of six different animals
tossed up in a fricassee.   Strange contrariety of conduct:
they pity, and they eat the objects of their compassion!   The
lion roars with terror over its captive; the tiger sends forth
its hideous shriek to intimidate its prey; no creature shows
any fondness for its short-lived prisoner, except a man and a
cat.

Man was born to live with innocence and simplicity, but he
has deviated from nature; he was born to share the bounties
of Heaven, but he has monopolized them; he was born to
govern the brute creation, but he is become their tyrant.   If
an epicure now should happen to surfeit on his last night's
feast, twenty animals the next day are to undergo the most
exquisite tortures, in order to provoke his appetite to another
guilty meal.   Hail, O ye simple, honest Brahmins of the East;
ye inoffensive friends of all that were born to happiness as
well as you; you never sought a short-lived pleasure from
the miseries of other creatures!   You never studied the tor-
menting arts of ingenious refinement; you never surfeited
upon a guilty meal!   How much more purified and refined
are all your sensations than ours! you distinguish every element with the utmost precision; a stream untasted before is a
new luxury, a change of air is a new banquet, too refined for
Western imaginations to conceive.

Though the Europeans do not hold the transmigration of
souls, yet one of their doctors has, with great force of argument and great plausibility of reasoning, endeavored to prove
that the bodies of animals are the habitations of demons and
wicked spirits, which are obliged to reside in these prisons till
the resurrection pronounces their everlasting punishment;
but are previously condemned to suffer all the pains and hardships inflicted upon them by man, or by each other, here.   If
this be the case, it may frequently happen that, while we whip
pigs to death or boil live lobsters, we are putting some old

acquaintance, some near relation, to excruciating tortures, and are serving him up to the very same table where he was once the most welcome companion.

"Kabul," says the Zend-Avesta,[1] "was born on the rushy banks of the river Mawra: his possessions were great, and his luxuries kept pace with the affluence of his fortune; he hated the harmless Brahmins, and despised their holy religion; every day his table was decked out with the flesh of a hundred different animals, and his cooks had a hundred different ways of dressing it, to solicit even satiety.

"Notwithstanding all his eating, he did not arrive at old age; he died of a surfeit caused by intemperance. Upon this, his soul was carried off, in order to take its trial before a select assembly of the souls of those animals which his gluttony had caused to be slain, and who were now appointed his judges.

"He trembled before a tribunal to every member of which he had formerly acted as an unmerciful tyrant: he sought for pity, but found none disposed to grant it. 'Does he not remember,' cries the angry boar, 'to what agonies I was put, not to satisfy his hunger, but his vanity? I was first hunted to death, and my flesh scarce thought worthy of coming once to his table. Were my advice followed, he should do penance in the shape of a hog, which in life he most resembled.'

"'I am rather,' cries a sheep upon the bench, 'for having him suffer under the appearance of a lamb; we may then send him through four or five transmigrations in the space of a month.' 'Were my voice of any weight in the assembly,' cries a calf, 'he should rather assume such a form as mine; I was bled every day, in order to make my flesh white, and at last killed without mercy.' 'Would it not be wiser,' cries a hen, 'to cram him in the shape of a fowl, and then smother him in his own blood, as I was served?' The majority of the assembly were pleased with this punishment, and were going to condemn him without further delay, when the ox rose up to give his

---

[1] The name of the sacred books which the descendants of the ancient Persians assert that they received, more than four thousand years ago, from Zoroaster, or Zerdusht.

opinion. 'I am informed,' says this counsellor, 'that the prisoner at the bar has left a wife with child behind him. By my knowledge in divination, I foresee that this child will be a son, decrepit, feeble, sickly, a plague to himself and all about him. What say you, then, my companions, if we condemn the father to animate the body of his own son, and by this means make him feel in himself those miseries his intemperance must otherwise have entailed upon his posterity?' The whole court applauded the ingenuity of his torture; they thanked him for his advice. Kabul was driven once more to revisit the earth; and his soul, in the body of his own son, passed a period of thirty years loaded with misery, anxiety, and disease."

LETTER XVI.

OF FALSEHOOD PROPAGATED BY BOOKS SEEMINGLY SINCERE.

From the Same.

I KNOW not whether I am more obliged to the Chinese missionaries for the instruction I have received from them, or prejudiced by the falsehoods they have made me believe. By them I was told that the Pope was universally allowed to be a man, and placed at the head of the Church; in England, however, they plainly prove him to be a whore in man's clothes, and often burn him in effigy as an impostor. A thousand books have been written on either side of the question; priests are eternally disputing against each other; and those mouths that want argument are filled with abuse. Which party must I believe, or shall I give credit to neither? When I survey the absurdities and falsehoods with which the books of the Europeans are filled, I thank Heaven for having been born in China, and that I have sagacity enough to detect imposture.

The Europeans reproach us with false history and fabulous chronology; how should they blush to see their own books, many of which are written by the doctors of their religion, filled with the most monstrous fables, and attested with the utmost solemnity. The bounds of a letter do not permit me to mention all the absurdities of this kind which in my reading I have met with. I shall confine myself to the accounts which some of their lettered men give of the persons of some of the inhabitants on our globe; and not satisfied with the most solemn asseverations, they sometimes pretend to have been eye-witnesses of what they describe.

A Christian doctor, in one of his principal performances,[1] says that it was not impossible for a whole nation to have but one eye in the middle of the forehead. He is not satisfied with leaving it in doubt; but in another work[2] assures us that the fact was certain, and that he himself was an eye-witness of it. "When," says he, "I took a journey into Ethiopia, in company with several other servants of Christ, in order to preach the Gospel there, I beheld, in the southern provinces of that country, a nation which had only one eye in the midst of their foreheads."

You will no doubt be surprised, reverend Fum, with this author's effrontery; but, alas, he is not alone in this story; he has only borrowed it from several others who wrote before him. Solinus creates another nation of Cyclops, the Arimaspians, who inhabit those countries that border on the Caspian Sea. This author goes on to tell us of a people of India, who have but one leg and one eye, and yet are extremely active, run with great swiftness, and live by hunting. These people we scarce know how to pity or admire; but the men whom Pliny calls Cynamolci, who have got the heads of dogs, really deserve our compassion; instead of language, they express their sentiments by barking. Solinus confirms what Pliny mentions; and Simon Mayole, a French bishop,[3] talks of them as of particular and familiar acquaintances. "After passing the deserts of Egypt," says he, "we meet with the Kunokephaloi, who inhabit those regions that border

---

[1] Augustin. de Civit. Dei, lib. xvi. p. 422.—GOLDSMITH.

[2] Id. ad fratres in Eremo.   Serm. xxxvii.—GOLDSMITH.

[3] Simon Maiolo was *an Italian*, and bishop of Volturara.   He was born at Asti in 1520, and died in 1597.

on Ethiopia; they live by hunting; they cannot speak, but whistle; their chins resemble a serpent's head; their hands are armed with long sharp claws; their breast resembles that of a greyhound; and they excel in swiftness and agility." Would you think it, my friend, that these odd kind of people are, notwithstanding their figure, excessively delicate? Not even an alderman's wife, or Chinese mandarin, can excel them in this particular. "These people," continues our faithful bishop, "never refuse wine; love roast and boiled meat; they are particularly curious in having their meat well dressed, and spurn at it if in the least tainted. When the Ptolemies reigned in Egypt," says he, a little farther on, "those men with dogs' heads taught grammar and music." For men who had no voices to teach music, and who could not speak, to teach grammar is, I confess, a little extraordinary. Did ever the disciples of Fohi broach anything more ridiculous?

Hitherto we have seen men with heads strangely deformed and with dogs' heads; but what would you say if you heard of men without any heads at all? Pomponius Mela, Solinus, and Aulus Gellius describe them to our hand: "The Blemiæ have a nose, eyes, and mouth on their breasts; or, as others will have it, placed on their shoulders."

One would think that these authors had an antipathy to the human form, and were resolved to make a new figure of their own; but let us do them justice. Though they sometimes deprive us of a leg, an arm, a head, or some such trifling part of the body, they often as liberally bestow upon us something that we wanted before. Simon Mayole seems our particular friend in this respect: if he has denied heads to one part of mankind, he has given tails to another. He describes many of the English of his time, which is more than a hundred years ago,[1] as having tails. His own words are as follows: "In England there are some families which have tails, as a punishment for deriding an Augustin friar sent by St. Greg-

---

[1] This is a mistake. Maiolo's "Dies Caniculares," etc., was published at Rome, in 1576. A translation, by Rosset, appeared at Paris in 1643, with this title, "Les Jours Caniculaires; c'est à dire, vingt-trois excellents Discours des Choses Naturelles et Surnaturelles."

ory, and who preached in Dorsetshire. They sewed the tails of different animals to his clothes; but soon they found those tails entailed on them and their posterity forever." It is certain that the author had some ground for this description. Many of the English wear tails to their wigs to this very day, as a mark, I suppose, of the antiquity of their families, and perhaps as a symbol of those tails with which they were formerly distinguished by nature.[1]

You see, my friend, there is nothing so ridiculous that has not at some time been said by some philosopher. The writers of books in Europe seem to think themselves authorized to say what they please; and an ingenious philosopher among them[2] has openly asserted that he would undertake to persuade the whole republic of readers to believe that the sun was neither the cause of light nor heat, if he could only get six philosophers on his side. Farewell.

LETTER XVII.

OF THE WAR NOW CARRIED ON BETWEEN FRANCE AND ENGLAND, WITH ITS FRIVOLOUS MOTIVES.

From the Same.

WERE an Asiatic politician to read the treaties of peace and friendship that have been annually making for more than a hundred years among the inhabitants of Europe, he would probably be surprised how it should ever happen that Christian princes could quarrel among each other. Their compacts for peace are drawn up with the utmost precision, and ratified with the greatest solemnity; to these each party promises a

---

[1] Little did Goldsmith imagine that, within ten years of the period at which he was writing, not, indeed, an Italian bishop, but a grave Scotch judge would step forward to maintain that orang-outangs are of the human species, and that even in the Bay of Bengal there exists a whole nation of men with tails. See MONBODDO, *Orig. of Language*, vol. i. lib. ii. ch. 3.

[2] Fontenelle.—GOLDSMITH.

sincere and inviolable obedience, and all wears the appearance of open friendship and unreserved reconciliation.

Yet, notwithstanding those treaties, the people of Europe are almost continually at war. There is nothing more easy than to break a treaty ratified in all the usual forms, and yet neither party be the aggressor. One side, for instance, breaks a trifling article by mistake; the opposite party, upon this, makes a small but premeditated reprisal; this brings on a return of greater from the other; both sides complain of injuries and infractions; war is declared; they beat; are beaten; some two or three hundred thousand men are killed; they grow tired; leave off just where they began; and so sit coolly down to make new treaties.[1]

The English and French seem to place themselves foremost among the champion states of Europe. Though parted by a narrow sea, yet are they entirely of opposite characters; and from their vicinity are taught to fear and admire each other. They are at present engaged in a very destructive war, have already spilled much blood, are excessively irritated, and all upon account of one side's desiring to wear greater quantities of *furs* than the other.

The pretext of the war is about some lands a thousand leagues off—a country cold, desolate, and hideous; a country belonging to a people who were in possession from time immemorial. The savages of Canada claim a property in the country in dispute; they have all the pretensions which long possession can confer. Here they had reigned for ages without rivals in dominion, and knew no enemies but the prowling bear or insidious tiger; their native forests produced all the

---

[1] " But what most show'd the vanity of life,
 Was to behold the nations all on fire,
 In cruel broils engag'd, and deadly strife:
 Most Christian kings inflam'd by black desire,
 With honorable ruffians in their hire,
 Cause war to rage, and blood around to pour;
 Of this sad work when each begins to tire,
 They sit them down just where they were before,
 Till for new scenes of woe peace shall their force restore."
       THOMSON, *Castle of Indolence.*

necessaries of life, and they found ample luxury in the enjoyment. In this manner they might have continued to live to
eternity, had not the English been informed that those countries produced furs in great abundance. From that moment
the country became an object of desire: it was found that
furs were things very much wanted in England; the ladies
edged some of their clothes with furs, and muffs were worn
both by gentlemen and ladies. In short, furs were found in-
dispensably necessary for the happiness of the state; and the
king was consequently petitioned to grant, not only the country of Canada, but all the savages belonging to it, to the subjects of England, in order to have the people supplied with
proper quantities of this necessary commodity.

So very reasonable a request was immediately complied
with, and large colonies were sent abroad to procure furs, and
take possession. The French, who were equally in want of
furs (for they were as fond of muffs and tippets as the English), made the very same request to their monarch, and met
with the same gracious reception from their king, who generously granted what was not his to give. Wherever the
French landed they called the country their own; and the
English took possession, wherever they came, upon the same
equitable pretensions. The harmless savages made no opposition; and, could the intruders have agreed together, they
might peaceably have shared this desolate country between
them. But they quarrelled about the boundaries of their set-
tlements, about grounds and rivers to which neither side
could show any other right than that of power, and which
neither could occupy but by usurpation. Such is the contest, that no honest man can heartily wish success to either
party.

The war has continued for some time with various success.
At first the French seemed victorious, but the English have of
late dispossessed them of the whole country in dispute. Think
not, however, that success on one side is the harbinger of
peace; on the contrary, both parties must be heartily tired to
effect even a temporary reconciliation. It should seem the
business of the victorious party to offer terms of peace; but

there are many in England who, encouraged by success, are for still protracting the war.

The best English politicians, however, are sensible that to keep their present conquests would be rather a burden than an advantage to them ; rather a diminution of their strength than an increase of power.   It is in the politic as in the human constitution : if the limbs grow too large for the body, their size, instead of improving, will diminish the vigor of the whole.   The colonies should always bear an exact proportion to the mother country ; when they grow populous they grow powerful, and by becoming powerful they become independent also.   Thus, subordination is destroyed, and a country swallowed up in the extent of its own dominions.   The Turkish empire would be more formidable were it less extensive, were it not for those countries which it can neither command nor give entirely away ; which it is obliged to protect, but from which it has no power to exact obedience.

Yet, obvious as these truths are, there are many Englishmen who are for transplanting new colonies into this late acquisition, for peopling the deserts of America with the refuse of their countrymen, and (as they express it) with the waste of an exuberant nation.   But who are those unhappy creatures who are to be thus drained away ?   Not the sickly, for they are unwelcome guests abroad as well as at home ; nor the idle, for they would starve as well behind the Appalachian mountains as in the streets of London.   This refuse is composed of the laborious and enterprising, of such men as can be serviceable to their country at home ; of men who ought to be regarded as the sinews of the people, and cherished with every degree of political indulgence.   And what are the commodities which this colony, when established, is to produce in return ?   Why, raw silk, hemp, and tobacco.   England, therefore, must make an exchange of her best and bravest subjects for raw silk, hemp, and tobacco ; her hardy veterans and honest tradesmen must be trucked for a box of snuff or a silk petticoat.   Strange absurdity !   Surely the politics of the Daures are not more strange, who sell their religion, their wives, and their liberty for a glass bead or a paltry penknife.   Farewell.

LETTER XVIII.

THE STORY OF THE CHINESE MATRON.[1]

From the Same.

THE English love their wives with much passion, the Hollanders with much prudence; the English, when they give their hands, frequently give their hearts; the Dutch give the hand, but keep the heart wisely in their own possession. The English love with violence, and expect violent love in return; the Dutch are satisfied with the slightest acknowledgment, for they give little away. The English expend many of the matrimonial comforts in the first year; the Dutch frugally husband out their pleasures, and are always constant because they are always indifferent.

There seems very little difference between a Dutch bridegroom and a Dutch husband. Both are equally possessed of the same cool unexpecting serenity; they can see neither elysium nor paradise behind the curtain; and Yiffrow is not more a goddess on the wedding-night than after twenty years' matrimonial acquaintance. On the other hand, many of the English marry in order to have one happy month in their lives: they seem incapable of looking beyond that period; they unite in hopes of finding rapture, and, disappointed in that, disdain ever to accept of happiness. From hence we see open hatred ensue; or what is worse, concealed disgust under the appearance of fulsome endearment. Much formality, great civility, and studied compliments are exhibited in public; cross looks, sulky silence, or open recrimination fill up their hours of private entertainment.

Hence I am taught, whenever I see a new-married couple

---

[1] The agreeable little story of which Goldsmith has here given an abridgment was translated from the Chinese into French by Père Dentrecolles, superintendent-general of the French missionaries in China, who died at Pekin in 1741.

more than ordinarily fond before faces, to consider them as
attempting to impose upon the company or themselves; either
hating each other heartily, or consuming that stock of love in
the beginning of their course which should serve them through
their whole journey. Neither side should expect those instances of kindness which are inconsistent with true freedom
or happiness to bestow. Love, when founded in the heart,
will show itself in a thousand unpremeditated sallies of fondness; but every cool, deliberate exhibition of the passion only
argues little understanding, or great insincerity.

Choang was the fondest husband and Hansi the most en-
dearing wife in all the kingdom of Korea: they were a pattern of conjugal bliss; the inhabitants of the country around
saw and envied their felicity; wherever Choang came, Hansi
was sure to follow; and in all the pleasures of Hansi, Choang
was admitted a partner. They walked hand-in-hand wherever they appeared, showing every mark of mutual satisfaction; embracing, kissing, their mouths were forever joined,
and, to speak in the language of anatomy, it was with them
one perpetual anastomosis.

Their love was so great that it was thought nothing could
interrupt their mutual peace; when an accident happened
which, in some measure, diminished the husband's assurance
of his wife's fidelity; for love so refined as his was subject to
a thousand little disquietudes.

Happening to go one day alone among the tombs that lay
at some distance from his house, he there perceived a lady
dressed in the deepest mourning (being clothed all over in
white [1]), fanning the wet clay that was raised over one of the
graves with a large fan, which she held in her hand. Choang,
who had early been taught wisdom in the school of Lao, was
unable to assign a cause for her present employment, and
coming up, civilly demanded the reason. " Alas," replied the
lady, her eyes bathed in tears, "how is it possible to survive
the loss of my husband, who lies buried in this grave! He

---

[1] " The mourning for the nearest relations in the first degree shall be worn for
three years, and shall be made of the coarsest white cloth, without being sewed at
the borders."—STAUNTON, *Laws of China*, p. 75.

was the best of men, the tenderest of husbands; with his dying breath he bid me never marry again[1] till the earth over his grave should be dry; and here you see me steadily resolving to obey his will, and endeavoring to dry it with my fan. I have employed two whole days in fulfilling his commands, and am determined not to marry till they are punctually obeyed, even though his grave should take up four days in drying."

Choang, who was struck with the widow's beauty, could not, however, avoid smiling at her haste to be married; but concealing the cause of his mirth, civilly invited her home, adding that he had a wife who might be capable of giving her some consolation. As soon as he and his guest were returned he imparted to Hansi in private what he had seen, and could not avoid expressing his uneasiness that such might be his own case, if his dearest wife should one day happen to survive him.

It is impossible to describe Hansi's resentment at so unkind a suspicion. As her passion for him was not only great, but extremely delicate, she employed tears, anger, frowns, and exclamations, to chide his suspicions; the widow herself was inveighed against; and Hansi declared she was resolved never to sleep under the same roof with a wretch who, like her, could be guilty of such barefaced inconstancy. The night was cold and stormy; however, the stranger was obliged to seek another lodging, for Choang was not disposed to resist, and Hansi would have her way.

The widow had scarce been gone an hour, when an old disciple of Choang's, whom he had not seen for many years, came to pay him a visit. He was received with the utmost ceremony, placed in the most honorable seat at supper, and the wine began to circulate with great freedom. Choang and Hansi exhibited open marks of mutual tenderness and unfeigned reconciliation; nothing could equal their apparent happiness; so fond a husband, so obedient a wife, few could

---

[1] In China second marriages are rare on the part of women, and reflect some discredit on the widows.

behold without regretting their own infelicity. When, lo! their happiness was at once disturbed by a most fatal accident. Choang fell lifeless in an apoplectic fit upon the floor. Every method was used, but in vain, for his recovery. Hansi was at first inconsolable for his death; after some hours, however, she found spirits to read his last will. The ensuing day she began to moralize and talk wisdom; the next day she was able to comfort the young disciple; and on the third, to shorten a long story, they both agreed to be married.

There was now no longer mourning in the apartments; the body of Choang was now thrust into an old coffin, and placed in one of the meanest rooms, there to lie unattended until the time prescribed by law for his interment. In the mean time Hansi and the young disciple were arrayed in the most magnificent habits; the bride wore in her nose a jewel of immense price, and her lover was dressed in all the finery of his former master, together with a pair of artificial whiskers that reached down to his toes. The hour of their nuptials was arrived; the whole family sympathized with their approaching happiness; the apartments were brightened up with lights that diffused the most exquisite perfume, and a lustre more bright than noonday. The lady expected her youthful lover in an inner apartment with impatience; when his servant, approaching with terror in his countenance, informed her, that his master was fallen into a fit, which would certainly be mortal, unless the heart of a man lately dead could be obtained, and applied to his breast. She scarcely waited to hear the end of his story, when, tucking up her clothes, she ran with a mattock in her hand to the coffin where Choang lay, resolving to apply the heart of her dead husband as a cure for the living. She therefore struck the lid with the utmost violence. In a few blows the coffin flew open, when the body, which to all appearance had been dead, began to move. Terrified at the sight, Hansi dropped the mattock, and Choang walked out, astonished at his own situation, his wife's unusual magnificence, and her more amazing surprise. He went among the apartments, unable to conceive the cause of so much splendor. He was not long in suspense before his domestics informed him of every transaction since he first became insensible. He could scarcely believe what they told him, and went in pursuit of Hansi herself in order to receive more certain information, or to reproach her infidelity. But she prevented his reproaches; he found her weltering in blood; for she had stabbed herself to the heart, being unable to survive her shame and disappointment.

Choang, being a philosopher, was too wise to make any loud lamentations: he thought it best to bear his loss with serenity; so, mending up the old coffin where he had lain himself, he placed his faithless spouse in his room; and unwilling that so many nuptial preparations should be expended in vain, he the same night married the widow with the large fan.

As they both were apprised of the foibles of each other beforehand, they knew how to excuse them after marriage. They lived together for many years in great tranquillity, and not expecting rapture, made a shift to find contentment. Farewell.

LETTER XIX.

THE ENGLISH METHOD OF TREATING WOMEN CAUGHT IN ADULTERY.—THE RUSSIAN METHOD.

To the Same.

THE gentleman dressed in black, who was my companion through Westminster Abbey, came yesterday to pay me a visit; and after drinking tea we both resolved to take a walk together, in order to enjoy the freshness of the country, which now begins to resume its verdure. Before we got out of the suburbs, however, we were stopped in one of the streets by a crowd of people, gathered in a circle round a man and his wife, who seemed too loud and too angry to be understood. The people were highly pleased with the dispute, which upon inquiry we found to be between Dr. Cacafogo, an apothecary, and his wife. The doctor, it seems, coming unexpectedly into his wife's apartment, found a gentleman there, in circumstances not in the least equivocal.

The doctor, who was a person of nice honor, resolving to revenge the flagrant insult, immediately flew to the chimney-piece, and taking down a rusty blunderbuss, drew the trigger upon the defiler of his bed: the delinquent would certainly have been shot through the head, but that the piece had not been charged for many years. The gallant made a shift to escape through the window, but the lady still remained; and, as she well knew her husband's temper, undertook to manage the quarrel without a second. He was furious, and she loud; their noise had gathered all the mob who charitably assembled on the occasion, not to prevent, but to enjoy the quarrel.

"Alas!" said I to my companion, "what will become of this unhappy creature thus caught in adultery? Believe me, I pity her from my heart; her husband, I suppose, will show her no mercy. Will they burn her as in India, or behead her as in Persia? Will they load her with stripes as in Turkey, or keep her in perpetual imprisonment as with us in China?[1] Prithee, what is the wife's punishment in England for such offences?" "When a lady is thus caught tripping," replied my companion, "they never punish her, but the husband." "You surely jest," interrupted I; "I am a foreigner, and you would abuse my ignorance!" "I am really serious," returned he; "Dr. Cacafogo has caught his wife in the act; but, as he had no witnesses, his small testimony goes for nothing; the consequence, therefore, of his discovery will be, that she will be packed off to live among her relations, and the doctor must be obliged to allow her a separate maintenance." "Amazing!" cried I; "is it not enough that she is permitted to live separate from the object she detests, but must he give her money to keep her in spirits too?" "That he must," said my guide, "and be called a cuckold by all his neighbors into the bargain. The men will laugh at him, the ladies will pity him; and all that his warmest friends can say in his favor will be, that 'the poor good soul has never had any harm in him.'" "I want patience," interrupted I; "what! are there no private chastise-

---

[1] In China women can never be imprisoned except for capital offences, or for adultery.

ments for the wife; no schools of penitence to show her her folly; no blows for such delinquents?"[1] "Pshaw, man," replied he, smiling, "if every delinquent among us were to be treated in your manner, one-half of the kingdom would flog the other."

I must confess, my dear Fum, that if I were an English husband, of all things I would take care not to be jealous, nor busily pry into those secrets my wife was pleased to keep from me. Should I detect her infidelity, what is the consequence? If I calmly pocket the abuse, I am laughed at by her and her gallant; if I talk my griefs aloud like a tragedy hero, I am laughed at by the whole world. The course then I would take would be, whenever I went out, to tell my wife where I was going, lest I should unexpectedly meet her abroad in company with some dear deceiver. Whenever I returned, I would use a peculiar rap at the door, and give four loud hems as I walked deliberately up the staircase. I would never inquisitively peep under her bed, or look behind the curtains. And even though I knew the captain was there, I would calmly take a dish of my wife's cool tea, and talk of the army with reverence.

Of all nations the Russians seem to me to behave most wisely in such circumstances. The wife promises her husband never to let him see her transgressions of this nature; and he as punctually promises, whenever she is so detected, without the least anger, to beat her without mercy; so they both know what each has to expect; the lady transgresses, is beaten, taken again into favor, and all goes on as before.

When a Russian young lady, therefore, is to be married, her father, with a cudgel in his hand, asks the bridegroom whether he chooses this virgin for his bride; to which the other replies in the affirmative. Upon this, the father, turning the lady three times round, and giving her three strokes with his cudgel on the back—"My dear," cries he, "these are the last blows you are ever to receive from your tender father; I re-

---

[1] "Criminal intercourse with a married woman shall be punished with eighty blows; deliberate intrigue with a married or unmarried woman shall be punished with one hundred blows."—STAUNTON, *Laws of China*, p. 404.

sign my authority and my cudgel to your husband; he knows better than I the use of either." The bridegroom knows decorums too well to accept of the cudgel abruptly; he assures the father that the lady will never want it, and that he would not, for the world, make any use of it. But the father, who knows what the lady may want better than he, insists upon his acceptance; upon this there follows a scene of Russian politeness, while one refuses, and the other offers the cudgel. The whole, however, ends with the bridegroom's taking it; upon which the lady drops a courtesy in token of obedience, and the ceremony proceeds as usual.

There is something excessively fair and open in this method of courtship; by this both sides are prepared for all the matrimonial adventures that are to follow. Marriage has been compared to a game of skill for life: it is generous thus in both parties to declare they are sharpers in the beginning. In England, I am told, both sides use every art to conceal their defects from each other before marriage, and the rest of their lives may be regarded as doing penance for their former dissimulation. Farewell.

LETTER XX.

SOME ACCOUNT OF THE REPUBLIC OF LETTERS IN ENGLAND.

From the Same.

THE Republic of Letters is a very common expression among the Europeans; and yet when applied to the learned of Europe is the most absurd that can be imagined, since nothing is more unlike a republic than the society which goes by that name. From this expression one would be apt to imagine that the learned were united into a single body, joining their interests and concurring in the same design. From this, one might be apt to compare them to our literary societies in China, where each acknowledges a just subordination, and all contribute to build the temple of science, without attempting, from ignorance or envy, to obstruct each other.

But very different is the state of learning here; every member of this fancied republic is desirous of governing, and none willing to obey; each looks upon his fellow as a rival, not an assistant, in the same pursuit. They calumniate, they injure, they despise, they ridicule each other; if one man writes a book that pleases, others shall write books to show that he might have given still greater pleasure, or should not have pleased. If one happens to hit upon something new, there are numbers ready to assure the public that all this was no novelty to them or the learned; that Cardanus, or Brunus, or some other author too dull to be generally read, had anticipated the discovery. Thus, instead of uniting like the members of a commonwealth, they are divided into almost as many factions as there are men; and their jarring constitution, instead of being styled a republic of letters, should be entitled an anarchy of literature.

It is true there are some of superior abilities who reverence and esteem each other; but their mutual admiration is not sufficient to shield off the contempt of the crowd. The wise are but few, and they praise with a feeble voice; the vulgar are many, and roar in reproaches. The truly great seldom unite in societies; have few meetings, no cabals; the dunces hunt in full cry till they have run down a reputation, and then snarl and fight with each other about dividing the spoil. Here you may see the compilers and the book-answerers of every month, when they have cut up some respectable name, most frequently reproaching each other with stupidity and dulness; resembling the wolves of the Russian forest, who prey upon venison or horse-flesh when they can get it, but in cases of necessity lying in wait to devour each other. While they have new books to cut up they make a hearty meal; but if this resource should unhappily fail, then it is that critics eat up critics, and compilers rob from compilations.

Confucius observes that it is the duty of the learned to unite society more closely, and to persuade men to become citizens of the world; but the authors I refer to are not only

for disuniting society but kingdoms also : if the English are
at war with France, the dunces of France think it their duty
to be at war with those of England.   Thus Fréron, one of
their first-rate scribblers, thinks proper to characterize all the
English writers in the gross.   " Their whole merit," says he,
" consists in exaggeration and often in extravagance ; correct
their pieces as you please, there still remains a leaven which
corrupts the whole.   They sometimes discover genius, but not
the smallest share of taste ;   England is not a soil for the
plants of genius to thrive in."   This is open enough, with not
the least adulation in the picture ; but hear what a Frenchman of acknowledged abilities says upon the same subject :
" I am at a loss to determine in what we excel the English, or
where they excel us ; when I compare the merits of both in
any one species of literary composition, so many reputable
and pleasing writers present themselves from either country
that my judgment rests in suspense ; I am pleased with the
disquisition, without finding the object of my inquiry."   But
lest you should think the French alone are faulty in this respect, hear how an English journalist delivers his sentiments
of them.   " We are amazed," says he, " to find so many works
translated from the French, while we have such numbers neglected of our own.   In our opinion, notwithstanding their
fame throughout the rest of Europe, the French are the most
contemptible reasoners (we had almost said writers) that can
be imagined.   However, nevertheless, excepting," etc.   Another English writer — Shaftesbury, if I remember — on the
contrary, says that the French authors are pleasing and judicious, more clear, more methodical, and entertaining than those
of his own country.

From these opposite pictures we perceive that the good
authors of either country praise and the bad revile each
other ; and yet, perhaps, you will be surprised that indifferent
writers should thus be the most apt to censure, as they have
the most to apprehend from recrimination ; you may perhaps
imagine that such as are possessed of fame themselves should
be most ready to declare their opinions, since what they say
might pass for decision.   But the truth happens to be that

the great are solicitous only of raising their own reputations, while the opposite class, alas ! are solicitous of bringing every reputation down to a level with their own.

But let us acquit them of malice and envy. A critic is often guided by the same motives that direct his author : the author endeavors to persuade us that he has written a good book; the critic is equally solicitious to show that he could write a better, had he thought proper. A critic is a being possessed of all the vanity but not the genius of a scholar; incapable, from his native weakness, of lifting himself from the ground, he applies to contiguous merit for support; makes the sportive sallies of another's imagination his serious employment; pretends to take our feelings under his care; teaches where to condemn, where to lay the emphasis of praise; and may with as much justice be called a man of taste as the Chinese, who measures his wisdom by the length of his nails.[1]

If, then, a book, spirited or humorous, happens to appear in the republic of letters, several critics are in waiting to bid the public not to laugh at a single line of it, for themselves had read it, and they know what is most proper to excite laughter. Other critics contradict the fulminations of this tribunal, call them all spiders, and assure the public that they ought to laugh without restraint. Another set are in the mean time quietly employed in writing notes to the book, intended to show the particular passages to be laughed at; when these are out, others still there are who write notes upon notes; thus a single new book employs not only the paper-makers, the printers, the pressmen, the bookbinders, the hawkers, but twenty critics, and as many compilers. In short, the body of the learned may be compared to a Persian army, where there are many pioneers, several sutlers, numberless servants, women and children in abundance, and but few soldiers. Adieu.

---

[1] " In China it is fashionable in both men and women to allow the nails of the left hand to grow to an inordinate length, until they assume an appearance very like the claws of the bradypus, as represented in Sir Charles Bell's work on the ' Hand.' The brittleness of the nail rendering it liable to break, they have been known sometimes to protect it, when very long, by means of thin slips of bamboo." —Davis's *Chinese*, vol. i. p. 267.

LETTER XXI.

THE CHINESE GOES TO SEE A PLAY.

To the Same.

THE English are as fond of seeing plays acted as the Chinese; but there is a vast difference in the manner of conducting them. We play our pieces in the open air, the English theirs under cover; we act by daylight, they by the blaze of torches. One of our plays continues eight or ten days successively;[1] an English piece seldom takes up above four hours in the representation.

My companion in black, with whom I am now beginning to contract an intimacy, introduced me a few nights ago to the play-house, where we placed ourselves conveniently at the foot of the stage. As the curtain was not drawn before my arrival, I had an opportunity of observing the behavior of the spectators, and indulging those reflections which novelty generally inspires.

The richest in general were placed in the lowest seats, and

---

[1] "The Chinese Government give countenance to spectacles for the people, by permitting them to be erected in every street by subscriptions among the inhabitants. The principal public occasions of these performances are certain annual festivals of a religious nature, when temporary theatres, constructed of bamboos and mats, are erected in front of their temples, or in open spaces through their towns, the spectacle being continued for several days together. The players, in general, come literally under our legal definition of vagabonds, as they consist of strolling bands of ten or a dozen, whose merit and rank in their profession, and consequently their pay, differ widely according to circumstances. The female parts are never performed by women, but generally by boys. They have no scenical deception to assist the story, and the odd expedients to which they are in consequence sometimes driven are not many degrees above Nick Bottom's 'bush of thorns and a lanthorn, to present the person of Moonshine.' Thus, a general is ordered upon an expedition to a distant province; he brandishes a whip, or takes in his hand the reins of a bridle, and striding three or four times round the stage, in the midst of a tremendous crash of gongs, drums, and trumpets, he stops short, and tells the audience where he has arrived."—DAVIS's *View of the Chinese Drama.*

the poor rose above them in degrees proportioned to their poverty. The order of precedence seemed here inverted: those who were undermost all the day now enjoyed a temporary eminence, and became masters of the ceremonies. It was they who called for the music, indulging every noisy freedom, and testifying all the insolence of beggary in exaltation.

They who held the middle region seemed not so riotous as those above them, nor yet so tame as those below; to judge by their looks, many of them seemed strangers there as well as myself; they were chiefly employed, during this period of expectation, in eating oranges, reading the story of the play, or making assignations.

Those who sat in the lowest rows, which are called the pit, seemed to consider themselves as judges of the merit of the poet and the performers; they were assembled partly to be amused, and partly to show their taste; appearing to labor under that restraint which an affectation of superior discernment generally produces. My companion, however, informed me that not one in a hundred of them knew even the first principles of criticism; that they assumed the right of being censors because there was none to contradict their pretensions; and that every man who now called himself a connoisseur became such to all intents and purposes.

Those who sat in the boxes appeared in the most unhappy situation of all. The rest of the audience came merely for their own amusement, these rather to furnish out a part of the entertainment themselves. I could not avoid considering them as acting parts in dumb show; not a courtesy or nod that was not the result of art; not a look nor a smile that was not designed for murder. Gentlemen and ladies ogled each other through spectacles; for my companion observed that blindness was of late become fashionable; all affected indifference and ease, while their hearts at the same time burnt for conquest. Upon the whole, the lights, the music, the ladies in their gayest dresses, the men with cheerfulness and expectation in their looks, all conspired to make a most agreeable picture, and to fill a heart that sympathizes at human happiness with an expressible serenity.

II.—11

The expected time for the play to begin at last arrived; the curtain was drawn, and the actors came on. A woman, who personated a queen, came in courtesying to the audience, who clapped their hands upon her appearance. Clapping of hands is, it seems, the manner of applauding in England; the manner is absurd, but every country, you know, has its peculiar absurdities. I was equally surprised, however, at the submission of the actress, who should have considered herself as a queen, as at the little discernment of the audience, who gave her such marks of applause before she attempted to deserve them. Preliminaries between her and the audience being thus adjusted, the dialogue was supported between her and a most hopeful youth, who acted the part of her confidant. They both appeared in extreme distress, for it seems the queen had lost a child some fifteen years before, and still kept its dear resemblance next her heart, while her kind companion bore a part in her sorrows.

Her lamentations grew loud; comfort is offered, but she detests the very sound: she bids them preach comfort to the winds. Upon this her husband comes in, who, seeing the queen so much afflicted, can himself hardly refrain from tears or avoid partaking in the soft distress. After thus grieving through three scenes, the curtain dropped for the first act.

"Truly," said I to my companion, "these kings and queens are very much disturbed at no very great misfortune. Certain I am, were people of humbler stations to act in this manner, they would be thought divested of common-sense." I had scarce finished this observation, when the curtain rose, and the king came on in a violent passion. His wife had, it seems, refused his proffered tenderness, had spurned his royal embrace; and he seemed resolved not to survive her fierce disdain. After he had thus fretted and the queen had fretted through the second act, the curtain was let down once more.

"Now," says my companion, "you perceive the king to be a man of spirit; he feels at every pore: one of your phlegmatic sons of clay would have given the queen her own way, and let her come to herself by degrees; but the king is for immediate

tenderness, or instant death: death and tenderness are leading passions of every modern buskined hero; this moment
they embrace and the next stab, mixing daggers and kisses in
every period."

I was going to second his remarks, when my attention was
engrossed by a new object: a man came in balancing a straw
upon his nose, and the audience were clapping their hands in
all the raptures of applause. "To what purpose," cried I, "does
this unmeaning figure make his appearance? is he a part of
the plot?" "Unmeaning do you call him?" replied my friend
in black; "this is one of the most important characters of the
whole play; nothing pleases the people more than the seeing
a straw balanced: there is a great deal of meaning in the
straw; there is something suited to every apprehension in the
sight; and a fellow possessed of talents like these is sure of
making his fortune."[1]

The third act now began, with an actor who came to inform us that he was the villain of the play, and intended to
show strange things before all was over. He was joined by
another, who seemed as much disposed for mischief as he;
their intrigues continued through this whole division. "If
that be a villain," said I, "he must be a very stupid one to tell
his secrets without being asked; such soliloquies of late are
never admitted in China."

The noise of clapping interrupted me once more; a child of
six years old was learning to dance on the stage, which gave the
ladies and mandarins infinite satisfaction. "I am sorry," said
I, "to see the pretty creature so early learning so bad a trade;
dancing being, I presume, as contemptible here as it is in
China." Quite the reverse, interrupted my companion; dancing is a very reputable and genteel employment here; men
have a greater chance for encouragement from the merit of
their heels than their heads. One who jumps up and flour-

---

[1] The exhibitions of Mattocks, the celebrated balance-master, were at this time
much run after. Among other tricks, he would balance a straw with great adroit-
ness, sometimes on one hand, and sometimes on the other; and now and then he
would kick it with his foot to a considerable height, and catch it upon his nose, his
chin, or his forehead.

ishes his toes three times before he comes to the ground may have three hundred a year; he who flourishes them four times gets four hundred; but he who arrives at five is inestimable, and may demand what salary he thinks proper. The female dancers, too, are valued for this sort of jumping and crossing; and it is a cant word among them, that she deserves most who shows highest. But the fourth act is begun: let us be attentive."

In the fourth act the queen finds her long-lost child, now grown up into a youth of smart parts and great qualifications; wherefore she wisely considers that the crown will fit his head better than that of her husband, whom she knows to be a driveller. The king discovers her design, and here comes on the deep distress: he loves the queen, and he loves the kingdom; he resolves therefore, in order to possess both, that her son must die. The queen exclaims at his barbarity, is frantic with rage, and at length, overcome with sorrow, falls into a fit; upon which the curtain drops, and the act is concluded.

"Observe the art of the poet," cries my companion. "When the queen can say no more she falls into a fit. While thus her eyes are shut, while she is supported in the arms of Abigail, what horrors do we not fancy! We feel it in every nerve; take my word for it that fits are the true aposiopesis of modern tragedy."

The fifth act began, and a busy piece it was. Scenes shifting, trumpets sounding, mobs hallooing, carpets spreading, guards bustling from one door to another; gods, demons, daggers, racks, and ratsbane. But whether the king was killed, or the queen was drowned, or the son was poisoned, I have absolutely forgotten.

When the play was over I could not avoid observing that the persons of the drama appeared in as much distress in the first act as the last. "How is it possible," said I, "to sympathize with them through five long acts? Pity is but a short-lived passion; I hate to hear an actor mouthing trifles; neither startings, strainings, nor attitudes affect me, unless there be cause: after I have been once or twice deceived by those

unmeaning alarms, my heart sleeps in peace, probably unaffected by the principal distress.   There should be one great
passion aimed at by the actor as well as the poet; all the
rest should be subordinate, and only contribute to make that
the greater : if the actor, therefore, exclaims upon every occasion in the tones of despair, he attempts to move us too soon ;
he anticipates the blow, he ceases to affect, though he gains
our applause."

I scarce perceived that the audience were almost all departed ; wherefore, mixing with the crowd, my companion and I
got into the street, where, essaying a hundred obstacles, from
coach - wheels and palanquin - poles, like birds in their flight
through the branches of a forest, after various turnings, we
both at length got home in safety.   Adieu.

LETTER XXII.

THE CHINESE PHILOSOPHER'S SON MADE A SLAVE IN PERSIA.

From the Same.

THE letter which came by the way of Smyrna, and which
you sent me unopened, was from my son.   As I have permitted you to take copies of all those I sent to China, you
might have made no ceremony in opening those directed to
me.   Either in joy or sorrow my friend should participate in
my feelings.   It would give pleasure to see a good man
pleased at my success; it would give almost equal pleasure
to see him sympathize at my disappointment.

Every account I receive from the East seems to come loaded with some new affliction.   My wife and daughter were
taken from me, and yet I sustained the loss with intrepidity ;
my son is made a slave among barbarians, which was the only
blow that could have reached my heart : yes, I will indulge
the transports of nature for a little, in order to show I can
overcome them in the end.   True magnanimity consists not
in never falling, but in rising every time we fall.

When our mighty emperor had published his displeasure at my departure, and seized upon all that was mine, my son was privately secreted from his resentment. Under the protection and guardianship of Fum Hoam, the best and the wisest of all the inhabitants of China, he was for some time instructed in the learning of the missionaries and the wisdom of the East. But hearing of my adventures, and incited by filial piety, he was resolved to follow my fortunes and share my distress.

He passed the confines of China in disguise, hired himself as a camel-driver to a caravan that was crossing the deserts of Thibet, and was within one day's journey of the river Laur, which divides that country from India, when a body of wandering Tartars falling unexpectedly upon the caravan, plundered it, and made those who escaped their first fury slaves. By those he was led into the extensive and desolate regions that border on the shores of the Aral lake.

Here he lived by hunting, and was obliged to supply every day a certain proportion of the spoil, to regale his savage masters. His learning, his virtues, and even his beauty were qualifications that no way served to recommend him; they knew no merit but that of providing large quantities of milk and raw flesh; and were sensible of no happiness but that of rioting on the undressed meal.

Some merchants from Mesched, however, coming to trade with the Tartars for slaves, he was sold among the number, and led into the kingdom of Persia, where he is now detained. He is there obliged to watch the looks of a voluptuous and cruel master, a man fond of pleasure, yet incapable of refinement, whom many years' service in war has taught pride but not bravery.

That treasure which I still keep within my bosom, my child, my all that was left to me, is now a slave.[1] Good heavens, why was this? Why have I been introduced into this mortal apartment to be a spectator of my own misfortunes and the misfortunes of my fellow-creatures? Wherever I

---

[1] This whole apostrophe seems most literally translated from Ambulaaohamed, the Arabian poet.—GOLDSMITH.

turn, what a labyrinth of doubt, error, and disappointment appears! Why was I brought into being; for what purposes made; from whence have I come; whither strayed; or to what regions am I hastening? Reason cannot resolve. It lends a ray to show the horrors of my prison, but not a light to guide me to escape them. Ye boasted revelations of the earth, how little do you aid the inquiry!

How am I surprised at the inconsistency of the magi! their two principles of good and evil affright me. The Indian who bathes his visage in urine and calls it piety strikes me with astonishment. The Christian who believes in three gods is highly absurd. The Jews who pretend that Deity is pleased with the effusion of blood are not less displeasing. I am equally surprised that rational beings can come from the extremities of the earth in order to kiss a stone,[1] or scatter pebbles. How contrary to reason are those! and yet all pretend to teach me to be happy.

Surely all men are blind and ignorant of truth. Mankind wanders, unknowing his way, from morning till evening. Where shall we turn after happiness; or is it wisest to desist from the pursuit? Like reptiles in a corner of some stupendous palace, we peep from our holes, look about us, wonder at all we see, but are ignorant of the great architect's design. Oh, for a revelation of himself, for a plan of his universal system! Oh, for the reasons of our creation; or why were we created to be thus unhappy! If we are to experience no other felicity but what this life affords, then are we miserable indeed; if we are born only to look about us,[2] repine, and die, then has Heaven been guilty of injustice. If this life terminates my existence, I despise the blessings of Providence, and the wisdom of the giver; if this life be my all, let the following epitaph be written on the tomb of Altangi: "By my father's crimes I received this; by my own crimes I bequeath it to posterity!"

---

[1] The Black Stone at Mecca, which, according to tradition, fell from heaven during the life of Adam, and was restored to Paradise at the time of the deluge, but was brought to Abraham at the building of the Caaba.

[2] "Let us, since life can little more supply
Than just to look about us and to die," etc.—POPE, *Essay on Man.*

LETTER XXIII.

THE ENGLISH SUBSCRIPTION IN FAVOR OF THE FRENCH
PRISONERS COMMENDED.

To the Same.

Yet, while I sometimes lament the cause of humanity and the depravity of human nature, there now and then appear gleams of greatness that serve to relieve the eye, oppressed with the hideous prospect, and resemble those cultivated spots that are sometimes found in the midst of an Asiatic wilderness. I see many superior excellences among the English, which it is not in the power of all their follies to hide; I see virtues, which in other countries are known only to a few, practised here by every rank of people.

I know not whether it proceeds from their superior opulence that the English are more charitable than the rest of mankind; whether by being possessed of all the conveniences of life themselves, they have more leisure to perceive the uneasy situation of the distressed; whatever be the motive, they are not only the most charitable of any other nation, but most judicious in distinguishing the properest objects of compassion.

In other countries, the giver is generally influenced by the immediate impulse of pity; his generosity is exerted as much to relieve his own uneasy sensations, as to comfort the object in distress. In England, benefactions are of a more general nature. Some men of fortune and universal benevolence propose the proper objects; the wants and the merits of the petitioners are canvassed by the people; neither passion nor pity finds a place in the cool discussion; and charity is then only exerted when it has received the approbation of reason.

A late instance of this finely directed benevolence forces itself so strongly on my imagination that it, in a manner, reconciles me to pleasure, and once more makes me the universal

friend of man. The English and French have not only political reasons to induce them to mutual hatred, but often
the more prevailing motive of private interest to widen the
breach. A war between other countries is carried on collectively; army fights against army, and a man's own private
resentment is lost in that of the community; but in England
and France the individuals of each country plunder each
other at sea without redress, and consequently feel that animosity against each other which passengers do at a robber.
They have for some time carried on an expensive war, and
several captives have been taken on both sides: those made
prisoners by the French have been used with cruelty, and
guarded with unnecessary caution; those taken by the English, being much more numerous, were confined in the ordinary manner; and not being released by their countrymen,
began to feel all these inconveniences which arise from want
of covering and long confinement.

Their countrymen were informed of their deplorable situation; but they, more intent on annoying their enemies than
relieving their friends, refuse the least assistance. The English now saw thousands of their fellow-creatures starving in
every prison, forsaken by those whose duty it was to protect
them, laboring with disease, and without clothes to keep off
the severity of the season. National benevolence prevailed
over national animosity; their prisoners were, indeed, enemies,
but they were enemies in distress—they ceased to be hateful
when they no longer continued to be formidable; forgetting,
therefore, their national hatred, the men who were brave
enough to conquer were generous enough to forgive; and
they whom all the world seemed to have disclaimed at last
found pity and redress from those they attempted to subdue.
A subscription was opened, ample charities collected, proper
necessaries procured, and the poor gay sons of a merry nation
were once more taught to resume their former gayety.[1]

When I cast my eye over the list of those who contributed

---

[1] "Gay, sprightly land of mirth and social ease,
    Pleas'd with thyself, whom all the world can please."—*The Traveller*.

on this occasion, I find the names almost entirely English; scarce one foreigner appears among the number. It was for Englishmen alone to be capable of such exalted virtue. I own I cannot look over this catalogue of good men and philosophers without thinking better of myself, because it makes me entertain a more favorable opinion of mankind. I am particularly struck with one who writes these words upon the paper that enclosed his benefaction: "The mite of an Englishman, a Citizen of the World, to Frenchmen, prisoners of war, and naked." I only wish that he may find as much pleasure from his virtues as I have done in reflecting upon them; that alone will amply reward him. Such a one, my friend, is an honor to human nature; he makes no private distinctions of party; all that are stamped with the divine image of their Creator are friends to him; he is a native of the world; and the Emperor of China may be proud that he has such a countryman.

To rejoice at the destruction of our enemies is a foible grafted upon human nature, and we must be permitted to indulge it; the true way of atoning for such an ill-founded pleasure is thus to turn our triumph into an act of benevolence, and to testify our own joy by endeavoring to banish anxiety from others.

Hamti, the best and wisest emperor that ever filled the throne, after having gained three signal victories over the Tartars, who had invaded his dominions, returned to Nankin in order to enjoy the glory of his conquest. After he had rested for some days, the people, who are naturally fond of processions, impatiently expected the triumphal entry which emperors upon such occasions were accustomed to make; their murmurs came to the emperor's ear; he loved his people, and was willing to do all in his power to satisfy their just desires; he therefore assured them that he intended, upon the next Feast of the Lanterns,[1] to exhibit one of the most glorious triumphs that had ever been seen in China.

---

[1] "The first full-moon of the new year is the Feast of Lanterns, being a display of ingenuity and taste in the construction and mechanism of an infinite variety of lanterns made of silk, varnish, horn, paper, and glass; some of them supplied with

The people were in raptures at his condescension; and on the appointed day assembled at the gates of the palace with the most eager expectations. Here they waited for some time without seeing any of those preparations which usually precede a pageant. The lantern with ten thousand tapers was not yet brought forth; the fire-works which usually covered the city walls were not yet lighted; the people once more began to murmur at this delay; when, in the midst of their impatience, the palace gates flew open, and the emperor himself appeared, not in splendor or magnificence, but in an ordinary habit, followed by the blind, the maimed, and the strangers of the city, all in new clothes, and each carrying in his hand money enough to supply his necessities for the year. The people were at first amazed, but soon perceived the wisdom of their king, who taught them that to make one man happy was more truly great than having ten thousand captives groaning at the wheels of his chariot. Adieu.

LETTER XXIV.

THE VENDERS OF QUACK MEDICINES AND NOSTRUMS RIDICULED.

To the Same.

WHATEVER may be the merits of the English in other sciences, they seem peculiarly excellent in the art of healing. There is scarcely a disorder incident to humanity against which they are not possessed with a most infallible antidote. The professors of other arts confess the inevitable intricacy of things, talk with doubt, and decide with hesitation; but doubting is entirely unknown in medicine; the advertising professors here delight in cases of difficulty: be the disorder never so desperate or radical, you will find numbers in every street, who, by levelling a pill at the part affected, promise a

moving figures of men galloping on horseback, fighting, or performing various feats, together with numerous representations of beasts, birds, and other living creatures, the whole in full motion."—DAVIS's *Chinese*, vol. i. p. 306.

certain cure, without loss of time, knowledge of a bed-fellow, or hinderance of business.

When I consider the assiduity of this profession, their benevolence amazes me. They not only in general give their medicines for half value, but use the most persuasive remonstrances to induce the sick to come and be cured. Sure there must be something strangely obstinate in an English patient who refuses so much health on such easy terms. Does he take a pride in being bloated with a dropsy? does he find pleasure in the alternations of an intermittent fever? or feel as much satisfaction in nursing up his gout as he found pleasure in acquiring it? He must; otherwise he would never reject such repeated assurances of instant relief. What can be more convincing than the manner in which the sick are invited to be well? The doctor first begs the most earnest attention of the public to what he is going to propose; he solemnly affirms the pill was never found to want success; he produces a list of those who have been rescued from the grave by taking it. Yet, notwithstanding all this, there are many here who now and then think proper to be sick. Only sick, did I say? There are some who even think proper to die! Yes, by the head of Confucius, they die! though they might have purchased the health-restoring specific for half a crown at every corner.

I am amazed, my dear Fum Hoam, that these doctors, who know what an obstinate set of people they have to deal with, have never thought of attempting to revive the dead. When the living are found to reject their prescriptions, they ought in conscience to apply to the dead, from whom they can expect no such mortifying repulses; they would find in the dead the most complying patients imaginable; and what gratitude might they not expect from the patient's son, now no longer an heir, and his wife, now no longer a widow?

Think not, my friend, that there is anything chimerical in such an attempt; they already perform cures equally strange. What can be more truly astonishing than to see old age restored to youth, and vigor to the most feeble constitutions? Yet this is performed here every day; a simple electuary effects these wonders, even without the bungling ceremonies of having the patient boiled up in a kettle, or ground down in a mill.

Few physicians here go through the ordinary courses of education, but receive all their knowledge of medicine by immediate inspiration from heaven. Some are thus inspired even in the womb; and, what is very remarkable, understand their profession as well at three years old as at threescore. Others have spent a great part of their lives unconscious of any latent excellence, till a bankruptcy or a residence in jail have called their miraculous powers into exertion. And others still there are indebted to their superlative ignorance alone for success: the more ignorant the practitioner the less capable is he thought of deceiving. The people here judge as they do in the East, where it is thought absolutely requisite that a man should be an idiot before he pretend to be either a conjurer or a doctor.[1]

When a physician by inspiration is sent for, he never perplexes the patient by previous examination; he asks very few questions, and those only for form sake. He knows every disorder by intuition; he administers the pill or drop for every distemper; nor is more inquisitive than the farrier while he drenches a horse. If the patient lives, then has he one more to add to the surviving list; if he dies, then it may be justly said of the patient's disorder that, "as it was not cured, the disorder was incurable."[2]

---

[1] In China the medical profession is at a low ebb. They are utterly ignorant of anatomy, and never think of attempting blood-letting, amputation, or any considerable operation. The eunuchs about the palace are generally accounted the most eminent practitioners; but the great proportion of acting physicians are to be found among the lower classes of the community, and the multitude of quacks and nostrum-venders is immense.—See Barrow, p. 341.

[2] "When a physician has been unsuccessful he retires, with the common Chinese adage, 'that there is medicine for sickness, but none for fate.'"—Davis's *Chinese*, ii. p. 282.

LETTER XXV.

THE NATURAL RISE AND DECLINE OF KINGDOMS, EXEMPLIFIED IN THE HISTORY OF THE KINGDOM OF LAO.

From the Same.

I WAS some days ago in company with a politician, who very pathetically declaimed upon the miserable situation of his country. He assured me that the whole political machine was moving in a wrong track, and that scarce even abilities like his own could ever set it right again. "What have we," said he, "to do with the wars on the Continent? we are a commercial nation; we have only to cultivate commerce, like our neighbors the Dutch; it is our business to increase trade by settling new colonies; riches are the strength of a nation; and for the rest, our ships, our ships alone, will protect us." I found it vain to oppose my feeble arguments to those of a man who thought himself wise enough to direct even the ministry. I fancied, however, that I saw with more certainty, because I reasoned without prejudice; I therefore begged leave, instead of argument, to relate a short history. He gave me a smile at once of condescension and contempt, and I proceeded as follows to describe the rise and declension of the kingdom of Lao.

Northward of China, and in one of the doublings of the great wall, the fruitful province of Lao enjoyed its liberty, and a peculiar government of its own. As the inhabitants were on all sides surrounded by the wall, they feared no sudden invasion from the Tartars; and being each possessed of property, they were zealous in its defence.

The natural consequence of security and affluence in any country is a love of pleasure: when the wants of nature are supplied, we seek after the conveniences; when possessed of these, we desire the luxuries of life; and when every luxury is provided, it is then ambition takes up the man, and leaves

him still something to wish for. The inhabitants of the country, from primitive simplicity, soon began to aim at elegance,
and from elegance proceeded to refinement. It was now
found absolutely requisite, for the good of the state, that the
people should be divided. Formerly, the same hand that was
employed in tilling the ground, or in dressing up the manufactures, was also in time of need a soldier; but the custom
was now changed: for it was perceived that a man bred up
from childhood to the arts, either of peace or of war, became
more eminent by this means in his respective profession.
The inhabitants were, therefore, now distinguished into artisans and soldiers; and while those improved the luxuries of
life, these watched for the security of the people.

A country possessed of freedom has always two sorts of
enemies to fear—foreign foes who attack its existence from
without, and internal miscreants who betray its liberties
within. The inhabitants of Lao were to guard against both.
A country of artisans were most likely to preserve internal
liberty, and a nation of soldiers were fittest to repel a foreign
invasion. Hence naturally arose a division of opinion between the artisans and the soldiers of the kingdom. The
artisans, ever complaining that freedom was threatened by an
armed internal force, were for disbanding the soldiers, and insisted that their walls, their walls alone, were sufficient to repel the most formidable invasion; the warriors, on the contrary, represented the power of the neighboring kings, the
combinations formed against their state, and the weakness
of the wall, which every earthquake might overturn. While
this altercation continued, the kingdom might be justly said
to enjoy its greatest share of vigor : every order in the state,
by being watchful over each other, contributed to diffuse happiness equally, and balanced the state. The arts of peace
flourished, nor were those of war neglected; the neighboring
powers, who had nothing to apprehend from the ambition of
men whom they only saw solicitous, not for riches but freedom, were contented to traffic with them; they sent their
goods to be manufactured in Lao, and paid a large price for
them upon their return.

By these means, this people at length became moderately rich, and their opulence naturally invited the invader: a Tartar prince led an immense army against them, and they as bravely stood up in their own defence; they were still inspired with a love of their country; they fought the barbarous enemy with fortitude, and gained a complete victory.

From this moment, which they regarded as the completion of their glory, historians date their downfall. They had risen in strength by a love of their country, and fell by indulging ambition. The country possessed by the invading Tartars, seemed to them a prize that would not only render them more formidable for the future, but which would increase their opulence for the present; it was unanimously resolved, therefore, both by soldiers and artisans, that those desolate regions should be peopled by colonies from Lao. When a trading nation begins to act the conqueror, it is then perfectly undone: it subsists in some measure by the support of its neighbors: while they continue to regard it without envy or apprehension, trade may flourish; but when once it presumes to assert as its right, what it only enjoyed as a favor, each country reclaims that part of commerce which it has power to take back, and turns it into some other channel more honorable, though perhaps less convenient.

Every neighbor now began to regard with jealous eyes this ambitious commonwealth, and forbade their subjects any future intercourse with them. The inhabitants of Lao, however, still pursued the same ambitious maxims: it was from their colonies alone they expected riches; and riches, said they, are strength, and strength is security. Numberless were the migrations of the desperate and enterprising of this country, to people the desolate dominions lately possessed by the Tartar. Between these colonies and the mother-country a very advantageous traffic was at first carried on; the republic sent their colonies large quantities of the manufactures of the country, and they in return provided the republic with an equivalent in ivory and ginseng. By this means the inhabitants became immensely rich, and this produced an equal degree of voluptuousness; for men who have much money will always find some fantastical modes of enjoyment. How shall I mark the steps by which they declined? Every colony in process of time spreads over the whole country where it first was planted. As it grows more populous it becomes more polite; and those manufactures for which it was in the beginning obliged to others, it learns to dress up itself. Such was the case with the colonies of Lao; they, in less than a century, became a powerful and a polite people, and the more polite they grew, the less advantageous was the commerce which still subsisted between them and others. By this means the mother-country, being abridged in its commerce, grew poorer, but not less luxurious. Their former wealth had introduced luxury; and wherever luxury once fixes, no art can either lessen or remove it. Their commerce with their neighbors was totally destroyed, and that with their colonies was every day naturally and necessarily declining; they still, however, preserved the insolence of wealth without a power to support it, and persevered in being luxurious while contemptible from poverty. In short, the state resembled one of those bodies bloated with disease, whose bulk is only a symptom of its wretchedness.

Their former opulence only rendered them more impotent, as those individuals who are reduced from riches to poverty are of all men the most unfortunate and helpless. They had imagined, because their colonies tended to make them rich upon the first acquisition, they would still continue to do so; they now found, however, that on themselves alone they should have depended for support; that colonies ever afford but temporary affluence, and when cultivated and polite are no longer useful. From such a concurrence of circumstances they soon became contemptible. The Emperor Honti invaded them with a powerful army. Historians do not say whether their colonies were too remote to lend assistance, or else were desirous of shaking off their dependence; but certain it is, they scarce made any resistance; their walls were now found but a weak defence, and they at length were obliged to acknowledge subjection to the Empire of China.

Happy, very happy, might they have been had they known

II.—12

when to bound their riches and their glory; had they known that extending empire is often diminishing power;[1] that countries are ever strongest which are internally powerful; that colonies, by draining away the brave and enterprising, leave the country in the hands of the timid and the avaricious; that walls give little protection unless manned with resolution; that too much commerce may injure a nation as well as too little; and that there is a wide difference between a conquering and a flourishing empire.[2] Adieu.

LETTER XXVI.

THE CHARACTER OF THE MAN IN BLACK, WITH SOME INSTANCES OF HIS INCONSISTENT CONDUCT.

From the Same.

THOUGH fond of many acquaintances, I desire an intimacy only with a few. The man in black whom I have often mentioned is one whose friendship I could wish to acquire, because he possesses my esteem. His manners, it is true, are tinctured with some strange inconsistencies; and he may be justly termed a humorist in a nation of humorists. Though he is generous even to profusion, he affects to be thought a prodigy of parsimony and prudence; though his conversation be replete with the most sordid and selfish maxims, his heart is dilated with the most unbounded love. I have known him profess himself a man-hater, while his cheek was glowing with compassion; and while his looks were softened into pity I have heard him use the language of the most unbounded ill-nature. Some affect humanity and tenderness, others boast

---

[1] "Extended empire, like expanded gold,
    Exchanges solid strength for feeble splendor."—JOHNSON's *Irene.*

[2] "Ye friends to truth, ye statesmen who survey
    The rich man's joys increase, the poor's decay,
    'Tis yours to judge how wide the limits stand
    Between a splendid and a happy land."—*The Deserted Village.*

of having such dispositions from nature ; but he is the only man I ever knew who seemed ashamed of his natural benevolence. He takes as much pains to hide his feelings as any hypocrite would to conceal his indifference ; but on every unguarded moment the mask drops off, and reveals him to the most superficial observer.[1]

In one of our late excursions into the country, happening to discourse upon the provision that was made for the poor in England, he seemed amazed how any of his countrymen could be so foolishly weak as to relieve occasional objects of charity, when the laws had made such ample provision for their support. " In every parish-house," says he, " the poor are supplied with food, clothes, fire, and a bed to lie on ; they want no more ; I desire no more myself ; yet still they seem discontented. I am surprised at the inactivity of our magistrates in not taking up such vagrants, who are only a weight upon the industrious ; I am surprised that the people are found to relieve them, when they must be at the same time sensible that it in some measure encourages idleness, extravagance, and imposture. Were I to advise any man for whom I had the least regard, I would caution him by all means not to be imposed upon by their false pretences ; let me assure you, sir, they are impostors, every one of them, and rather merit a prison than relief."

He was proceeding in this strain earnestly to dissuade me from an imprudence of which I am seldom guilty, when an old man, who still had about him the remnants of tattered finery, implored our compassion. He assured us that he was no common beggar, but forced into the shameful profession to support a dying wife and five hungry children. Being prepossessed against such falsehoods, his story had not the least influence upon me ; but it was quite otherwise with the

---

[1] " I have often affected bluntness to avoid the imputation of flattery, and have frequently seemed to overlook those merits too obvious to escape notice, and pretended disregard to those instances of good-nature and good-sense which I could not fail tacitly to applaud ; and all this lest I should be ranked among the grinning tribe who say ' Very well' to all that is said," etc.—*Goldsmith to Mrs. Jane Lawder*, Aug. 15th, 1758.

man in black: I could see it visibly operate upon his countenance, and effectually interrupt his harangue. I could easily
perceive that his heart burnt to relieve the five starving
children, but he seemed ashamed to discover his weakness to
me. While he thus hesitated between compassion and pride,
I pretended to look another way, and he seized this opportunity of giving the poor petitioner a piece of silver, bidding
him at the same time, in order that I should hear, go work
for his bread, and not tease passengers with such impertinent
falsehoods for the future.

As he fancied himself quite unperceived, he continued as
we proceeded to rail against beggars with as much animosity
as before; he threw in some episodes on his own amazing
prudence and economy, with his profound skill in discovering
impostors; he explained the manner in which he would deal
with beggars were he a magistrate; hinted at enlarging some
of the prisons for their reception, and told two stories of
ladies that were robbed by beggarmen. He was beginning a
third to the same purpose when a sailor with a wooden leg
once more crossed our walks, desiring our pity and blessing
our limbs. I was for going on without taking any notice, but
my friend, looking wishfully upon the poor petitioner, bid me
stop, and he would show me with how much ease he could at
any time detect an impostor.

He now, therefore, assumed a look of importance, and in
an angry tone began to examine the sailor, demanding in
what engagement he was thus disabled and rendered unfit
for service. The sailor replied, in a tone as angrily as he,
that he had been an officer on board a private ship-of-war,
and that he had lost his leg abroad, in defence of those who
did nothing at home. At this reply all my friend's importance vanished in a moment; he had not a single question
more to ask; he now only studied what method he should
take to relieve him unobserved. He had, however, no easy
part to act, as he was obliged to preserve the appearance of
ill-nature before me, and yet relieve himself by relieving the
sailor. Casting, therefore, a furious look upon some bundles
of chips which the fellow carried in a string at his back, my

friend demanded how he sold his matches; but, not waiting for a reply, desired in a surly tone to have a shilling's worth. The sailor seemed at first surprised at his demand, but soon recollecting himself, and presenting his whole bundle, "Here master," says he, "take all my cargo, and a blessing into the bargain."

It is impossible to describe with what an air of triumph my friend marched off with his new purchase; he assured me that he was firmly of opinion that those fellows must have stolen their goods, who could thus afford to sell them for half value. He informed me of several different uses to which those chips might be applied; he expatiated largely upon the savings that would result from lighting candles with a match, instead of thrusting them into the fire. He averred, that he would as soon have parted with a tooth as his money to those vagabonds, unless for some valuable consideration. I cannot tell how long this panegyric upon frugality and matches might have continued, had not his attention been called off by another object more distressful than either of the former. A woman in rags, with one child in her arms, and another on her back, was attempting to sing ballads, but with such a mournful voice that it was difficult to determine whether she was singing or crying. A wretch who, in the deepest distress, still aimed at good-humor was an object my friend was by no means capable of withstanding; his vivacity and his discourse were instantly interrupted; upon this occasion his very dissimulation had forsaken him. Even in my presence he immediately applied his hands to his pockets, in order to relieve her; but guess his confusion when he found he had already given away all the money he carried about him to former objects. The misery painted in the woman's visage was not half so strongly expressed as the agony in his. He continued to search for some time, but to no purpose, till, at length recollecting himself, with a face of ineffable good-nature, as he had no money, he put into her hands his shilling's worth of matches.

LETTER XXVII.

THE HISTORY OF THE MAN IN BLACK.

To the Same.

As there appeared something reluctantly good in the character of my companion, I must own it surprised me what could be his motives for thus concealing virtues which others take such pains to display. I was unable to repress my desire of knowing the history of a man who thus seemed to act under continual restraint, and whose benevolence was rather the effect of appetite than reason.

It was not, however, till after repeated solicitations he thought proper to gratify my curiosity. "If you are fond," says he, "of hearing hair-breadth 'scapes, my history must certainly please; for I have been for twenty years upon the very verge of starving, without ever being starved.

"My father, the younger son of a good family, was possessed of a small living in the Church.[1] His education was above his fortune, and his generosity greater than his education. Poor as he was, he had his flatterers still poorer than himself; for every dinner he gave them they returned an equivalent in praise; and this was all he wanted. The same ambition that actuates a monarch at the head of an army influenced my father at the head of his table; he told the story of the ivy-tree, and that was laughed at; he repeated the jest of the two scholars and one pair of breeches, and the company laughed at that; but the story of Taffy in the sedan chair was sure to set the table in a roar. Thus his pleasure increased in proportion to the pleasure he gave; he loved all the world, and he fancied all the world loved him.

---

[1] In this story are contained portions of Goldsmith's own early history.

" As his fortune was but small, he lived up to the very extent of it; he had no intentions of leaving his children money, for that was dross; he was resolved they should have learning, for learning, he used to observe, was better than silver or gold. For this purpose, he undertook to instruct us himself; and took as much pains to form our morals as to improve our understanding. We were told that universal benevolence was what first cemented society; we were taught to consider all the wants of mankind as our own; to regard 'the human face divine' with affection and esteem; he wound us up to be mere machines of pity, and rendered us incapable of withstanding the slightest impulse, made either by real or fictitious distress; in a word, we were perfectly instructed in the art of giving away thousands before we were taught the more necessary qualifications of getting a farthing.

" I cannot avoid imagining that, thus refined by his lessons out of all my suspicion, and divested of even all the little cunning which nature had given me, I resembled, upon my first entrance into the busy and insidious world, one of those gladiators who were exposed without armor in the amphitheatre at Rome. My father, however, who had only seen the world on one side, seemed to triumph in my superior discernment; though my whole stock of wisdom consisted in being able to talk like himself upon subjects that once were useful, because they were then topics of the busy world, but that now were utterly useless, because connected with the busy world no longer.

" The first opportunity he had of finding his expectations disappointed was at the very middling figure I made in the university; he had flattered himself that he should soon see me rising into the foremost rank in literary reputation, but was mortified to find me utterly unnoticed and unknown. His disappointment might have been partly ascribed to his having overrated my talents, and partly to my dislike of mathematical reasonings, at a time when my imagination and memory, yet unsatisfied, were more eager after new objects than desirous of reasoning upon those I knew. This did not, however, please my tutors, who observed indeed, that I was a little dull; but at the same time allowed that I seemed to be very good-natured, and had no harm in me.[1]

"After I had resided at college seven years, my father died, and left me—his blessing. Thus shoved from shore, without ill-nature to protect, or cunning to guide, or proper stores to subsist me in so dangerous a voyage, I was obliged to embark in the wide world at twenty-two. But, in order to settle in life, my friends advised (for they always advise when they begin to despise us)—they advised me, I say, to go into orders.

"To be obliged to wear a long wig when I liked a short one, or a black coat when I generally dressed in brown, I thought was such a restraint upon my liberty that I absolutely rejected the proposal. A priest in England is not the same mortified creature with a bonze in China: with us, not he that fasts best, but eats best, is reckoned the best liver; yet I rejected a life of luxury, indolence, and ease, from no other consideration but that boyish one of dress. So that my friends were now perfectly satisfied I was undone; and yet they thought it a pity for one who had not the least harm in him, and was so very good-natured.

"Poverty naturally begets dependence, and I was admitted as flatterer to a great man. At first I was surprised that the situation of a flatterer at a great man's table could be thought disagreeable; there was no great trouble in listening attentively when his lordship spoke, and laughing when he looked round for applause. This even good-manners might have obliged me to perform. I found, however, too soon, that his lordship was a greater dunce than myself; and from that very moment my power of flattery was at an end. I now rather aimed at setting him right than at receiving his absurdities with submission: to flatter those we do not know is an easy task; but to flatter our intimate acquaintances, all whose foibles are strongly in our eye, is drudgery insupportable. Every time I now opened my lips in praise, my false-

---

[1] "Who can possibly doubt the original from whom the man in black's experiences were taken?"—FORSTER'S *Life of Goldsmith*, vol. i. p. 35.

hood went to my conscience; his lordship soon perceived me to be unfit for service; I was therefore discharged, my patron at the same time being graciously pleased to observe that he believed I was tolerably good-natured, and had not the least harm in me.

"Disappointed in ambition, I had recourse to love. A young lady, who lived with her aunt, and was possessed of a pretty fortune in her own disposal, had given me, as I fancied, some reasons to expect success. The symptoms by which I was guided were striking. She had always laughed with me at her awkward acquaintance, and at her aunt among the number; she always observed that a man of sense would make a better husband than a fool, and I as constantly applied the observation in my own favor. She continually talked, in my company, of friendship and the beauties of the mind, and spoke of Mr. Shrimp my rival's high-heeled shoes with detestation. These were circumstances which I thought strongly in my favor; so, after resolving and re-resolving, I had courage enough to tell her my mind. Miss heard my proposal with serenity, seeming at the same time to study the figures of her fan. Out at last it came. There was but one small objection to complete our happiness; which was no more, than—that she was married three months before to Mr. Shrimp, with high-heeled shoes! By way of consolation, however, she observed that, though I was disappointed in her, my addresses to her aunt would probably kindle her into sensibility, as the old lady always allowed me to be very good-natured, and not to have the least share of harm in me.

"Yet still I had friends, numerous friends, and to them I was resolved to apply. O friendship! thou fond soother of the human breast, to thee we fly in every calamity; to thee the wretched seek for succor; on thee the care-tired son of misery fondly relies; from thy kind assistance the unfortunate always hopes relief, and may be ever sure of—disappointment! My first application was to a City scrivener, who had frequently offered to lend me money when he knew I did not want it. I informed him that now was the time to put his friendship to the test; that I wanted to borrow a couple of hundreds for a certain occasion, and was resolved to take it up from him. 'And pray, sir,' cried my friend, 'do you want all this money?' 'Indeed I never wanted it more,' returned I. 'I am sorry for that,' cries the scrivener, 'with all my heart; for they who want money when they come to borrow, will always want money when they should come to pay.'

"From him I flew with indignation to one of the best friends I had in the world, and made the same request. 'Indeed, Mr. Drybone,' cries my friend, 'I always thought it would come to this. You know, sir, I would not advise you but for your own good; but your conduct has hitherto been ridiculous in the highest degree, and some of your acquaintance always thought you a very silly fellow. Let me see, you want two hundred pounds. Do you want only two hundred, sir, exactly?' 'To confess a truth,' returned I, 'I shall want three hundred; but then I have another friend, from whom I can borrow the rest.' 'Why, then,' replied my friend, 'if you would take my advice (and you know I should not presume to advise you but for your own good), I would recommend it to you to borrow the whole sum from that other friend; and then one note will serve for all, you know.'

"Poverty now began to come fast upon me; yet, instead of growing more provident or cautious as I grew poor, I became every day more indolent and simple. A friend was arrested for fifty pounds; I was unable to extricate him except by becoming his bail. When at liberty he fled from his creditors, and left me to take his place. In prison I expected greater satisfactions than I had enjoyed at large. I hoped to converse with men in this new world, simple and believing like myself; but I found them as cunning and as cautious as those in the world I had left behind. They sponged up my money while it lasted, borrowed my coals and never paid for them, and cheated me when I played at cribbage. All this was done because they believed me to be very good-natured, and knew that I had no harm in me.

"Upon my first entrance into this mansion, which is to some the abode of despair, I felt no sensations different from those I experienced abroad. I was now on one side the door, and those who were unconfined were on the other; this was all the difference between us. At first, indeed, I felt some uneasiness, in considering how I should be able to provide this week for the wants of the week ensuing; but after some time, if I found myself sure of eating one day, I never troubled my head how I was to be supplied another. I seized every precarious meal with the utmost good-humor; indulged no rants of spleen at my situation; never called down heaven and all the stars to behold me dining upon a halfpenny-worth of radishes; my very companions were taught to believe that I liked salad better than mutton. I contented myself with thinking that all my life I should either eat white bread or brown; considered that all that happened was best; laughed when I was not in pain, took the world as it went, and read Tacitus often, for want of more books and company.

" How long I might have continued in this torpid state of simplicity I cannot tell, had I not been roused by seeing an old acquaintance, whom I knew to be a prudent blockhead, preferred to a place in the Government. I now found that I had pursued a wrong track, and that the true way of being able to relieve others was first to aim at independence myself; my immediate care, therefore, was to leave my present habitation, and make an entire reformation in my conduct and behavior. For a free, open, undesigning deportment I put on that of closeness, prudence, and economy. One of the most heroic actions I ever performed, and for which I shall praise myself as long as I live, was the refusing half a crown to an old acquaintance, at the time when he wanted it and I had it to spare; for this alone I deserve to be decreed an ovation.

" I now, therefore, pursued a course of uninterrupted frugality, seldom wanted a dinner, and was consequently invited to twenty. I soon began to get the character of a saving hunks that had money, and insensibly grew into esteem. Neighbors have asked my advice in the disposal of their daughters; and I have always taken care not to give any. I have contracted a friendship with an alderman, only by observing that if we take a farthing from a thousand pounds it

will be a thousand pounds no longer. I have been invited to
a pawnbroker's table by pretending to hate gravy; and am
now actually upon treaty of marriage with a rich widow for
only having observed that the bread was rising. If ever I
am asked a question, whether I know it or not, instead of answering, I only smile and look wise. If a charity is proposed,
I go about with the hat, but put nothing in myself. If a
wretch solicits my pity, I observe that the world is filled with
impostors, and take a certain method of not being deceived,
by never relieving. In short, I now find the truest way of
finding esteem, even from the indigent, is — to give away
nothing, and thus have much in our power to give."

LETTER XXVIII.

ON THE GREAT NUMBER OF OLD MAIDS AND BACHELORS IN LONDON.—SOME OF THE CAUSES.

To the Same.

LATELY in company with my friend in black, whose conversation is now both my amusement and instruction, I could
not avoid observing the great numbers of old bachelors
and maiden ladies with which this city seems to be overrun.
"Sure, marriage," said I, "is not sufficiently encouraged, or
we should never behold such crowds of battered beaux and
decayed coquettes still attempting to drive a trade they have
been so long unfit for, and swarming upon the gayety of the
age. I behold an old bachelor in the most contemptible
light, as an animal that lives upon the common stock without
contributing his share; he is a beast of prey, and the laws
should make use of as many stratagems and as much force to
drive the reluctant savage into the toils as the Indians when
they hunt the hyena or the rhinoceros. The mob should be
permitted after him; boys might play tricks on him with
impunity; every well-bred company should laugh at him;
and if, when turned of sixty, he offered to make love, his

mistress might spit in his face, or, what would be perhaps a greater punishment, should fairly grant him the favor.

" As for old maids," continued I, " they should not be treated with so much severity, because I suppose none would be so if they could. No lady in her senses would choose to make a subordinate figure at christenings and lyings-in, when she might be the principal herself; nor curry favor with a sister-in-law, when she might command a husband; nor toil in preparing custards, when she might lie abed and give directions how they ought to be made; nor stifle all her sensations in demure formality, when she might with matrimonial freedom shake her acquaintance by the hand, and wink at a *double entendre*. No lady could be so very silly as to live single if she could help it. I consider an unmarried lady declining into the vale of years as one of those charming countries bordering on China, that lies waste for want of proper inhabitants. We are not to accuse the country, but the ignorance of its neighbors, who are insensible of its beauties, though at liberty to enter and cultivate the soil."

" Indeed, sir," replied my companion, " you are very little acquainted with the English ladies, to think they are old maids against their will. I dare venture to affirm that you can hardly select one of them all who has not had frequent offers of marriage, which either pride or avarice has not made her reject. Instead of thinking it a disgrace, they take every occasion to boast of their former cruelty; a soldier does not exult more when he counts over the wounds he has received than a female veteran when she relates the wounds she has formerly given: exhaustless when she begins a narrative of the former death-dealing power of her eyes. She tells of the knight in gold lace, who died with a single frown, and never rose again till—he was married to his maid; of the squire who, being cruelly denied, in a rage flew to the window and, lifting up the sash, threw himself in an agony—into his armchair; of the parson who, crossed in love, resolutely swallowed opium, which banished the stings of despised love by—making him sleep. In short, she talks over her former losses with pleasure, and, like some tradesmen, finds consolation in the many bankruptcies she has suffered.

" For this reason, whenever I see a superannuated beauty still unmarried, I tacitly accuse her either of pride, avarice, coquetry, or affectation.   There's Miss Jenny Tinderbox—I once remember her to have had some beauty, and a moderate fortune.   Her elder sister happened to marry a man of quality, and this seemed as a statute of virginity against poor Jane. Because there was one lucky hit in the family, she was resolved not to disgrace it by introducing a tradesman.   By thus rejecting her equals, and neglected or despised by her superiors, she now acts in the capacity of tutoress to her sister's children, and undergoes the drudgery of three servants, without receiving the wages of one.

" Miss Squeeze was a pawnbroker's daughter; her father had early taught her that money was a very good thing, and left her a moderate fortune at his death.   She was so perfectly sensible of the value of what she had got, that she was resolved never to part with a farthing without an equality on the part of her suitor: she thus refused several offers made her by people who wanted to better themselves, as the saying is, and grew old and ill-natured, without ever considering that she should have made an abatement in her pretensions, from her face being pale and marked with the small-pox.

" Lady Betty Tempest, on the contrary, had beauty, with fortune and family.   But, fond of conquest, she passed from triumph to triumph.   She had read plays and romances, and there had learned that a plain man of common-sense was no better than a fool; such she refused, and sighed only for the gay, giddy, inconstant, and thoughtless.   After she had thus rejected hundreds who liked her, and sighed for hundreds who despised her, she found herself insensibly deserted; at present she is company only for her aunts and cousins, and sometimes makes one in a country dance, with only one of the chairs for a partner, casts off round a joint-stool, and sets to a corner cupboard.   In a word, she is treated with civil contempt from every quarter, and placed, like a piece of old-fashioned lumber, merely to fill up a corner.

"But Sophronia, the sagacious Sophronia, how shall I mention her? She was taught to love Greek, and hate the men from her very infancy; she has rejected fine gentlemen because they were not pedants, and pedants because they were not fine gentlemen; her exquisite sensibility has taught her to discover every fault in every lover, and her inflexible justice has prevented her pardoning them: thus she rejected several offers, till the wrinkles of age had overtaken her; and now, without one good feature in her face, she talks incessantly of the beauties of the mind." Farewell.

LETTER XXIX.

A DESCRIPTION OF A CLUB OF AUTHORS.

From the Same.

WERE we to estimate the learning of the English by the number of books that are every day published among them, perhaps no country, not even China itself, could equal them in this particular. I have reckoned not less than twenty-three new books published in one day; which upon computation makes eight thousand three hundred and ninety-five in one year. Most of these are not confined to one single science, but embrace the whole circle. History, politics, poetry, mathematics, metaphysics, and the philosophy of nature, are all comprised in a manual not larger than that in which our children are taught the letters. If, then, we suppose the learned of England to read but an eighth part of the works which daily come from the press—and sure none can pretend to learning upon less easy terms—at this rate every scholar will read a thousand books in one year. From such a calculation you may conjecture what an amazing fund of literature a man must be possessed of who thus reads three new books every day, not one of which but contains all the good things that ever were said or written.

And yet I know not how it happens, but the English are

not in reality so learned as would seem from this calculation.
We meet but few who know all arts and sciences to perfection; whether it is that the generality are incapable of such
extensive knowledge, or that the authors of those books are
not adequate instructors. In China, the emperor himself
takes cognizance of all the doctors in the kingdom who profess authorship.[1] In England, every man may be an author
that can write; for they have by law a liberty not only of
saying what they please, but of being also as dull as they
please.

Yesterday I testified my surprise to the man in black,
where writers could be found in sufficient number to throw
off the books I daily saw crowding from the press. I at first
imagined that their learned seminaries might take this method of instructing the world. But to obviate this objection,
my companion assured me, that the doctors of colleges never
wrote, and that some of them had actually forgotten their
reading. "But if you desire," continued he, "to see a collection of authors, I fancy I can introduce you this evening
to a club, which assembles every Saturday at seven, at the
sign of 'The Broom,' near Islington,[2] to talk over the business of the last and the entertainment of the week ensuing."
I accepted his invitation; we walked together, and entered
the house some time before the usual hour for the company
assembling.

My friend took this opportunity of letting me into the
characters of the principal members of the club, not even the

---

[1] "One of the most remarkable national peculiarities of China is their extraordinary addiction to letters, and the very honorable pre-eminence which, from the most
remote period, has been universally conceded to that class which is exclusively devoted to literary pursuits. Everything that is subservient to, or connected with,
literary objects in China is carried to a degree of refinement, and blended with all
their ordinary concerns of pleasure and of business, in a way that may seem extravagant and puerile. Their customary reverence for letters is such that they
will not tread upon written or printed paper."—Sir GEORGE STAUNTON'S *Miscellaneous Notices*, p. ii. chap. vi.

[2] Islington was one of Goldsmith's frequent resorts and occasional residences.
Some of the supposed authors in this and the succeeding letter were no doubt
real characters.

host excepted—who, it seems, was once an author himself, but preferred by a bookseller to this situation as a reward for his former services.

"The first person," said he, "of our society is Doctor Non-entity, a metaphysician. Most people think him a profound scholar; but as he seldom speaks, I cannot be positive in that particular; he generally spreads himself before the fire, sucks his pipe, talks little, drinks much, and is reckoned very good company. I'm told he writes indexes to perfection; he makes essays on the origin of evil, philosophical inquiries upon any subject, and draws up an answer to any book upon twenty-four hours' warning. You may distinguish him from the rest of the company by his long gray wig, and the blue handkerchief round his neck.

"The next to him in merit and esteem is Tim Syllabub, a droll creature; he sometimes shines as a star of the first magnitude among the choice spirits of the age; he is reckoned equally excellent at a rebus, a riddle, a bawdy song, and a hymn for the Tabernacle. You will know him by his shabby finery, his powdered wig, dirty shirt, and broken silk stockings.

"After him succeeds Mr. Tibbs, a very useful hand; he writes receipts for the bite of a mad dog, and throws off an Eastern tale to perfection; he understands the business of an author as well as any man, for no bookseller alive can cheat him. You may distinguish him by the peculiar clumsiness of his figure and the coarseness of his coat; however, though it be coarse (as he frequently tells the company), he has paid for it.

"Lawyer Squint is the politician of the society; he makes speeches for Parliament, writes addresses to his fellow-sub-jects, and letters to noble commanders; he gives the history of every new play, and finds 'seasonable thoughts' upon every occasion." My companion was proceeding in his description, when the host came running in, with terror on his counte-nance, to tell us that the door was beset with bailiffs. "If that be the case, then," says my companion, "we had as good be going; for I am positive we shall not see one of the com-

II.—13

pany this night." Wherefore, disappointed, we were both obliged to return home: he to enjoy the oddities which compose his character alone, and I to write as usual to my friend the occurrences of the day.   Adieu.

LETTER XXX.

THE PROCEEDINGS OF THE CLUB OF AUTHORS.

From the Same.

By my last advices from Moscow I find the caravan has not yet departed for China.   I still continue to write, expecting that you may receive a large number of my letters at once.   In them you will find rather a minute detail of English peculiarities, than a general picture of their manners or disposition.   Happy it were for mankind if all travellers would thus, instead of characterizing a people in general terms, lead us into a detail of those minute circumstances which first influenced their opinion.   The genius of a country should be investigated with a kind of experimental inquiry; by this means we should have more precise and just notions of foreign nations, and detect travellers themselves when they happened to form wrong conclusions.

My friend and I repeated our visit to the club of authors; where, upon our entrance, we found the members all assembled and engaged in a loud debate.

The poet, in shabby finery, holding a manuscript in his hand, was earnestly endeavoring to persuade the company to hear him read the first book of an heroic poem which he had composed the day before.   But against this all the members very warmly objected.   They knew no reason why any member of the club should be indulged with a particular hearing, when many of them had published whole volumes which had never been looked in.   They insisted that the law should be observed, where reading in company was expressly noticed. It was in vain that the plaintiff pleaded the peculiar merit of

his piece: he spoke to an assembly insensible to all his remonstrances; the book of laws was opened, and read by the
secretary, where it was expressly enacted, " That whatsoever
poet, speech-maker, critic, or historian should presume to engage the company by reading his own works, he was to lay
down sixpence previous to opening the manuscript, and
should be charged one shilling an hour while he continued
reading: the said shilling to be equally distributed among
the company as a recompense for their trouble."

Our poet seemed at first to shrink at the penalty, hesitating
for some time whether he should deposit the fine, or shut up
the poem; but looking round, and perceiving two strangers·
in the room, his love of fame outweighed his prudence, and
laying down the sum by law established, he insisted on his
prerogative.

A profound silence ensuing, he began by explaining his
design. "Gentlemen," says he, "the present piece is not one
of your common epic poems, which come from the press like
paper kites in summer; there are none of your Turnuses or
Didos in it; it is an heroical description of Nature. I only
beg you'll endeavor to make your souls unison with mine,
and hear with the same enthusiasm with which I have written. The poem begins with the description of an author's
bedchamber; the picture was sketched in my own apartment, for you must know, gentlemen, that I am myself the
hero." Then putting himself into the attitude of an orator,
with all the emphasis of voice and action, he proceeded:

> " Where the Red Lion flaring o'er the way
>   Invites each passing stranger that can pay;
>   Where Calvert's butt, and Parson's black champagne,
>   Regale the drabs and bloods of Drury Lane;
>   There in a lonely room, from bailiffs snug,
>   The muse found Scroggen stretch'd beneath a rug.
>   A window patch'd with paper lent a ray,
>   That dimly show'd the state in which he lay:
>   The sanded floor that grits beneath the tread;
>   The humid wall with paltry pictures spread;
>   The royal game of goose was there in view,
>   And the twelve rules the royal martyr drew;

> The seasons fram'd with listing found a place,
> And brave Prince William show'd his lamp-black face:[1]
> The morn was cold: he views with keen desire
> The rusty grate, unconscious of a fire;
> With beer and milk arrears the frieze was scored,
> And five crack'd teacups dress'd the chimney-board;
> A nightcap deck'd his brows instead of bay,
> A cap by night—a stocking all the day!"

With this last line he seemed so much elated that he was unable to proceed. "There, gentlemen," cries he—"there is a description for you; Rabelais's bed-chamber is but a fool to it.

> 'A cap by night—a stocking all the day!'—

there is sound and sense, and truth and nature in the trifling compass of ten little syllables."

He was too much employed in self-admiration to observe the company; who, by nods, winks, shrugs, and stifled laughter, testified every mark of contempt. He turned severally to each for their opinion, and found all, however, ready to applaud. One swore it was inimitable; another said it was damn'd fine; and a third cried out in a rapture, "Carissimo!" At last, addressing himself to the president, "And pray, Mr. Squint," says he, "let us have your opinion." "Mine!" answered the president, taking the manuscript out of the author's hand—"may this glass suffocate me, but I think it equal to anything I have seen; and I fancy," continued he, doubling up the poem, and forcing it into the author's pocket, "that you will get great honor when it comes out; so I shall beg leave to put it in. We will not intrude upon your good-nature, in desiring to hear more of it at present; *ex ungue Herculem*, we are satisfied, perfectly satisfied." The author made two or three attempts to pull it out a second time, and the president made as many to prevent him. Thus, though with reluctance, he was at last obliged to sit down, contented with the commendations for which he had paid.

When this tempest of poetry and praise was blown over,

---

[1] "And Prussia's monarch show'd his lamp-black face."—See GOLDSMITH'S Letter to his brother, in Vol. IV.

one of the company changed the subject, by wondering how any man could be so dull as to write poetry at present, since prose itself would hardly pay. "Would you think it, gentlemen?" continued he, "I have actually written last week sixteen prayers, twelve bawdy jests, and three sermons, all at the rate of sixpence apiece; and what is still more extraordinary, the bookseller has lost by the bargain. Such sermons would once have gained me a prebend's stall; but now, alas! we have neither piety, taste, nor humor among us. Positively, if this season does not turn out better than it has begun, unless the ministry commit some blunders to furnish us with a new topic of abuse, I shall resume my old business of working at the press, instead of finding it employment."

The whole club seemed to join in condemning the season, as one of the worst that had come for some time; a gentleman particularly observed that the nobility were never known to subscribe worse than at present. "I know not how it happens," said he; "though I follow them up as close as possible yet I can hardly get a single subscription in a week. The houses of the great are as inaccessible as a frontier garrison at midnight. I never see a nobleman's door half-opened that some surly porter or footman does not stand full in the breach. I was yesterday to wait with a subscription-proposal upon my Lord Squash, the creolian. I had posted myself at his door the whole morning, and just as he was getting into his coach thrust my proposal snug into his hand, folded up in the form of a letter from myself. He just glanced at the superscription, and not knowing the hand, consigned it to his valet-de-chambre; this respectable personage treated it as his master, and put it into the hands of the porter; the porter grasped my proposal frowning; and measuring my figure from top to toe, put it back into my own hands unopened."

"To the devil I pitch all the nobility!" cries a little man, in a peculiar accent; "I am sure they have of late used me most scurvily. You must know, gentlemen, some time ago, upon the arrival of a certain noble duke from his travels, I set myself down, and vamped up a fine, flaunting poetical panegyric, which I had written in such a strain that I fancied it would have even wheedled milk from a mouse. In this I represented the whole kingdom welcoming his grace to his native soil, not forgetting the loss France and Italy would sustain in their arts by his departure. I expected to touch for a bank-bill at least; so folding up my verses in gilt paper, I gave my last half-crown to a genteel servant to be the bearer. My letter was safely conveyed to his grace, and the servant, after four hours' absence, during which time I led the life of a fiend, returned with a letter four times as big as mine. Guess my ecstasy at the prospect of so fine a return. I eagerly took the packet into my hands, that trembled to receive it. I kept it some time unopened before me, brooding over the expected treasure it contained; when, opening it, as I hope to be saved, gentlemen, his grace had sent me in payment for my poem, no bank-bills, but six copies of verse, each longer than mine, addressed to him upon the same occasion."

" A nobleman," cries a member who had hitherto been silent, " is created as much for the confusion of us authors as the catchpoll. I'll tell you a story, gentlemen, which is as true as that this pipe is made of clay. When I was delivered of my first book, I owed my tailor for a suit of clothes; but that is nothing new, you know, and may be any man's case as well as mine. Well, owing him for a suit of clothes, and hearing that my book took very well, he sent for his money, and insisted upon being paid immediately; though I was at that time rich in fame, for my book ran like wildfire, yet I was very short in money, and being unable to satisfy his demand, prudently resolved to keep my chamber, preferring a prison of my own choosing at home to one of my tailor's choosing abroad. In vain the bailiffs used all their arts to decoy me from my citadel; in vain they sent to let me know that a . gentleman wanted to speak with me at the next tavern; in vain they came with an urgent message from my aunt in the country; in vain I was told that a particular friend was at the point of death, and desired to take his last farewell; I was deaf, insensible, rock, adamant; the bailiffs could make no impression on my hard heart, for I effectually kept my liberty by never stirring out of the room."

" This was very well for a fortnight; when one morning I received a most splendid message from the Earl of Doomsday, importing that he had read my book, and was in raptures with every line of it; he impatiently longed to see the author, and had some designs which might turn out greatly to my advantage. I paused upon the contents of this message, and found there could be no deceit, for the card was gilt at the edges, and the bearer, I was told, had quite the looks of a gentleman. Witness, ye powers, how my heart triumphed at my own importance! I saw a long perspective of felicity before me; I applauded the taste of the times, which never saw genius forsaken; I had prepared a set introductory speech for the occasion, five glaring compliments for his lordship, and two more modest for myself. The next morning, therefore, in order to be punctual to my appointment, I took coach, and ordered the fellow to drive to the street and house mentioned in his lordship's address. I had the precaution to pull up the window as I went along to keep off the busy part of mankind, and, big with expectation, fancied the coach never went fast enough. At length, however, the wished-for moment of its stopping arrived; this for some time I impatiently expected, and letting down the window in a transport, in order to take a previous view of his lordship's magnificent palace and situation, I found—poison to my sight! I found myself, not in an elegant street, but a paltry lane; not at a nobleman's door, but the door of a sponging-house; I found the coachman had all this while been driving me to jail, and I saw the bailiff, with a devil's face, coming out to secure me."

To a philosopher no circumstance, however trifling, is too minute; he finds instruction and entertainment in occurrences which are passed over by the rest of mankind as low, trite, and indifferent; it is from the number of these particulars, which to many appear insignificant, that he is at last enabled to form general conclusions. This, therefore, must be my excuse for sending so far as China accounts of manners and follies which, though minute in their own nature, serve more truly to characterize this people than histories of their public treaties, courts, ministers, negotiations, and ambassadors. Adieu.

LETTER XXXI.

THE PERFECTION OF THE CHINESE IN THE ART OF GARDEN-
ING.—DESCRIPTION OF A CHINESE GARDEN.

From the Same.

THE English have not yet brought the art of gardening to the same perfection with the Chinese, but have lately begun to imitate them: nature is now followed with greater assiduity than formerly; the trees are suffered to shoot out into the utmost luxuriance; the streams, no longer forced from their native beds, are permitted to wind along the valleys; spontaneous flowers take place of the finished parterre, and the enamelled meadow of the shaven green.

Yet still the English are far behind us in this charming art; their designers have not yet attained a power of uniting instruction with beauty. A European will scarcely conceive my meaning, when I say that there is scarce a garden in China which does not contain some fine moral, couched under the general design, where one is not taught wisdom as he walks, and feels the force of some noble truth or delicate precept, resulting from the disposition of the groves, streams, or grottoes. Permit me to illustrate what I mean by a description of my gardens at Quamsi. My heart still hovers round those scenes of former happiness with pleasure; and I find a satisfaction in enjoying them at this distance, though but in imagination.

You descended from the house between two groves of trees, planted in such a manner that they were impenetrable to the eye; while on each hand the way was adorned with all that was beautiful in porcelain, statuary, and painting. This passage from the house opened into an area surrounded with rocks, flowers, trees, and shrubs, but all so disposed as if each was the spontaneous production of nature. As you proceeded forward on this lawn, to your right and left hand were two gates, opposite each other, of very different architecture and design; and before you lay a temple built rather with minute elegance than ostentation.

The right-hand gate was planned with the utmost simplicity, or rather rudeness; ivy clasped round the pillars, the baleful cypress hung over it; time seemed to have destroyed all the smoothness and regularity of the stone; two champions with lifted clubs appeared in the act of guarding its access; dragons and serpents were seen in the most hideous attitudes, to deter the spectator from approaching; and the perspective view that lay behind seemed dark and gloomy to the last degree; the stranger was tempted to enter only from the motto —*Pervia Virtuti.*

The opposite gate was formed in a very different manner; the architecture was light, elegant, and inviting; flowers hung in wreaths round the pillars; all was finished in the most exact and masterly manner; the very stone of which it was built still preserved its polish; nymphs, wrought by the hand of a master, in the most alluring attitudes, beckoned the stranger to approach; while all that lay behind, as far as the eye could reach, seemed gay, luxuriant, and capable of affording endless pleasure. The motto itself contributed to invite him, for over the gate were written these words—*Facilis Descensus.*

By this time I fancy you begin to perceive that the gloomy gate was designed to represent the road to virtue; the opposite, the more agreeable passage to vice. It is but natural to suppose that the spectator was always tempted to enter by the gate which offered him so many allurements. I always in these cases left him to his choice; but generally found that he took to the left, which promised most entertainment.

Immediately upon his entering the gate of vice the trees and flowers were disposed in such a manner as to make the most pleasing impression; but, as he walked farther on, he insensibly found the garden assume the air of a wilderness, the landscapes began to darken, the paths grew more intricate, he appeared to go downward, frightful rocks seemed to hang over his head, gloomy caverns, unexpected precipices, awful ruins, heaps of unburied bones, and terrifying sounds caused by unseen waters, began to take place of what at first appeared so lovely; it was in vain to attempt returning—the labyrinth was too much perplexed for any but myself to find the way back. In short, when sufficiently impressed with the horrors of what he saw, and the imprudence of his choice, I brought him by a hidden door a shorter way back into the area from whence at first he had strayed.

The gloomy gate now presented itself before the stranger; and though there seemed little in its appearance to tempt his curiosity, yet, encouraged by the motto, he gradually proceeded. The darkness of the entrance, the frightful figures that seemed to obstruct his way, the trees of a mournful green, conspired at first to disgust him; as he went forward, however, all began to open and wear a more pleasing appearance; beautiful cascades, beds of flowers, trees loaded with fruit or blossoms, and unexpected brooks improved the scene; he now found that he was ascending, and, as he proceeded, all nature grew more beautiful; the prospect widened as he went higher, even the air itself seemed to become more pure. Thus pleased and happy from unexpected beauties, I at last led him to an arbor from whence he could view the garden and the whole country around, and where he might own that the road to virtue terminated in happiness.

Though from this description you may imagine that a vast tract of ground was necessary to exhibit such a pleasing variety in, yet be assured I have seen several gardens in England take up ten times the space which mine did without half the beauty. A very small extent of ground is enough for an elegant taste: the greater room is required if magnificence is in view. There is no spot, though ever so little, which a skilful designer might not thus improve so as to convey a delicate allegory, and impress the mind with truths the most useful and necessary. Adieu.[1]

---

[1] This letter was written shortly after the appearance of Sir William (then Mr.) Chambers's work on Chinese Temples, etc. "Sir William's description of Chinese gardening is a mere prose work of imagination, without a shadow of foundation in reality. Their taste is, indeed, extremely defective and vicious on this particular

LETTER XXXII.

OF THE DEGENERACY OF SOME OF THE ENGLISH NOBILITY.—A
MUSHROOM FEAST AMONG THE TARTARS.

From the Same.

In a late excursion with my friend into the country, a gentleman with a blue ribbon tied round his shoulder, and in a chariot drawn by six horses, passed swiftly by us, attended with a numerous train of captains, lackeys, and coaches filled with women. When we were recovered from the dust raised by this cavalcade, and could continue our discourse without danger of suffocation, I observed to my companion that all this state and equipage, which he seemed to despise, would in China be regarded with the utmost reverence, because such distinctions were always the reward of merit; the greatness of a mandarin's retinue being a most certain mark of the superiority of his abilities or virtue.

"The gentleman who has now passed us," replied my companion, "has no claims from his own merit to distinction; he is possessed neither of abilities nor virtue; it is enough for him that one of his ancestors was possessed of these qualities two hundred years before him. There was a time, indeed, when his family deserved their titles, but they are long since degenerated, and his ancestors for more than a century have been more and more solicitous to keep up the breed of their dogs and horses than that of their children. This very nobleman, simple as he seems, is descended from a race of statesmen and heroes; but, unluckily, his great-grandfather marry-

---

point, and, as an improvement of nature, ranks much on a par with the cramping of their women's feet. The only exception exists in the gardens, or rather parks, of the emperor at Yuen-ming-yuen, which Mr. Barrow describes as grand both in plan and extent; but for a subject to emulate these would be almost criminal, even if it were possible."—Davis's *Chinese*, vol. i. p. 367.

ing a cook-maid, and she having a trifling passion for his lordship's groom, they somehow crossed the strain, and produced
an heir who took after his mother in his great love to good
eating, and his father in a violent affection for horse-flesh.
These passions have for some generations passed on from
father to son, and are now become the characteristics of the
family, his present lordship being equally remarkable for his
kitchen and his stable."

"But such a nobleman," cried I, " deserves our pity, thus
placed in so high a sphere of life, which only the more exposes to contempt. A king may confer titles, but it is personal merit alone that insures respect. I suppose," added I,
" that such men are despised by their equals, neglected by
their inferiors, and condemned to live among involuntary dependents in irksome solitude ?"

"You are still under a mistake," replied my companion,
" for, though this nobleman is a stranger to generosity, though
he takes twenty opportunities in a day of letting his guests
know how much he despises them ; though he is possessed
neither of taste, wit, nor wisdom ; though incapable of improving others by his conversation, and never known to enrich
any by his bounty, yet for all this his company is eagerly
sought after : he is a lord, and that is as much as most people
desire in a companion. Quality and title have such allurements that hundreds are ready to give up all their own importance, to cringe, to flatter, to look little, and to pall every pleasure in constraint, merely to be among the great, though without the least hopes of improving their understanding or shar-
ing their generosity ; they might be happy among their equals,
but those are despised for company, where they are despised
in turn. You saw what a crowd of humble cousins, card-
ruined beaux, and captains on half-pay were willing to make
up this great man's retinue down to his country-seat. Not
one of all these that could not lead a more comfortable life at
home in their little lodging of three shillings a week, with their
lukewarm dinner, served up between two pewter plates from
a cook's-shop. Yet, poor devils ! they are willing to undergo
the impertinence and pride of their entertainer merely to be

thought to live among the great ; they are willing to pass the summer in bondage, though conscious they are taken down only to approve his lordship's taste upon every occasion, to tag all his stupid observations with a *very true*, to praise his stable, and descant upon his claret and cookery."

"The pitiful humiliations of the gentlemen you are now describing," said I, "puts me in mind of a custom among the Tartars of Koreki not entirely dissimilar to this we are now considering.[1] The Russians, who trade with them, carry thither a kind of mushrooms, which they exchange for furs of squirrels, ermines, sables, and foxes. These mushrooms the rich Tartars lay up in large quantities for the winter, and when a nobleman makes a mushroom feast all the neighbors around are invited. The mushrooms are prepared by boiling, by which the water acquires an intoxicating quality, and is a sort of drink which the Tartars prize beyond all other. When the nobility and ladies are assembled, and the ceremonies usual between people of distinction over, the mushroom-broth goes freely round ; they laugh, talk *double entendre*, grow fuddled, and become excellent company. The poorer sort, who love mushroom-broth to distraction as well as the rich, but cannot afford it at the first hand, post themselves on these occasions round the huts of the rich, and watch the opportunity of the ladies and gentlemen as they come down to pass their liquor ; and, holding a wooden bowl, catch the delicious fluid, very little altered by filtration, being still strongly tinctured with the intoxicating quality. Of this they drink with the utmost satisfaction, and thus they get as drunk and as jovial as their betters."

"Happy nobility !" cries my companion, "who can fear no diminution of respect, unless by being seized with stranguary, and who when most drunk are most useful ! Though we have not this custom among us, I foresee that if it were introduced we might have many a toad-eater in England ready to drink from the wooden bowl on these occasions, and to

---

[1] Van Stralenberg, a writer of credit, gives the same account of his people. *Vide* "An Historico-geographical Description of the North-eastern Parts of Europe and Asia," etc.—GOLDSMITH.

praise the flavor of his lordship's liquor. As we have different classes of gentry, who knows but we may see a lord holding the bowl to a minister, a knight holding it to his lordship, and a simple squire drinking it double distilled from the loins of knighthood? For my part, I shall never for the future hear a great man's flatterers haranguing in his praise that I shall not fancy I behold the wooden bowl; for I can see no reason why a man who can live easily and happily at home should bear the drudgery of decorum and the impertinence of his entertainer, unless intoxicated with a passion for all that was quality; unless he thought that whatever came from the great was delicious, and had the tincture of the mushroom in it." Adieu.

LETTER XXXIII.

THE MANNER OF WRITING AMONG THE CHINESE.—THE EASTERN
TALES OF MAGAZINES, ETC., RIDICULED.

From the Same.

I AM disgusted, O Fum Hoam, even to sickness disgusted. Is it possible to bear the presumption of those islanders, when they pretend to instruct me in the ceremonies of China! They lay it down as a maxim, that every person who comes from thence must express himself in metaphor; swear by Allah, rail against wine, and behave, and talk, and write like a Turk or Persian. They make no distinction between our elegant manners and the voluptuous barbarities of our Eastern neighbors. Wherever I come, I raise either diffidence or astonishment; some fancy me no Chinese, because I am formed more like a man than a monster; and others wonder to find one born five thousand miles from England endued with common-sense. "Strange," say they, "that a man who has received his education at such a distance from London should have common-sense: to be born out of England, and yet have common-sense! Impossible! He must be some Englishman in disguise; his very visage has nothing of the true exotic barbarity."

I yesterday received an invitation from a lady of distinction, who it seems had collected all her knowledge of Eastern manners from fictions every day propagated here, under the titles of Eastern Tales and Oriental Histories. She received me very politely, but seemed to wonder that I neglected bringing opium and a tobacco-box. When chairs were drawn for the rest of the company, I was assigned my place on a cushion on the floor. It was in vain that I protested the Chinese used chairs as in Europe; she understood decorum too well to entertain me with the ordinary civilities.

I had scarcely been seated according to her directions, when the footman was ordered to pin a napkin under my chin; this I protested against as being no way Chinese; however, the whole company, who it seems were a club of connoisseurs, gave it unanimously against me, and the napkin was pinned accordingly.

It was impossible to be angry with people who seemed to err only from an excess of politeness, and I sat contented, expecting their importunities were now at an end; but as soon as ever dinner was served the lady demanded whether I was for a plate of bears' claws[1] or a slice of birds' nests?[2] As these were dishes with which I was utterly unacquainted, I was desirous of eating only what I knew, and therefore begged to be helped from a piece of beef that lay on the side-table. My request at once disconcerted the whole company. A Chinese eat beef! that could never be! there was no local propriety in Chinese beef, whatever there might be in Chinese pheasant. "Sir," said my entertainer, "I think I have some reasons to fancy myself a judge of these matters; in short, the Chinese never eat beef;[3] so that I must be permitted to recommend the pillau. There was never better

---

[1] "The paws of these animals, which abound in fat, are eaten by the Chinese as a delicacy."—DAVIS's *Chinese*, vol. ii. p. 338.

[2] "This is a dish in which the Chinese are perfect epicures. The substance thus served up is reduced into very thin filaments, transparent as isinglass and resembling vermicelli."—*Ibid.*, vol. i. p. 323.

[3] "The general prevalence of Buddhism is probably the reason that beef is scarcely ever used by the Chinese. They, however, make no difficulty whatever of dogs, cats, and even rats."—*Ibid.*, vol. i. p. 334.

dressed at Pekin ; the saffron and rice are well boiled, and the spices in perfection."

I had no sooner begun to eat what was laid before me than I found the whole company as much astonished as before: it seems I made no use of my chopsticks. A grave gentleman, whom I take to be an author, harangued very learnedly (as the company seemed to think) upon the use which was made of them in China. He entered into a long argument with himself about their first introduction, without once appealing to me, who might be supposed best capable of silencing the inquiry. As the gentleman, therefore, took my silence for a mark of his own superior sagacity, he was resolved to pursue the triumph; he talked of our cities, mountains, and animals as familiarly as if he had been born in Quamsi, but as erroneously as if a native of the moon. He attempted to prove that I had nothing of the true Chinese cut in my visage; showed that my cheek-bones should have been higher, and my forehead broader. In short, he almost reasoned me out of my country, and effectually persuaded the rest of the company to be of his opinion.

I was going to expose his mistakes, when it was insisted that I had nothing of the true Eastern manner in my delivery. "This gentleman's conversation," says one of the ladies, who was a great reader, "is like our own, mere chit-chat and common-sense: there is nothing like sense in the true Eastern style, where nothing more is required but sublimity. Oh, for a history of Aboulfaouris, the grand voyager—of genii, magicians, rocks, bags of bullets, giants, and enchanters, where all is great, obscure, magnificent, and unintelligible !—" " I have written many a sheet of Eastern tale myself," interrupts the author, " and I defy the severest critic to say but that I have stuck close to the true manner. I have compared a lady's chin to the snow upon the mountains of Bomek; a soldier's sword to the clouds that obscure the face of heaven. If riches are mentioned, I compared them to the flocks that graze the verdant Tefflis; if poverty, to the mists that veil the brow of Mount Baku. I have used *thee* and *thou* upon all occasions; I have described fallen stars, and splitting mountains, not forgetting the little houris, who make a pretty figure in every description. But you shall hear how I generally begin: 'Eben-ben-bolo, who was the son of Ban, was born on the foggy summits of Benderabassi. His beard was whiter than the feathers which veil the breast of the penguin; his eyes were like the eyes of doves when washed by the dews of the morning; his hair, which hung like the willow weeping over the glassy stream, was so beautiful that it seemed to reflect its own brightness; and his feet were as the feet of a wild deer which fleeth to the tops of the mountains.' There, there is the true Eastern taste for you; every advance made toward sense is only a deviation from sound. Eastern tales should always be sonorous, lofty, musical, and unmeaning."

I could not avoid smiling to hear a native of England attempt to instruct me in the true Eastern idiom; and after he looked round some time for applause, I presumed to ask him whether he had ever travelled into the East, to which he replied in the negative. I demanded whether he understood Chinese or Arabic, to which also he answered as before. "Then, how, sir," said I, "can you pretend to determine upon the Eastern style, who are entirely unacquainted with the Eastern writings? Take, sir, the word of one who is professedly a Chinese, and who is actually acquainted with the Arabian writers, that what is palmed upon you daily for an imitation of Eastern writing no way resembles their manner, either in sentiment or diction. In the East similes are seldom used, and metaphors almost wholly unknown; but in China particularly the very reverse of what you allude to takes place: a cool, phlegmatic method of writing prevails there. The writers of that country, ever more assiduous to instruct than to please, address rather the judgment than the fancy. Unlike many authors of Europe, who have no consideration of the reader's time, they generally leave more to be understood than they express.

"Besides, sir, you must not expect from an inhabitant of China the same ignorance, the same unlettered simplicity, that you find in a Turk, Persian, or native of Peru. The Chinese
II.—14

are versed in the sciences as well as you, and are masters of
several arts unknown to the people of Europe. Many of
them are instructed not only in their own national learning,
but are perfectly well acquainted with the languages and
learning of the West. If my word in such a case is not to be
taken, consult your own travellers on this head, who affirm
that the scholars of Pekin and Siam sustain theological theses
in Latin. 'The college of Masprend, which is but a league
from Siam,' says one of your travellers,[1] 'came in a body to
salute our ambassador. Nothing gave me more sincere pleasure than to behold a number of priests, venerable both from
age and modesty, followed by a number of youths of all nations—Chinese, Japanese, Tonquinese, of Cochin-China, Pegu,
and Siam—all willing to pay their respects in the most polite
manner imaginable. A Cochin-Chinese made an excellent
Latin oration upon this occasion; he was succeeded and even
outdone by a student of Tonquin, who was as well skilled in
the Western learning as any scholar of Paris.' Now, sir, if
youths who never stirred from home are so perfectly skilled
in your laws and learning, surely more must be expected
from one like me, who have travelled so many thousand
miles, who have conversed familiarly for several years with
the English factors established at Canton, and the missionaries sent us from every part of Europe. The unaffected of
every country nearly resemble each other; and a page of our
Confucius and of your Tillotson have scarce any material difference. Paltry affectation, strained allusions, and disgusting
finery are easily attained by those who choose to wear them;
and they are but too frequently the badges of ignorance or
of stupidity, whenever it would endeavor to please."

I was proceeding in my discourse, when, looking round, I
perceived the company no way attentive to what I attempted
with so much earnestness to enforce. One lady was whisper-
ing her that sat next, another was studying the merits of a fan,
a third began to yawn, and the author himself fell fast asleep.

---

[1] "'Journal, ou Suite du Voyage de Siam, en forme de Lettres familières, fait
en 1685 et 1686, par N. L. D. C., p. 174, edit. Amstelod. 1686.'"—GOLDSMITH.

I thought it, therefore, high time to make a retreat; nor did the company seem to show any regret at my preparations for departure; even the lady who had invited me with the most mortifying insensibility saw me seize my hat and rise from my cushion; nor was I invited to repeat my visit, because it was found that I aimed at appearing rather a reasonable creature than an outlandish idiot.   Adieu.

LETTER XXXIV.

OF THE PRESENT RIDICULOUS PASSION OF THE NOBILITY FOR PAINTING.

To the Same.

THE polite arts are in this country subject to as many revolutions as its laws or politics; not only the objects of fancy and dress, but even of delicacy and taste, are directed by the capricious influence of fashion.   I am told there has been a time when poetry was universally encouraged by the great, when men of the first rank not only patronized the poet, but produced the finest models for his imitation.   It was then the English sent forth those glowing rhapsodies which we have so often read over together with rapture; poems big with all the sublimity of Mencius,[1] and supported by reasoning as strong as that of Zimpo.

The nobility are ever fond of wisdom, but they are also fond of having it without study; to read poetry required

---

[1] " Ranking next to Confucius (*similis aut secundus*) is the celebrated Mencius, so called by the Jesuits, from his Chinese name, Meng-tse.   He lived about a century after his great predecessor, whose doctrines he still further illustrated and promoted, and left behind him the *fourth* of the sacred books bearing his own name. Mencius lived to the age of eighty-four.   Kea-tsing, an emperor of the Ming dynasty, made one of his real or supposed descendants in the *fifty-sixth* generation a member of the Hânlin college.   'If,' as Dr. Morrison observes, 'the persons who now profess to be the posterity of Confucius and Mencius be really so, their families are probably the most ancient in the world.'   It would be difficult to find even a Welsh pedigree to compete with them."—DAVIS'S *Chinese*, vol. ii. p. 55.

thought, and the English nobility were not fond of thinking;
they soon, therefore, placed their affections upon music, because in this they might indulge a happy vacancy, and yet
still have pretensions to delicacy and taste as before. They
soon brought their numerous dependents into an approbation
of their pleasures, who in turn led their thousand imitators
to feel or feign a similitude of passion. Colonies of singers
were now imported from abroad at a vast expense, and it was
expected the English would soon be able to set examples to
Europe. All these expectations, however, were soon dissipated. In spite of the zeal which fired the great, the ignorant vulgar refused to be taught to sing, refused to undergo
the ceremonies which were to initiate them in the singing
fraternity; thus the colony from abroad dwindled by degrees, for they were of themselves unfortunately incapable
of propagating the breed.

Music having thus lost its splendor, painting is now become
the sole object of fashionable care. The title of connoisseur
in that art is at present the safest passport into every fashionable society; a well-timed shrug, an admiring attitude, and
one or two exotic tones of exclamation are sufficient qualifications for men of low circumstances to curry favor. Even
some of the young nobility are themselves early instructed in
handling the pencil, while their happy parents, big with expectation, foresee the walls of every apartment covered with
the manufactures of their posterity.

But many of the English are not content with giving all
their time to this art at home; some young men of distinction are found to travel through Europe, with no other intent
than that of understanding and collecting pictures, studying
seals, and describing statues. On they travel from this cabinet of curiosities to that gallery of pictures; waste the prime
of life in wonder; skilful in pictures, ignorant in men; yet
impossible to be reclaimed, because their follies take shelter
under the names of delicacy and taste.

It is true, painting should have due encouragement; as the
painter can undoubtedly fit up our apartments in a much
more elegant manner than the upholsterer; but I should

think a man of fashion makes but an indifferent exchange, who lays out all that time in furnishing his house which he should have employed in the furniture of his head.   A person who shows no other symptoms of taste than his cabinet or gallery, might as well boast to me of the furniture of his kitchen.[1]

I know no other motive but vanity that induces the great to testify such an inordinate passion for pictures: after the piece is bought, and gazed at eight or ten days successively, the purchaser's pleasure must surely be over; all the satisfaction he can then have is to show it to others; he may be considered as the guardian of a treasure of which he makes no manner of use: his gallery is furnished, not for himself, but the connoisseur, who is generally some humble flatterer, ready to feign a rapture he does not feel, and as necessary to the happiness of a picture-buyer, as gazers are to the magnificence of an Asiatic procession.

I have enclosed a letter from a youth of distinction, on his travels, to his father in England; in which he appears addicted to no vice, seems obedient to his governor, of a good natural disposition, and fond of improvement; but at the same time, early taught to regard cabinets and galleries as the only proper schools of improvement, and to consider a skill in pictures as the properest knowledge for a man of quality:

"My Lord,—We have been but two days at Antwerp; wherefore I have sat down as soon as possible to give you some account of what we have seen since our arrival, desirous of letting no opportunity pass without writing to so good a father.   Immediately upon alighting from our Rotterdam machine, my governor, who is immoderately fond of paintings, and at the same time an excellent judge, would let no time pass till we paid our respects to the church of the Virgin-mother, which contains treasure beyond estimation.   We took

---

[1] "I can have no expectations in an address of this kind either to add to your reputation, or to establish my own.   You can gain nothing from my admiration, *as I am ignorant of that art* in which you are said to excel."—GOLDSMITH, *Dedication of The Deserted Village to Sir Joshua Reynolds.*

an infinity of pains in knowing its exact dimensions, and differed half a foot in our calculation; so I leave that to some succeeding information. I really believe my governor and I could have lived and died there. There is scarcely a pillar in the whole church that is not adorned by a Rubens, a Vander Meulen, a Vandyke, or a Wouverman. What attitudes, carnations, and draperies! I am almost induced to pity the English, who have none of those exquisite pieces among them. As we are willing to let slip no opportunity of doing business, we immediately after went to wait on Mr. Hogendorp, whom you have so frequently commended for his judicious collection. His cameos are indeed beyond price; his intaglios not so good. He showed us one of an officiating flamen, which he thought to be an antique; but my governor, who is not to be deceived in these particulars, soon found it to be an arrant *cinque cento*. I could not, however, sufficiently admire the genius of Mr. Hogendorp, who has been able to collect, from all parts of the world, a thousand things which nobody knows the use of. Except your lordship and my governor, I do not know anybody I admire so much. He is indeed a surprising genius.

"The next morning early, as we were resolved to take the whole day before us, we sent our compliments to Mr. Van Sprokcken, desiring to see his gallery, which request he very politely complied with. His gallery measures fifty feet by twenty, and is well filled; but what surprised the most of all was to see a holy family just like your lordship's, which this ingenious gentleman assures me is the true original. I own this gave me inexpressible uneasiness, and I fear it will to your lordship, as I had flattered myself that the only original was in your lordship's possession. I would advise you, however, to take yours down till its merit can be ascertained, my governor assuring me that he intends to write a long dissertation to prove its originality. One might study in this city for ages, and still find something new. We went from this to view the cardinal's statues, which are really very fine; there were three spintria executed in a very masterly manner, all arm-in-arm; the torse which I heard you talk so much of is at last discovered to be a Hercules spinning, and not a Cleopatra bathing, as your lordship had conjectured. There has been a treatise written to prove it.

"My Lord Firmly is certainly a Goth, a Vandal—no taste in the world for painting. I wonder how any call him a man of taste. Passing through the streets of Antwerp a few days ago, and observing the nakedness of the inhabitants, he was so barbarous as to observe, that he thought the best method the Flemings could take was to sell their pictures and buy clothes. Ah, Coglione! We shall go to-morrow to Mr. Carwarden's cabinet, and the next day we shall see the curiosities collected by Van Ran; and the day after we shall pay a visit to Mount Calvary, and after that— But I find my paper finished; so, with the most sincere wishes for your lordship's happiness, and with hopes, after having seen Italy, that centre of pleasure, to return home worthy the care and expense which has been generously laid out in my improvement, I remain, my lord, yours," etc.

LETTER XXXV.

THE PHILOSOPHER'S SON DESCRIBES A LADY, HIS FELLOW-CAPTIVE.

From Hingpo, a slave in Persia, to Altangi, a travelling philosopher of China, by the way of Moscow.

FORTUNE has made me the slave of another, but nature and inclination render me entirely subservient to you; a tyrant commands my body, but you are master of my heart. And yet let not thy inflexible nature condemn me when I confess that I find my soul shrink with my circumstances. I feel my mind not less than my body bend beneath the rigors of servitude; the master whom I serve grows every day more formidable. In spite of reason, which should teach me to despise him, his hideous image fills even my dreams with horror.

A few days ago, a Christian slave, who wrought in the gardens, happening to enter an arbor where the tyrant was entertaining the ladies of his harem with coffee, the unhappy captive was instantly stabbed to the heart for his intrusion. I have been preferred to his place, which, though less laborious than my former station, is yet more ungrateful, as it brings me nearer him whose presence excites sensations at once of disgust and apprehension.

Into what a state of misery are the modern Persians fallen! A nation famous for setting the world an example of freedom is now become a land of tyrants and a den of slaves.[1] The houseless Tartar of Kamtchatka, who enjoys his herbs and his fish in unmolested freedom, may be envied, if compared to the thousands who pine here in hopeless servitude, and curse the day that gave them being. Is this just dealing, Heaven! to render millions wretched to swell up the happiness of a few? Cannot the powerful of this earth be happy without our sighs and tears? Must every luxury of the great be woven from the calamities of the poor? It must, it must surely be that this jarring, discordant life is but the prelude to some future harmony: the soul, attuned to virtue here, shall go from hence to fill up the universal choir where Tien presides in person; where there shall be no tyrants to frown, no shackles to bind, nor no whips to threaten; where I shall once more meet my father with rapture, and give a loose to filial piety; where I shall hang on his neck, and hear the wisdom of his lips, and thank him for all the happiness to which he has introduced me.

The wretch whom fortune has made my master has lately purchased several slaves of both sexes; among the rest I hear a Christian captive talked of with admiration. The eunuch who bought her, and who is accustomed to survey beauty with indifference, speaks of her with emotion. Her pride, however, astonishes her attendant slaves not less than her beauty. It is reported that she refuses the warmest solicitations of her haughty lord; he has even offered to make her one of his four wives upon changing her religion and conforming to his. It is probable she cannot refuse such extraor-

---

[1] "A land of tyrants, and a den of slaves,
Her wretches seek dishonorable graves."—*The Traveller.*

dinary offers, and her delay is perhaps intended to enhance her favors.

I have just now seen her; she inadvertently approached the place without a veil where I sat writing. She seemed to regard the heavens alone with fixed attention: there her most ardent gaze was directed. Genius of the sun! what unexpected softness! what animated grace! her beauty seemed the transparent covering of virtue. Celestial beings could not wear a look of more perfection, while sorrow humanized her form, and mixed my admiration with pity. I rose from the bank on which I sat, and she retired; happy that none observed us, for such an interview might have been fatal.

I have regarded, till now, the opulence and the power of my tyrant without envy. I saw him with a mind incapable of enjoying the gift of fortune, and consequently regarded him as one loaded, rather than enriched, with its favors; but at present, when I think that so much beauty is reserved only for him; that so many charms should be lavished on a wretch incapable of feeling the greatness of the blessing, I own I feel a reluctance to which I have hitherto been a stranger.

But let not my father impute those uneasy sensations to so trifling a cause as love. No, never let it be thought that your son, and the pupil of the wise Fum Hoam, could stoop to so degrading a passion. I am only displeased at seeing so much excellence so unjustly disposed of.

The uneasiness which I feel is not for myself, but for the beautiful Christian. When I reflect on the barbarity of him for whom she is designed, I pity, indeed I pity her; when I think that she must only share one heart, who deserves to command a thousand, excuse me if I feel an emotion which universal benevolence extorts from me. As I am convinced that you take a pleasure in those sallies of humanity, and are particularly pleased with compassion, I could not avoid discovering the sensibility with which I felt this beautiful stranger's distress. I have for a while forgot, in hers, the miseries of my own hopeless situation: the tyrant grows every day more severe; and love, which softens all other minds into tenderness, seems only to have increased his severity. Adieu.

LETTER XXXVI.

THE BEAUTIFUL CAPTIVE CONSENTS TO MARRY HER LORD.

From the Same.

THE whole harem is filled with a tumultuous joy. Zelis, the beautiful captive, has consented to embrace the religion of Mohammed, and become one of the wives of the fastidious Persian. It is impossible to describe the transport that sits on every face on this occasion. Music and feasting fill every apartment; the most miserable slave seems to forget his chains, and sympathizes with the happiness of Mostadad. The herb we tread beneath our feet is not made more for our use than every slave around him for their imperious master; mere machines of obedience, they wait with silent assiduity, feel his pains, and rejoice in his exultation. Heavens! how much is requisite to make one man happy!

Twelve of the most beautiful slaves, and I among the number, have got orders to prepare for carrying him in triumph to the bridal apartment. The blaze of perfumed torches is to imitate the day; the dancers and singers are hired at a vast expense. The nuptials are to be celebrated on the approaching feast of Barboura, when a hundred taels in gold are to be distributed among the barren wives, in order to pray for fertility from the approaching union.

What will not riches procure! A hundred domestics, who curse the tyrant in their souls, are commanded to wear a face of joy, and they are joyful. A hundred flatterers are ordered to attend, and they fill his ears with praise. Beauty, all-commanding beauty, sues for admittance, and scarcely receives an answer: even love itself seems to wait upon fortune, or, though the passion be only feigned, yet it wears every appearance of sincerity; and what greater pleasure can even true sincerity confer, or what would the rich have more?

Nothing can exceed the intended magnificence of the bridegroom but the costly dresses of the bride: six eunuchs in the most sumptuous habits are to conduct him to the nuptial couch, and wait his orders. Six ladies, in all the magnificence of Persia, are directed to undress the bride. Their business is to assist, to encourage her, to divest her of every encumbering part of her dress—all but the last covering, which, by an artful complication of ribbons, is purposely made difficult to unloose, and with which she is to part reluctantly even to the joyful possessor of her beauty.

Mostadad, O my father, is no philosopher; and yet he seems perfectly contented with ignorance. Possessed of numberless slaves, camels, and women, he desires no greater possession. He never opened the page of Mencius, and yet all the slaves tell me that he is happy.

Forgive the weakness of my nature if I sometimes feel my heart rebellious to the dictates of wisdom, and eager for happiness like his. Yet why wish for his wealth with his ignorance—to be, like him, incapable of sentimental pleasures, incapable of feeling the happiness of making others happy, incapable of teaching the beautiful Zelis philosophy?

What! shall I, in a transport of passion, give up the golden mean, the universal harmony, the unchanging essence, for the possession of a hundred camels, as many slaves, thirty-five beautiful horses, and seventy-three fine women? First blast me to the centre! degrade me beneath the most degraded! pare my nails, ye powers of Heaven! ere I would stoop to such an exchange. What! part with philosophy, which teaches me to suppress my passions instead of gratifying them, which teaches me even to divest my soul of passion, which teaches serenity in the midst of tortures; philosophy, by which even now I am so very serene, and so very much at ease, to be persuaded to part with it for any other enjoyment! Never, never, even though persuasion spoke in the accents of Zelis!

A female slave informs me that the bride is to be arrayed in a tissue of silver, and her hair adorned with the largest pearls of Ormus. But why tease you with particulars in which we both are so little concerned? The pain I feel in separation throws a gloom over my mind, which in this scene of universal joy I fear may be attributed to some other cause. How wretched are those who are, like me, denied even the last resource of misery—their tears! Adieu.

LETTER XXXVII.

THE PHILOSOPHER'S SON BEGINS TO BE DISGUSTED IN THE PUR-
SUIT OF WISDOM.—AN ALLEGORY TO PROVE ITS FUTILITY.

From the Same.

I BEGIN to have doubts whether wisdom be alone sufficient to make us happy: whether every step we make in refine-ment is not an inlet into new disquietudes. A mind too vig-orous and active serves only to consume the body to which it is joined, as the richest jewels are soonest found to wear their settings.

When we rise in knowledge, as the prospect widens the ob-jects of our regard become more obscure, and the unlettered peasant, whose views are only directed to the narrow sphere around him, beholds Nature with a finer relish, and tastes her blessings with a keener appetite, than the philosopher whose mind attempts to grasp a universal system.

As I was some days ago pursuing this subject among a circle of my fellow-slaves, an ancient Guebre of the number, equally remarkable for his piety and wisdom, seemed touched with my conversation, and desired to illustrate what I had been saying with an allegory taken from the Zend-Avesta of Zoroaster. "By this we shall be taught," says he, "that they who travel in pursuit of wisdom walk only in a circle, and after all their labor at last return to their pristine igno-rance; and in this also we shall see that enthusiastic confi-dence or unsatisfying doubts terminate all our inquiries.

"In early times, before myriads of nations covered the earth, the whole human race lived together in one valley. The simple inhabitants, surrounded on every side by lofty mountains, knew no other world but the little spot to which they were confined. They fancied the heavens bent down to meet the mountain tops, and formed an impenetrable wall to surround them. None had ever yet ventured to climb the steepy cliff in order to explore those regions that lay beyond it; they knew the nature of the skies only from a tradition, which mentioned their being made of adamant. Traditions make up the reasonings of the simple, and serve to silence every inquiry.

"In this sequestered vale, blessed with all the spontaneous productions of nature—the honeyed blossom, the refreshing breeze, the gliding brook, and golden fruitage—the simple inhabitants seemed happy in themselves, in each other; they desired no greater pleasure, for they knew of none greater; ambition, pride, and envy were vices unknown among them; and from this peculiar simplicity of its possessors the country was called the Valley of Ignorance.

"At length, however, an unhappy youth, more aspiring than the rest, undertook to climb the mountain's side, and examine the summits which were hitherto deemed inaccessible. The inhabitants from below gazed with wonder at his intrepidity; some applauded his courage, others censured his folly; still, however, he proceeded towards the place where the earth and heavens seemed to unite, and at length arrived at the wished-for height, with extreme labor and assiduity.

"His first surprise was to find the skies not, as he expected, within his reach, but still as far off as before; his amazement increased when he saw a wide-extended region lying on the opposite side of the mountain; but it rose to astonishment when he beheld a country at a distance more beautiful and alluring than even that he had just left behind.

"As he continued to gaze with wonder, a genius, with a look of infinite modesty, approaching, offered to be his guide and instructor. 'The distant country, which you so much admire,' says the angelic being, 'is called the Land of Certainty; in that charming retreat sentiment contributes to refine every sensual banquet; the inhabitants are blessed with every solid enjoyment, and still more blessed in a perfect consciousness of their own felicity; ignorance in that country is wholly unknown; all there is satisfaction without alloy, for every pleasure first undergoes the examination of reason. As for me, I am called the Genius of Demonstration, and am stationed here in order to conduct every adventurer to that land of happiness through those intervening regions you see overhung with fogs and darkness, and horrid with forests, cataracts, caverns, and various other shapes of danger. But follow me, and in time I may lead you to that distant desirable land of tranquillity.'

"The intrepid traveller immediately put himself under the direction of the genius, and both journeying on together with a slow but agreeable pace, deceived the tediousness of the way by conversation. The beginning of the journey seemed to promise true satisfaction, but as they proceeded forward the skies became more gloomy and the way more intricate; they often inadvertently approached the brow of some frightful precipice, or the brink of a torrent, and were obliged to measure back their former way. The gloom increasing as they proceeded, their pace became more slow; they paused at every step, frequently stumbled, and their distrust and timidity increased. The Genius of Demonstration now, therefore, advised his pupil to grope upon hands and feet, as a method, though more slow, yet less liable to error.

"In this manner they attempted to pursue their journey for some time, when they were overtaken by another genius, who, with a precipitate pace, seemed travelling the same way. He was instantly known by the other to be the Genius of Probability. He wore two wide-extended wings at his back, which incessantly waved without increasing the rapidity of his motion; his countenance betrayed a confidence that the ignorant might mistake for sincerity, and he had but one eye, which was fixed in the middle of his forehead.

"'Servant of Hormizda,' cried he, approaching the mortal pilgrim, 'if thou art travelling to the Land of Certainty, how is it possible to arrive there under the guidance of a genius who proceeds forward so slowly, and is so little acquainted

with the way?   Follow me; we shall soon perform the journey to where every pleasure awaits our arrival.'

"The peremptory tone in which this genius spoke, and the
speed with which he moved forward, induced the traveller to
change his conductor, and leaving his modest companion behind, he proceeded forward with his more confident director,
seeming not a little pleased at the increased velocity of his
motion.

"But soon he found reasons to repent.   Whenever a torrent crossed their way his guide taught him to despise the
obstacle by plunging him in; whenever a precipice presented he was directed to fling himself forward.   Thus, each moment miraculously escaping, his repeated escapes only served
to increase his guide's temerity.   He led him, therefore, for-
wards, amid infinite difficulties, till they arrived at the borders of an ocean, which appeared unnavigable from the black
mists that lay upon its surface.   Its unquiet waves were of
the darkest hue, and gave a lively representation of the various agitations of the human mind.

"The Genius of Probability now confessed his temerity,
owned his being an improper guide to the Land of Certainty,
a country where no mortal had ever been permitted to arrive;
but at the same time offered to supply the traveller with another conductor, who should carry him to the Land of Confidence, a region where the inhabitants lived with the utmost
tranquillity, and tasted almost as much satisfaction as if in the
Land of Certainty.   Not waiting for a reply, he stamped three
times on the ground, and called forth the Demon of Error, a
gloomy fiend of the servants of Arimanes.   The yawning
earth gave up the reluctant savage, who seemed unable to
bear the light of the day.   His stature was enormous, his color
black and hideous; his aspect betrayed a thousand varying
passions, and he spread forth pinions that were fitted for the
most rapid flight.   The traveller at first was shocked at the
spectre; but finding him obedient to superior power, he assumed his former tranquillity.

"'I have called you to duty,' cries the genius to the demon, 'to bear on your back a son of mortality over the Ocean

of Doubts into the Land of Confidence; I expect you'll perform your commission with punctuality. And as for you,' continued the genius, addressing the traveller, 'when once I have bound this fillet round your eyes, let no voice of persuasion, nor threats the most terrifying, induce you to unbind it in order to look round; keep the fillet fast, look not at the ocean below, and you may certainly expect to arrive at a region of pleasure.'

"Thus saying, and the traveller's eyes being covered, the demon, muttering curses, raised him on his back, and, instantly upborne by his strong pinions, directed his flight among the clouds. Neither the loudest thunder nor the most angry tempest could persuade the traveller to unbind his eyes. The demon directed his flight downwards, and skimmed the surface of the ocean; a thousand voices, some with loud invectives, others in the sarcastic tones of contempt, vainly endeavored to persuade him to look round; but he still continued to keep his eyes covered, and would in all probability have arrived at the happy land had not flattery effected what other means could not perform; for now he heard himself welcomed on every side to the promised land, and a universal shout of joy was sent forth at his safe arrival. The wearied traveller, desirous of seeing the long-wished-for country, at length pulled the fillet from his eyes and ventured to look round him. But he had unloosed the band too soon; he was not yet above half-way over. The demon, who was still hovering in the air, and had produced those sounds only in order to deceive, was now freed from his commission; wherefore, throwing the astonished traveller from his back, the unhappy youth fell headlong into the subjacent Ocean of Doubts, from whence he never after was seen to rise."

LETTER XXXVIII.

THE CHINESE PHILOSOPHER PRAISES THE JUSTICE OF A LATE BRITISH SENTENCE.

From Lien Chi Altangi, to Fum Hoam, first President of the Ceremonial Academy at Pekin, in China.

When Parmenio, the Grecian, had done something which excited a universal shout from the surrounding multitude, he was instantly struck with the doubt that what had their approbation must certainly be wrong; and, turning to a philosopher who stood near him, "Pray, sir," says he, "pardon me; I fear I have been guilty of some absurdity."

You know that I am not less than him a despiser of the multitude; you know that I equally detest flattery to the great; yet so many circumstances have concurred to give a lustre to the latter part of the present English monarch's reign, that I cannot withhold my contribution of praise; I cannot avoid acknowledging the crowd, for once, just in their unanimous approbation.

Yet think not the battles gained, dominion extended, or enemies brought to submission are the virtues which at present claim my admiration. Were the reigning monarch only famous for his victories, I should regard his character with indifference; the boast of heroism in this enlightened age is justly regarded as a qualification of a very subordinate rank, and mankind now begin to look with becoming horror on these foes to man. The virtue in this aged monarch, which I have at present in view, is one of a much more exalted nature, is one the most difficult of attainment, is the least praised, of all kingly virtues, and yet deserves the greatest praise: the virtue I mean is justice—a strict administration of justice, without severity and without favor.

Of all virtues this is the most difficult to be practised by

II.—15

a king who has a power to pardon. All men, even tyrants themselves, lean to mercy when unbiassed by passions or interest; the heart naturally persuades to forgiveness, and, pursuing the dictates of this pleasing deceiver, we are led to prefer our private satisfaction to public utility. What a thorough love for the public, what a strong command over the passions, what a finely-conducted judgment must he possess, who opposes the dictates of reason to those of his heart, and prefers the future interest of his people to his own immediate satisfaction!

If still, to a man's own natural bias for tenderness, we add the numerous solicitations made by a criminal's friends for mercy; if we survey a king not only opposing his own feelings, but reluctantly refusing those he regards, and this to satisfy the public, whose cries he may never hear, whose gratitude he may never receive—this surely is true greatness! Let us fancy ourselves for a moment in this just old man's place, surrounded by numbers, all soliciting the same favor, a favor that nature disposes us to grant, where the inducements to pity are laid before us in the strongest light, suppliants at our feet, some ready to resent a refusal, none opposing a compliance; let us, I say, suppose ourselves in such a situation, and I fancy we should find ourselves more apt to act the character of good-natured men than of upright magistrates.

What contributes to raise justice above all other kindly virtues is, that it is seldom attended with a due share of applause, and those who practise it must be influenced by greater motives than empty fame: the people are generally well pleased with a remission of punishment, and all that wears the appearance of humanity; it is the wise alone who are capable of discerning that impartial justice is the truest mercy; they know it to be very difficult at once to compassionate and yet condemn an object that pleads for tenderness.

I have been led into this commonplace train of thought by a late striking instance in this country of the impartiality of justice, and of the king's inflexible resolution of inflicting punishment where it was justly due. A man of the first quality,[1] in a fit either of passion, melancholy, or madness, murdered his servant: it was expected that his station in life would have lessened the ignominy of his punishment; however, he was arraigned, condemned, and underwent the same degrading death with the meanest malefactor. It was well considered that virtue alone is true nobility; and that he whose actions sink him even beneath the vulgar has no right to those distinctions which should be the rewards only of merit: it was, perhaps, considered that crimes were more heinous among the higher classes of people, as necessity exposes them to fewer temptations.

Over all the East, even China not excepted, a person of the same quality guilty of such a crime might, by giving up a share of his fortune to the judge, buy off his sentence. There are several countries, even in Europe, where the servant is entirely the property of his master: if a slave kills his lord, he dies by the most excruciating tortures; but if the circumstances are reversed, a small fine buys off the punishment of the offender. Happy the country where all are equal, and where those who sit as judges have too much integrity to receive a bribe, and too much honor to pity, from a similitude of the prisoner's title or circumstances with their own! Such is England; yet think not that it was always equally famed for this strict impartiality. There was a time, even here, when title softened the rigors of the law, when dignified wretches were suffered to live, and continue for years an equal disgrace to justice and nobility.

To this day, in a neighboring country, the great are often most scandalously pardoned for the most scandalous offences. A person is still alive among them who has more than once deserved the most ignominious severity of justice.[2] His being of the blood royal, however, was thought a sufficient atone-

---

[1] Earl Ferrers, hanged at Tyburn, 5th May, 1760, for murdering his steward. "Two petitions from the earl's mother and all his family were presented to the king; who said, as the House of Lords had unanimously found him guilty, he would not interfere."—HORACE WALPOLE *to Sir Horace Mann*, vol. iii. p. 353. See also *The Citizen of the World*, Letter XLV. p. 250.

[2] The Prince of Charolais.

ment for his being a disgrace to humanity. This remarkable personage took pleasure in shooting at the passengers below, from the top of his palace; and in this most princely amusement he usually spent some time every day. He was at length arraigned by the friends of a person whom in this manner he had killed, and was found guilty of the charge, and condemned to die. His merciful monarch pardoned him in consideration of his rank and quality. The unrepenting criminal soon after renewed his usual entertainment, and in the same manner killed another man. He was a second time condemned; and, strange to think, a second time received his majesty's pardon! Would you believe it? A third time the very same man was guilty of the very same offence; a third time, therefore, the laws of his country found him guilty—I wish for the honor of humanity I could suppress the rest—a third time he was pardoned! Will you not think such a story too extraordinary for belief? will you not think me describing the savage inhabitants of Congo? Alas! the story is but too true, and the country where it was transacted regards itself as the politest in Europe! Adieu.

LETTER XXXIX.

DESCRIPTION OF TRUE POLITENESS.—TWO LETTERS OF DIFFERENT
COUNTRIES, BY LADIES FALSELY THOUGHT POLITE AT HOME.

From Lien Chi Altangi to ——, Merchant, in Amsterdam.

CEREMONIES are different in every country; but true politeness is everywhere the same. Ceremonies, which take up so much of our attention, are only artificial helps which ignorance assumes, in order to imitate politeness, which is the result of good-sense and good-nature. A person possessed of those qualities, though he had never seen a court, is truly agreeable; and if without them would continue a clown, though he had been all his life a gentleman-usher.

How would a Chinese, bred up in the formalities of an

Eastern court, be regarded, should he carry all his good-manners beyond the Great Wall? How would an Englishman, skilled in all the decorums of Western good-breeding, appear at an Eastern entertainment: would he not be reckoned more fantastically savage than even his unbred footman?

Ceremony resembles that base coin which circulates through a country by the royal mandate: it serves every purpose of real money at home, but is entirely useless if carried abroad; a person who should attempt to circulate his native trash in another country would be thought either ridiculous or culpable. He is truly well-bred who knows when to value and when to despise those national peculiarities which are regarded by some with so much observance: a traveller of taste at once perceives that the wise are polite all the world over, but that fools are polite only at home.

I have now before me two very fashionable letters upon the same subject, both written by ladies of distinction; one of whom leads the fashion in England, and the other sets the ceremonies of China: they are both regarded in their respective countries by all the beau-monde as standards of taste and models of true politeness, and both give us a true idea of what they imagine elegant in their admirers. Which of them understands true politeness, or whether either, you shall be at liberty to determine. The English lady writes thus to her female confidante:

" As I live, my dear Charlotte, I believe the colonel will carry it at last; he is a most irresistible fellow, that's flat. So well-dressed, so neat, so sprightly, and plays about one so agreeably, that I vow he has as much spirits as the Marquis of Monkeyman's Italian greyhound. I first saw him at Ranelagh; he shines there: he is nothing without Ranelagh, and Ranelagh nothing without him. The next day he sent a card and compliments, desiring to wait on mamma and me to the music subscription. He looked all the time with such irresistible impudence, that positively he had something in his face gave me as much pleasure as a pair-royal of naturals in my own hand. He waited on mamma and me the next morn-

ing to know how we got home: you must know the insidious
devil makes love to us both.   Rap went the footman at the
door; bounce went my heart: I thought he would have rat-
tled the house down.   Chariot drove up to the window, with
his footmen in the prettiest liveries: he has infinite taste,
that's flat.   Mamma has spent all the morning at her head;
but for my part I was in an undress to receive him; quite
easy, mind that; no way disturbed at his approach; mamma
pretended to be as *dégagée* as I, and yet I saw her blush in
spite of her.   Positively he is a most killing devil!   We did
nothing but laugh all the time he stayed with us; I never heard
so many very good things before.   At first he mistook mamma for my sister, at which she laughed; then he mistook my
natural complexion for paint, at which I laughed; and then
he showed us a picture in the lid of his snuffbox, at which
we all laughed.   He plays piquet so very ill, and is so very
fond of cards, and loses with such a grace, that positively he
has won me; I have got a cool hundred, but have lost my
heart.   I need not tell you that he is only a colonel of the
train-bands.   I am, dear Charlotte, yours forever,

                                        " BELINDA."

   The Chinese lady addresses her confidante, a poor relation
of the family, upon the same occasion; in which she seems to
understand decorums even better than the Western beauty.
You, who have resided so long in China, will readily acknowledge the picture to be taken from nature; and, by being acquainted with the Chinese customs, will better apprehend the
lady's meaning.

From Yaoua to Yaya.

   " Papa insists upon one, two, three, four hundred taels from
the colonel, my lover, before he parts with a lock of my hair!
Oh, how I wish the dear creature may be able to produce the
money and pay papa my fortune.   The colonel is reckoned
the politest man in all Shensi.   The first visit he paid at our
house, mercy! what stooping, and cringing, and stopping, and
fidgeting, and going back, and creeping forward, there was be-

tween him and papa; one would have thought he had got the seventeen books of ceremonies all by heart. When he was come into the hall he flourished his hands three times in a very graceful manner. Papa, who would not be outdone, flourished his four times; upon this the colonel began again, and both thus continued flourishing for some minutes in the politest manner imaginable.[1] I was posted in the usual place behind the screen, where I saw the whole ceremony through a slit. Of this the colonel was sensible, for papa informed him. I would have given the world to have shown him my little shoes, but had no opportunity. It was the first time I had ever the happiness of seeing any man but papa, and I vow, my dear Yaya, I thought my three souls would have actually fled from my lips. Ho! but he looked most charmingly; he is reckoned the best-shaped man in the whole province, for he is very fat and very short; but even those natural advantages are improved by his dress, which is fashionable past description. His head was close shaven, all but the crown, and the hair of that was braided into a most beautiful tail that, reaching down to his heels, was terminated by a bunch of yellow roses.[2] Upon his first entering the room I could easily perceive he had been highly perfumed with assafœtida. But then his looks—his looks, my dear Yaya, were irresistible. He kept his eyes steadfastly fixed on the wall during the whole ceremony, and I sincerely believe no accident could have discomposed his gravity, or drawn his eyes away. After a polite silence of two hours he gallantly begged to have the singing women introduced, purely for my amuse-

---

[1] In China the ordinary ceremony among equals is to join the closed hands and lift them two or three times towards the head, saying, *Haou; tsing, tsing;* that is, "Are you well? hail! hail!"

[2] In a Chinese novel, translated by Mr. Davis, called *Hung-how Mung*, or "The Red Chamber Dreams," is the following description of a Chinese dandy: "His beautiful nose was full and round, like the gall-bladder of a quadruped; and he had a face like the moon in the midst of autumn; from his head to the end of his tail, which dangled to the ankles, hung four strings of precious stones set in gold. His upper tunic was pink, spangled with flowers, his trousers and stockings were embroidered, and his shoes were of a deep red color, with thick white soles; ten thousand thoughts of love were collected in the corner of his eye."

ment. After one of them had for some time entertained us with her voice, the colonel and she retired for some minutes together. I thought they would never have come back. I must own he is a most agreeable creature. Upon his return they again renewed the concert, and he continued to gaze upon the wall as usual, when, in less than half an hour more, ho! but he retired out of the room with another. He is indeed a most agreeable creature.

"When he came to take his leave the whole ceremony began afresh; papa would see him to the door, but the colonel swore he would rather see the earth turned upside down than permit him to stir a single step, and papa was at last obliged to comply. As soon as he was got to the door papa went out to see him on horseback; here they continued half an hour bowing and cringing before one would mount or the other go in, but the colonel was at last victorious. He had scarce gone a hundred paces from the house, when papa, running out, hallooed after him, 'A good journey!' upon which the colonel returned, and would see papa into his house before ever he would depart. He was no sooner got home than he sent me a very fine present of duck eggs, painted of twenty different colors. His generosity I own has won me. I have ever since been trying over the eight letters of good-fortune,[1] and have great hopes. All I have to apprehend is that, after he has married me, and that I am carried to his house close shut up in my chair, when he comes to have the first sight of my face, he may shut me up a second time and send me back to papa. However, I shall appear as fine as possible; mamma and I have been to buy the clothes for my wedding. I am to have a new *foong hoâng* in my hair,[2] the beak of which will reach down to my nose; the milliner from

---

[1] The *pa-kua*, or eight mystical diagrams of Fo-hy.

[2] Unmarried women wear their hair hanging down in long tresses, and the putting up of the hair is one of the ceremonies preparatory to marriage. It is twisted up towards the back of the head, ornamented with flowers or jewels, and fastened with two bodkins stuck in crosswise. They sometimes wear an ornament representing the *foong hoâng*, or Chinese phœnix, composed of gold and jewels, the wings hovering, and the beak of the bird hanging over the forehead on an elastic spring."—DAVIS's *Chinese*, vol. i. p. 358.

whom we bought that and our ribbons cheated us as if she had no conscience, and so to quiet mine I cheated her.   All this is fair, you know.—I remain, my dear Yaya, your ever faithful   YAOUA."

LETTER XL.

THE ENGLISH STILL HAVE POETS, THOUGH NOT VERSIFIERS.

From the Same.

You have always testified the highest esteem for the English poets, and thought them not inferior to the Greeks, Romans, or even the Chinese in the art.   But it is now thought even by the English themselves that the race of their poets is extinct; every day produces some pathetic exclamation upon the decadence of taste and genius.   Pegasus, say they, has slipped the bridle from his mouth, and our modern bards attempt to direct his flight by catching him by the tail.

Yet, my friend, it is only among the ignorant that such discourses prevail; men of true discernment can see several poets still among the English, some of whom equal if not surpass their predecessors.   The ignorant term that alone poetry which is couched in a certain number of syllables in every line, where a vapid thought is drawn out into a number of verses of equal length, and perhaps pointed with rhymes at the end.   But glowing sentiment, striking imagery, concise expression, natural description, and modulated periods, are fully sufficient entirely to fill up my idea of this art, and make way to every passion.

If my idea of poetry, therefore, be just, the English are not at present so destitute of poetical merit as they seem to imagine.   I can see several poets in disguise among them; men furnished with that strength of soul, sublimity of sentiment, and grandeur of expression, which constitutes the character. Many of the writers of their modern odes, sonnets, tragedies, or rebuses, it is true, deserve not the name, though they have done nothing but clink rhymes and measure syllables for years together; their Johnsons and Smolletts are truly poets; though for aught I know they never made a single verse in their whole lives.

In every incipient language the poet and the prose writer are very distinct in their qualifications; the poet ever proceeds first—treading unbeaten paths, enriching his native funds, and employed in new adventures. The other follows with more cautious steps, and though slow in his motions, treasures up every useful or pleasing discovery. But when once all the extent and the force of the language is known, the poet then seems to rest from his labor, and is at length overtaken by his assiduous pursuer. Both characters are then blended into one; the historian and orator catch all the poet's fire, and leave him no real mark of distinction, except the iteration of numbers regularly returning. Thus, in the decline of ancient European learning, Seneca, though he wrote in prose, is as much a poet as Lucan, and Longinus, though but a critic, more sublime than Apollonius.

From this, then, it appears that poetry is not discontinued, but altered among the English at present; the outward form seems different from what it was, but poetry still continues internally the same: the only question remains, whether the metric feet used by the good writers of the last age, or the prosaic numbers employed by the good writers of this, be preferable? And here the practice of the last age appears to me superior: they submitted to the restraint of numbers and similar sounds; and this restraint, instead of diminishing, augmented the force of their sentiment and style. Fancy restrained may be compared to a fountain which plays highest by diminishing the aperture. Of the truth of this maxim in every language, every fine writer is perfectly sensible from his own experience, and yet to explain the reason would be perhaps as difficult as to make a frigid genius profit by the discovery.

There is still another reason in favor of the practice of the last age, to be drawn from the variety of modulation. The musical period in prose is confined to a very few changes; the

numbers in verse are capable of infinite variation. I speak
not now from the practice of modern verse-writers, few of
whom have any idea of musical variety, but run on in the
same monotonous flow through the whole poem, but rather
from the example of their former poets, who were tolerable
masters of this variety, and also from a capacity in the language of still admitting various unanticipated music.

Several rules have been drawn up for varying the poetic
measure, and critics have elaborately talked of accents and
syllables; but good-sense, and a fine ear which rules can never teach, are what alone can in such a case determine. The
rapturous flowings of joy, or the interruptions of indignation,
require accents placed entirely different, and a structure con-
sonant to the emotions they would express. Changing passions, and numbers changing with those passions, make the
whole secret of Western as well as Eastern poetry. In a
word, the great faults of the modern professed English poets
are, that they seem to want numbers which should vary with
the passion, and are more employed in describing to the imagination than striking at the heart.   Adieu.

LETTER XLI.

THE BEHAVIOR OF THE CONGREGATION IN ST. PAUL'S CATHE-
DRAL AT PRAYERS.

To the Same.

SOME time since I sent thee, O holy disciple of Confucius,
an account of the grand abbey or mausoleum of the kings and
heroes of this nation. I have since been introduced to a temple not so ancient, but far superior in beauty and magnificence. In this, which is the most considerable of the empire,
there are no pompous inscriptions, no flattery paid the dead,
but all is elegant and awfully simple. There are, however, a
few rags hung round the walls, which have, at a vast expense,
been taken from the enemy in the present war. The silk of

which they are composed, when new, might be valued at half a string of copper money in China; yet this wise people fitted out a fleet and an army in order to seize them; though now grown old, and scarcely capable of being patched up into a handkerchief. By this conquest the English are said to have gained, and the French to have lost, much honor. Is the honor of European nations placed only in tattered silk?

In this temple I was permitted to remain during the whole service; and were you not already acquainted with the religion of the English, you might, from my description, be inclined to believe them as grossly idolatrous as the disciples of Lao. The idol which they seem to address strides like a colossus over the door of the inner temple, which here, as with the Jews, is esteemed the most sacred part of the building. Its oracles are delivered in a hundred various tones, which seem to inspire the worshippers with enthusiasm and awe: an old woman, who appeared to be the priestess, was employed in various attitudes, as she felt the inspiration. When it began to speak all the people remained fixed in silent attention, nodding assent, looking approbation, appearing highly edified by those sounds which, to a stranger, might seem inarticulate and unmeaning.

When the idol had done speaking, and the priestess had locked up its lungs with a key, observing almost all the company leaving the temple, I concluded the service was over, and taking my hat, was going to walk away with the crowd, when I was stopped by the man in black, who assured me that the ceremony had scarcely yet begun. "What!" cried I, "do I not see almost the whole body of the worshippers leaving the church? Would you persuade me that such numbers who profess religion and morality would, in this shameless manner, quit the temple before the service was concluded? You surely mistake: not even the Kalmouks would be guilty of such an indecency, though all the object of their worship was but a joint-stool." My friend seemed to blush for his countrymen, assuring me that those whom I saw running away were only a parcel of musical blockheads, whose passion was merely for sounds, and whose heads were as empty as a fiddle-case. "Those who remain behind," says he, "are the true religious; they make use of music to warm their hearts, and to lift them to a proper pitch of rapture: examine their behavior, and you will confess there are some among us who practise true devotion."

I now looked round me as he directed, but saw nothing of that fervent devotion which he had promised: one of the worshippers appeared to be ogling the company through a glass; another was fervent, not in addresses to Heaven, but to his mistress; a third whispered, a fourth took snuff, and the priest himself, in a drowsy tone, read over the *duties* of the day.

"Bless my eyes!" cried I, as I happened to look toward the door, "what do I see? one of the worshippers fallen fast asleep, and actually sunk down on this cushion! He is now enjoying the benefit of a trance; or does he receive the influence of some mysterious vision?" "Alas! alas!" replied my companion, "no such thing; he has only had the misfortune of eating too hearty a dinner, and finds it impossible to keep his eyes open." Turning to another part of the temple, I perceived a young lady just in the same circumstances and attitude. "Strange," cried I; "can she too have overeaten herself?" "Oh, fie!" replied my friend, "you now grow censorious. She grow drowsy from eating too much! that would be profanation. She only sleeps now from having sat up all night at a brag party." "Turn me where I will, then," says I, "I can perceive no single symptom of devotion among the worshippers, except from that old woman in the corner, who sits groaning behind the long sticks of a mourning fan; she indeed seems greatly edified with what she hears." "Ay," replied my friend, "I knew we should find some to catch you; I know her; that is the deaf lady who lives in the cloisters."

In short, the remissness of behavior in almost all the worshippers, and some even of the guardians, struck me with surprise; I had been taught to believe that none were ever promoted to offices in the temple but men remarkable for their superior sanctity, learning, and rectitude; that there was no such thing heard of as persons being introduced into the church merely to oblige a senator, or provide for the younger branch of a noble family; I expected, as their minds were continually set upon heavenly things, to see their eyes directed there also, and hoped from their behavior to perceive their inclinations corresponding with their duty. But I am since informed that some are appointed to preside over temples they never visit; and, while they receive all the money, are contented with letting others do all the good. Adieu.

LETTER XLII.

THE HISTORY OF CHINA MORE REPLETE WITH GREAT ACTIONS THAN THAT OF EUROPE.

From Fum Hoam to Lien Chi Altangi, the discontented Wanderer, by the way of Moscow.

MUST I ever continue to condemn thy perseverance, and blame that curiosity which destroys thy happiness? What yet untasted banquet, what luxury yet unknown, has rewarded thy painful adventures? Name a pleasure which thy native country could not amply procure; frame a wish that might not have been satisfied in China. Why then such toil, and such danger, in pursuit of raptures within your reach at home?

The Europeans, you will say, excel us in sciences and in arts—those sciences which bound the aspiring wish, and those arts which tend to gratify even unrestrained desire. They may, perhaps, outdo us in the arts of building ships, casting cannons, or measuring mountains; but are they superior in the greatest of all arts, the art of governing kingdoms and ourselves?

When I compare the history of China with that of Europe, how do I exult in being a native of that kingdom which derives its original from the sun! Upon opening the Chinese history, I there behold an ancient extended empire, established by laws which nature and reason seem to have dictated.

The duty of children to their parents, a duty which nature implants in every breast, forms the strength of that government which has subsisted for time immemorial.[1] Filial obedience is the first and greatest requisite of a state; by this we become good subjects to our emperors, capable of behaving with just subordination to our superiors, and grateful dependants on heaven; by this we become fonder of marriage, in order to be capable of exacting obedience from others in our turn; by this we become good magistrates, for early submission is the truest lesson to those who would learn to rule. By this the whole state may be said to resemble one family, of which the emperor is the protector, father, and friend.

In this happy region, sequestered from the rest of mankind, I see a succession of princes who in general considered themselves as the fathers of their people; a race of philosophers who bravely combated idolatry, prejudice, and tyranny, at the expense of their private happiness and immediate reputation. Whenever a usurper or a tyrant intruded into the administration, how have all the good and great been united against him! Can European history produce an instance like that of the twelve mandarins, who all resolved to apprise the vicious emperor Tisiang of the irregularity of his conduct? He who first undertook the dangerous task was cut in two by the emperor's order; the second was ordered to be tormented, and then put to a cruel death; the third undertook the task with intrepidity, and was instantly stabbed by the tyrant's hand; in this manner they all suffered, except one. But, not to be turned from his purpose, the brave survivor entering the palace with the instruments of torture in his hand, "Here," cried he, addressing himself to the throne, " here, O Tisiang,

---

[1] "The vital and universally operating principle of the Chinese government is the duty of submission to parental authority, whether vested in the parents themselves or in their representatives, and which, although usually described under the pleasing appellation of filial piety, is much more properly to be considered as a general rule of action than as the expression of any particular sentiment of affection. It is inculcated with the greatest force in the writings of the first of their philosophers and legislators; it has survived each successive dynasty; and it continues to this day powerfully enforced both by positive laws and by public opinion."—SIR GEORGE STAUNTON.

are the marks your faithful subjects receive for their loyalty, I am wearied with serving a tyrant, and now come for my reward." The emperor, struck with his intrepidity, instantly forgave the boldness of his conduct, and reformed his own. What European annals can boast of a tyrant thus reclaimed to lenity?

When five brethren had set upon the great emperor Ginsong alone, with his sabre he slew four of them; he was struggling with the fifth, when his guards, coming up, were going to cut the conspirator into a thousand pieces. "No, no," cried the emperor, with a calm and placid countenance, "of all his brothers he is the only one remaining; at least let one of the family be suffered to live, that his aged parents may have somebody left to feed and comfort them."[1]

When Haitong, the last emperor of the house of Ming, saw himself besieged in his own city by the usurper, he was resolved to issue from his palace with six hundred of his guards and give the enemy battle; but they forsook him. Being thus without hopes, and choosing death rather than to fall alive into the hands of a rebel, he retired to his garden, conducting his little daughter, an only child, in his hand; there in a private arbor, unsheathing his sword, he stabbed the young innocent to the heart, and then despatched himself, leaving the following words written with his blood on the border of his vest: "Forsaken by my subjects, abandoned by my friends, use my body as you will, but spare, oh, spare my people!"[2]

---

[1] See Du Halde, tom. i. p. 424.

[2] "On the summit of the highest eminences were lofty trees surrounding summer-houses, and cabinets contrived for retreat and pleasure. One of these was pointed out as the last striking scene of the existence of that race of emperors who had built and beautified the whole of this magnificent palace. A man, whom fortune seemed for a while to favor, as if destined to become the head of a new dynasty in China, availed himself, toward the middle of the last century, of the weakness and luxury of the court, and of that indolence which, more than even luxury, had brought the former dynasties to ruin; with an army of Chinese, first collected under the hope of bringing about better times, and kept together afterwards by the tempting bait of plunder, he marched to the gates of Pekin. The ill-fated monarch, too slightly supported, and possessed of too little energy to resist, but with sentiments too elevated to brook submission to an enemy who had been

An empire which has thus continued invariably the same for such a long succession of ages ; which, though at last conquered by the Tartars, still preserves its ancient laws and learning, and may more properly be said to annex the dominions of Tartary to its empire than to admit a foreign conqueror ; an empire as large as Europe, governed by one law, acknowledging subjection to one prince, and experiencing but one revolution of any continuance in the space of four thousand years—this is something so peculiarly great, that I am naturally led to despise all other nations on the comparison. Here we see no religious persecutions, no enmity between mankind for difference in opinion. The disciples of Lao-keun, the idolatrous sectaries of Fohi, and the philosophical children of Confucius, only strive to show by their actions the truth of their doctrines.

Now turn from this happy, peaceful scene to Europe, the theatre of intrigue, avarice, and ambition. How many revolutions does it not experience in the compass even of one age! and to what do these revolutions tend but the destruction of thousands? Every great event is replete with some new calamity. The seasons of serenity are passed over in silence, their histories seem to speak only of the storm.

There we see the Romans extending their power over barbarous nations, and in turn becoming a prey to those whom they had conquered. We see those barbarians, when become Christians, engaged in continual war with the followers of Mahomet; or more dreadful still, destroying each other. We see councils in the earlier ages authorizing every iniquity; crusades spreading desolation in the country left as well as that to be conquered; excommunications freeing subjects from natural allegiance, and persuading to sedition; blood flowing in the fields and on scaffolds; tortures used as arguments to convince the recusant; to heighten the horror of the

---

his subject, and determining to save his offspring from the danger of dishonor, stabbed his only daughter, and put an end to his own life with a cord, in one of those edifices above-mentioned, which had been erected for far other purposes."— MACARTNEY, *Embassy*, vol. ii. p. 121.

II.—16

piece, behold it shaded with wars, rebellions, treasons, plots, politics, and poison.

And what advantage has any country of Europe obtained from such calamities? Scarce any. Their dissensions for more than a thousand years have served to make each other unhappy, but have enriched none. All the great nations still nearly preserve their ancient limits; none have been able to subdue the other, and so terminate the dispute. France, in spite of the conquests of Edward the Third and Henry the Fifth, notwithstanding the efforts of Charles the Fifth and Philip the Second, still remains within its ancient limits. Spain, Germany, Great Britain, Poland, the states of the North, are nearly still the same. What effect, then, has the blood of so many thousands, the destruction of so many cities, produced? Nothing either great or considerable. The Christian princes have lost, indeed, much from the enemies of Christendom, but they have gained nothing from each other. Their princes, because they preferred ambition to justice, deserve the character of enemies to mankind; and their priests, by neglecting morality for opinion, have mistaken the interests of society.

On whatever side we regard the history of Europe we shall perceive it to be a tissue of crimes, follies, and misfortunes; of politics without design, and wars without consequence. In this long list of human infirmity, a great character or a shining virtue may sometimes happen to arise, as we often meet a cottage or a cultivated spot in the most hideous wilderness; but for an Alfred, an Alphonso, a Frederic, or one Alexander the Third, we meet a thousand princes who have disgraced humanity.

LETTER XLIII.

AN APOSTROPHE ON THE SUPPOSED DEATH OF VOLTAIRE.

From Lien Chi Altangi to Fum Hoam, first President of the Ceremonial Academy at Pekin, in China.

WE have just received accounts here that Voltaire, the poet and philosopher of Europe, is dead.[1]   He is now beyond the reach of the thousand enemies who, while living, degraded his writings and branded his character.   Scarce a page of his latter productions that does not betray the agonies of a heart bleeding under the scourge of unmerited reproach.   Happy, therefore, at last in escaping from calumny; happy in leaving a world that was unworthy of him and his writings!

Let others, my friend, bestrew the hearses of the great with panegyric; but such a loss as the world has now suffered affects me with stronger emotions.   When a philosopher dies, I consider myself as losing a patron, an instructor, and a friend.   I consider the world as losing one who might serve to console her amid the desolations of war and ambition. Nature every day produces in abundance men capable of filling all the requisite duties of authority; but she is niggard in the birth of an exalted mind, scarcely producing in a century a single genius to bless and enlighten a degenerate age. Prodigal in the production of kings, governors, mandarins, chams, and courtiers, she seems to have forgotten, for more than three thousand years, the manner in which she once formed the brain of a Confucius; and well it is she has forgotten, when a bad world gave him so very bad a reception.

Whence, my friend, this malevolence which has ever pursued the great even to the tomb? whence this more than

---

[1] The account proved untrue.   Voltaire died on the 30th May, 1778.

fiend-like disposition of embittering the lives of those who would make us more wise and more happy ?

When I cast my eye over the fates of several philosophers, who have at different periods enlightened mankind, I must confess it inspires me with the most degrading reflections on humanity. When I read of the stripes of Mencius, the tortures of Tchin, the bowl of Socrates, and the bath of Seneca; when I hear of the persecutions of Dante, the imprisonment of Galileo, the indignities suffered by Montaigne, the banishment of Cartesius, the infamy of Bacon, and that even Locke himself escaped not without reproach; when I think on such subjects I hesitate whether most to blame the ignorance or the villany of my fellow-creatures.

Should you look for the character of Voltaire among the journalists and illiterate writers of the age, you will there find him characterized as a monster, with a head turned to wisdom, and a heart inclining to vice; the powers of his mind and the baseness of his principles forming a detestable contrast. But seek for his character among writers like himself, and you find him very differently described. You perceive him, in their accounts, possessed of good-nature, humanity, greatness of soul, fortitude, and almost every virtue; in this description those who might be supposed best acquainted with his character are unanimous. The Royal Prussian,[1] D'Argens,[2] Diderot,[3] D'Alembert, and Fontenelle conspire in drawing the picture, in describing the friend of man and the patron of every rising genius.

An inflexible perseverance in what he thought was right, and a generous detestation of flattery, formed the groundwork of this great man's character. From these principles many strong virtues and few faults arose: as he was warm in his friendship, and severe in his resentment, all that mention him seem possessed of the same qualities, and speak of him with rapture or detestation. A person of his eminence can have few indifferent as to his character; every reader must be an enemy or an admirer.

---

[1] Philosophe Sans Souci.—GOLDSMITH.   [2] Let. Chin.—GOLDSMITH.
[3] Encycloped.—GOLDSMITH.

This poet began the course of glory so early as the age of eighteen, and even then was author of a tragedy [1] which deserved applause. Possessed of a small patrimony, he preserved his independence in an age of venality, and supported the dignity of learning, by teaching his contemporary writers to live, like him, above the favors of the great. He was banished his native country for a satire upon the royal concubine. He had accepted the place of historian to the French king, but refused to keep it, when he found it was presented only in order that he should be the first flatterer of the state.

The great Prussian received him as an ornament to his kingdom, and had sense enough to value his friendship and profit by his instructions. In this court he continued, till an intrigue, with which the world seems hitherto unacquainted, obliged him to quit that country. His own happiness, the happiness of the monarch, of his sister, of a part of the court, rendered his departure necessary.

Tired at length of courts, and all the follies of the great, he retired to Switzerland, a country of liberty, where he enjoyed tranquillity and the muse. Here, though without any taste for magnificence himself, he usually entertained at his table the learned and polite of Europe, who were attracted by a desire of seeing a person from whom they had received so much satisfaction. The entertainment was conducted with the utmost elegance, and the conversation was that of philosophers. Every country that at once united liberty and science were his peculiar favorites. The being an Englishman was to him a character that claimed admiration and respect.

Between Voltaire and the disciples of Confucius there are many differences; however, being of a different opinion does not in the least diminish my esteem: I am not displeased with my brother because he happens to ask our father for favors in a different manner from me. Let his errors rest in peace, his excellences deserve admiration; let me with the wise admire his wisdom; let the envious and the ignorant ridicule his foibles; the folly of others is ever most ridiculous to those who are themselves most foolish. Adieu.

---

[1] "Amulius et Numitor," written before Voltaire had completed his thirteenth year.

LETTER XLIV.

WISDOM AND PRECEPT MAY LESSEN OUR MISERIES, BUT CAN NEVER INCREASE OUR POSITIVE SATISFACTIONS.

From Lien Chi Altangi to Hingpo, a Slave in Persia.

It is impossible to form a philosophic system of happiness which is adapted to every condition in life, since every person who travels in this great pursuit takes a separate road. The differing colors which suit different complexions are not more various than the different pleasures appropriated to particular minds. The various sects who have pretended to give lessons to instruct men in happiness have described their own particular sensations without considering ours, have only loaded their disciples with constraint, without adding to their real felicity.

If I find pleasure in dancing, how ridiculous would it be in me to prescribe such an amusement for the entertainment of a cripple: should he, on the other hand, place his chief delight in painting, yet would he be absurd in recommending the same relish to one who had lost the power of distinguishing colors. General directions are, therefore, commonly useless; and to be particular would exhaust volumes, since each individual may require a particular system of precepts to direct his choice.

Every mind seems capable of entertaining a certain quantity of happiness, which no institutions can increase, no circumstances alter, and entirely independent of fortune. Let any man compare his present fortune with the past, and he will probably find himself, upon the whole, neither better nor worse than formerly.

Gratified ambition, or irreparable calamity, may produce transient sensations of pleasure or distress. Those storms may discompose in proportion as they are strong, or the mind is pliant to their impression. But the soul, though at first lifted up by the event, is every day operated upon with diminished influence, and at length subsides into the level of its usual tranquillity. Should some unexpected turn of fortune take thee from fetters and place thee on a throne, exultation would be natural upon the change; but the temper, like the face, would soon resume its native serenity.

Every wish, therefore, which leads us to expect happiness somewhere else but where we are; every institution which teaches us that we should be better by being possessed of something new, which promises to lift us a step higher than we are, only lays a foundation for uneasiness, because it contracts debts which it cannot repay; it calls that a good which, when we have found it, will, in fact, add nothing to our happiness.

To enjoy the present, without regret for the past or solicitude for the future, has been the advice rather of poets than philosophers. And yet the precept seems more rational than is generally imagined. It is the only general precept respecting the pursuit of happiness that can be applied with propriety to every condition of life. The man of pleasure, the man of business, and the philosopher are equally interested in its disquisition. If we do not find happiness in the present moment, in what shall we find it? either in reflecting on the past, or prognosticating the future. But let us see how these are capable of producing satisfaction.

A remembrance of what is past, and an anticipation of what is to come seem to be the two faculties by which man differs most from other animals. Though brutes enjoy them in a limited degree, yet their whole life seems taken up in the present, regardless of the past and the future. Man, on the contrary, endeavors to derive his happiness, and experiences most of his miseries, from these two sources.

Is this superiority of reflection a prerogative of which we should boast, and for which we should thank nature; or is it a misfortune of which we should complain and be humble? Either from the abuse, or from the nature of things, it certainly makes our condition more miserable.

Had we a privilege of calling up, by the power of memory, only such passages as were pleasing, unmixed with such as were disagreeable, we might then excite at pleasure an ideal happiness, perhaps more poignant than actual sensation. But this is not the case: the past is never represented without some disagreeable circumstance which tarnishes all its beauty; the remembrance of an evil carries in it nothing agreeable, and to remember a good is always accompanied with regret. Thus we lose more than we gain by remembrance.

And we shall find our expectation of the future to be a gift more distressful even than the former. To fear an approaching evil is certainly a most disagreeable sensation; and in expecting an approaching good, we experience the inquietude of wanting actual possession.

Thus, whichever way we look, the prospect is disagreeable. Behind, we have left pleasures we shall never more enjoy, and therefore regret; and before, we see pleasures which we languish to possess, and are consequently uneasy till we possess them. Was there any method of seizing the present unembittered by such reflections, then would our state be tolerably easy.

This, indeed, is the endeavor of all mankind, who, untutored by philosophy, pursue as much as they can a life of amusement and dissipation. Every rank in life, and every size of understanding, seems to follow this alone; or, not pursuing it, deviates from happiness. The man of pleasure pursues dissipation by profession: the man of business pursues it not less, as every voluntary labor he undergoes is only dissipation in disguise. The philosopher himself, even while he reasons upon the subject, does it unknowingly, with a view of dissipating the thoughts of what he was, or what he must be.

The subject therefore comes to this: Which is the most perfect sort of dissipation—pleasure, business, or philosophy? which best serves to exclude those uneasy sensations which memory or anticipation produce?

The enthusiasm of pleasure charms only by intervals: the highest rapture lasts only for a moment; and all the senses seem so combined as to be soon tired into languor by the gratification of any one of them. It is only among the poets we hear of men changing to one delight when satiated with another. In nature it is very different; the glutton, when sated with the full meal, is unqualified to feel the real pleasure of drinking; the drunkard in turn finds few of those transports which lovers boast in enjoyment; and the lover, when cloyed, finds a diminution of every other appetite. Thus, after a full indulgence of any one sense, the man of pleasure finds a languor in all, is placed in a chasm between past and expected enjoyment, perceives an interval which must be filled up. The present can give no satisfaction, because he has already robbed it of every charm. A mind thus left without immediate employment naturally recurs to the past or future; the reflector finds that he was happy, and knows that he cannot be so now; he sees that he may yet be happy, and wishes the hour was come: thus every period of his continuance is miserable, except that very short one of immediate gratification. Instead of a life of dissipation, none has more frequent conversations with disagreeable *self* than he: his enthusiasms are but few and transient; his appetites, like angry creditors, continually making fruitless demands for what he is unable to pay, and the greater his former pleasure, the more impatient his expectations. A life of pleasure is therefore the most unpleasing life in the world.

Habit has rendered the man of business more cool in his desires; he finds less regret for past pleasures, and less solicitude for those to come. The life he now leads, though tainted in some measure with hope, is yet not afflicted so strongly with regret, and is less divided between short-lived rapture and lasting anguish. The pleasures he has enjoyed are not so vivid, and those he has to expect cannot consequently create so much anxiety.

The philosopher, who extends his regard to all mankind, must have a still smaller concern for what has already affected or may hereafter affect himself: the concerns of others make his whole study, and that study is his pleasure; and this pleasure is continuing in its nature, because it can be changed at will, leaving but few of these anxious intervals which are employed in remembrance or anticipation. The philosopher by this means leads a life of almost continued dissipation; and reflection, which makes the uneasiness and misery of others, serves as a companion and instructor to him.

In a word, positive happiness is constitutional, and incapable of increase; misery is artificial, and generally proceeds from our folly. Philosophy can add to our happiness in no other manner but by diminishing our misery: it should not pretend to increase our present stock, but make us economists of what we are possessed of. The great source of calamity lies in regret or anticipation: he, therefore, is most wise who thinks of the present alone, regardless of the past or the future. This is impossible to the man of pleasure; it is difficult to the man of business; and is in some measure attainable by the philosopher. Happy were we all born philosophers; all born with a talent of thus dissipating our own cares, by spreading them upon all mankind! Adieu.

LETTER XLV.

THE ARDOR OF THE PEOPLE OF LONDON IN RUNNING AFTER SIGHTS AND MONSTERS.

From Lien Chi Altangi to Fum Hoam, first President of the Ceremonial Academy at Pekin, in China.

THOUGH the frequent invitations I receive from men of distinction here might excite the vanity of some, I am quite mortified, however, when I consider the motives that inspire their civility. I am sent for, not to be treated as a friend, but to satisfy curiosity; not to be entertained, so much as wondered at; the same earnestness which excites them to see a Chinese would have made them equally proud of a visit from the rhinoceros.

From the highest to the lowest this people seem fond of sights and monsters. I am told of a person here who gets a very comfortable livelihood by making wonders and then selling or showing them to the people for money: no matter how insignificant they were in the beginning, by locking them up close, and showing for money, they soon become prodigies. His first essay in this way was to exhibit himself as a wax-work figure behind a glass door at a puppet-show. Thus, keeping the spectators at a proper distance, and having his head adorned with a copper crown, he looked "extremely natural, and very like the life itself." He continued this exhibition with success, till an involuntary fit of sneezing brought him to life before all the spectators, and consequently rendered him for that time as entirely useless as the peaceable inhabitant of a catacomb.

Determined to act the statue no more, he next levied contributions under the figure of an Indian king; and by painting his face and counterfeiting the savage howl, he frighted several ladies and children with amazing success. In this manner, therefore, he might have lived very comfortably, had he not been arrested for a debt that was contracted when he was the figure in wax-work: thus his face underwent an involuntary ablution, and he found himself reduced to his primitive complexion and indigence.

After some time, being freed from jail, he was now grown wiser, and instead of making himself a wonder was resolved only to make wonders. He learned the art of pasting up mummies, was never at a loss for an artificial *lusus naturæ;* nay, it has been reported that he has sold seven petrified lobsters of his own manufacture to a noted collector of rarities; but this the learned Cracovius Putridus has undertaken to refute in a very elaborate dissertation.

His last wonder was nothing more than a halter; yet by this halter he gained more than by all his former exhibitions. The people, it seems, had got it into their heads that a certain noble criminal[1] was to be hanged with a silken rope. Now, there was nothing they so much desired to see as this very rope, and he was resolved to gratify their curiosity: he there-

---

[1] Earl Ferrers: see Letter XXXVIII., p. 227. He was hanged in the dress he wore at his wedding. "The executioners fought for the rope with which he was hanged, and the one who lost it cried."—HORACE WALPOLE *to Sir Horace Mann,* vol. iii. p. 360.

fore got one made, not only of silk, but, to render it the more
striking, several threads of gold were intermixed. The people
paid their money only to see silk, but were highly satisfied
when they found it was mixed with gold into the bargain. It
is scarce necessary to mention that the projector sold his silken
rope for almost what it had cost him, as soon as the criminal
was known to be hanged in hempen materials.

By their fondness of sights one would be apt to imagine
that, instead of desiring to see things as they should be, they
are rather solicitous of seeing them as they ought not to be.
A cat with four legs is disregarded, though never so useful;
but if it has but two, and is consequently incapable of catching mice, it is reckoned inestimable, and every man of taste
is ready to raise the auction. A man, though in his person
faultless as an aerial genius, might starve ; but if stuck over
with hideous warts like a porcupine, his fortune is made forever, and he may propagate the breed with impunity and
applause.

A good woman in my neighborhood who was bred a habit-
maker, though she handled her needle tolerably well, could
scarcely get employment. But being obliged by an accident
to have both her hands cut off from the elbows, what would
in another country have been her ruin made her fortune here:
she now was thought more fit for her trade than before ; business flowed in apace, and all people paid for seeing the man-
tua-maker who wrought without hands.

A gentleman, showing me his collection of pictures, stopped
at one with peculiar admiration. "There," cries he, "is an
inestimable piece." I gazed at the picture for some time, but
could see none of those graces with which he seemed enraptured : it appeared to me the most paltry piece of the whole
collection. I therefore demanded where those beauties lay
of which I was yet insensible. "Sir," cries he, "the merit
does not consist in the piece, but in the manner in which it
was done. The painter drew the whole with his foot, and
held the pencil between his toes. I bought it at a very great
price ; for peculiar merit should ever be rewarded."

But these people are not more fond of wonders than liberal

in rewarding those who show them. From the wonderful dog of knowledge, at present under the patronage of the nobility, down to the man with the box, who professes to show "the most imitation of nature that was ever seen," they all live in luxury. A singing-woman shall collect subscriptions in her own coach-and-six; a fellow shall make a fortune by tossing a straw from his toe to his nose; one in particular has found that eating fire was the most ready way to live; and another who jingles several bells fixed to his cap is the only man that I know of who has received emolument from the labors of his head.

A young author, a man of good-nature and learning, was complaining to me some nights ago of this misplaced generosity of the times. "Here," says he, "have I spent part of my youth in attempting to instruct and amuse my fellow-creatures, and all my reward has been solitude, poverty and reproach; while a fellow, possessed of even the smallest share of fiddling merit, or who has perhaps learned to whistle double, is rewarded, applauded, and caressed!" "Prithee, young man," says I to him, "are you ignorant that in so large a city as this it is better to be an amusing than a useful member of society? Can you leap up and touch your feet four times before you come to the ground?" "No, sir." "Can you pimp for a man of quality?" "No, sir." "Can you stand upon two horses at full speed?" "No, sir." "Can you swallow a penknife?" "I can do none of these tricks." "Why, then," cried I, "there is no other prudent means of subsistence left but to apprise the town that you speedily intend to eat up your own nose, by subscription."

I have frequently regretted that none of our Eastern posture-masters or showmen have ever ventured to England. I should be pleased to see that money circulate in Asia which is now sent to Italy and France, in order to bring their vagabonds hither. Several of our tricks would undoubtedly give the English high satisfaction. Men of fashion would be greatly pleased with the postures as well as the condescension of our dancing-girls, and the ladies would equally admire the conductors of our fireworks. What an agreeable surprise would it be to see a huge fellow with whiskers flash a charged blunderbuss full in a lady's face without singeing her hair or melting her pomatum! Perhaps, when the first surprise was over, she might then grow familiar with danger; and the ladies might vie with each other in standing fire with intrepidity.

But of all the wonders of the East the most useful, and I should fancy the most pleasing, would be the looking-glass of Lao, which reflects the mind as well as the body. It is said that the Emperor Chusi used to make his concubines dress their heads and their hearts in one of these glasses every morning: while the lady was at her toilet he would frequently look over her shoulder; and it is recorded that, among the three hundred which composed his seraglio, not one was found whose mind was not even more beautiful than her person.

I make no doubt but a glass in this country would have the very same effect. The English ladies, concubines and all, would undoubtedly cut very pretty figures in so faithful a monitor. There, should we happen to peep over a lady's shoulder while dressing, we might be able to see neither gaming nor ill-nature; neither pride, debauchery, nor a love of gadding. We should find her, if any sensible defect appeared in the mind, more careful in rectifying it than plastering up the irreparable decays of the person; nay, I am even apt to fancy that ladies would find more real pleasure in this utensil in private than in any other bauble imported from China, though never so expensive or amusing.

LETTER XLVI.

THE LOOKING-GLASS OF LAO——A DREAM.

To the Same.

Upon finishing my last letter I retired to rest, reflecting upon the wonders of the glass of Lao, wishing to be possessed of one here, and resolved in such case to oblige every lady with a sight of it for nothing. What fortune denied me waking fancy supplied in a dream: the glass, I know not how, was put into my possession, and I could perceive several ladies approaching, some voluntarily, others driven forward against their wills, by a set of discontented genii, who by intuition I knew were their husbands.

The apartment in which I was to show away was filled with several gaming tables, as if just forsaken; the candles were burnt to the socket, and the hour was five o'clock in the morning. Placed at one end of the room, which was of prodigious length, I could more easily distinguish every female figure as she marched up from the door; but guess my surprise, when I could scarce perceive one blooming or agreeable face among the number! This, however, I attributed to the early hour, and kindly considered that the face of a lady just risen from bed ought always to find a compassionate advocate.

The first person who came up in order to view her intellectual face was a commoner's wife, who, as I afterwards found, being bred during her virginity in a pawnbroker's shop, now attempted to make up the defects of breeding and sentiment by the magnificence of her dress, and the expensiveness of her amusements. "Mr. Showman," cried she, approaching, "I am told you has something to show in that there sort of magic lanthorn, by which folks can see themselves on the inside: I protest, as my Lord Beetle says, I am sure it will be vastly pretty, for I have never seen anything like it before. But how: are we to strip off our clothes and be turned inside out? if so, as Lord Beetle says, I absolutely declare off; for I would not strip for the world before a man's face, and so I tells his lordship almost every night of his life." I informed the lady that I would dispense with the ceremony of stripping, and immediately presented my glass to her view.

As when a first-rate beauty, after having with difficulty escaped the small-pox, revisits her favorite mirror—that mirror which had repeated the flattery of every lover, and even added force to the compliment—expecting to see what had so often given her pleasure, she no longer beholds the cherried lip, the polished forehead, and speaking blush, but a hateful phiz quilted into a thousand seams by the hand of deformity, grief, resentment, and rage fill her bosom by turns; she blames the fates and the stars, but most of all the unhappy glass feels her resentment: so it was with the lady in question; she had never seen her own mind before, and was now shocked at its deformity. One single look was sufficient to satisfy her curiosity: I held up the glass to her face, and she shut her eyes; no entreaties could prevail upon her to gaze once more. She was even going to snatch it from my hands and break it in a thousand pieces. I found it was time, therefore, to dismiss her as incorrigible, and show away to the next that offered.

This was an unmarried lady, who continued in a state of virginity till thirty-six, and then admitted a lover when she despaired of a husband. No woman was louder at a revel than she, perfectly free-hearted, and almost in every respect a man; she understood ridicule to perfection, and was once known even to sally out in order to beat the watch. "Here, you, my dear, with the outlandish face," said she, addressing me, "let me take a single peep. Not that I care three damns what figure I may cut in the glass of such an old-fashioned creature; if I am allowed the beauties of the face by people of fashion, I know the world will be complaisant enough to toss me the beauties of the mind into the bargain." I held my glass before her as she desired, and must confess was shocked with the reflection. The lady, however, gazed for some time with the utmost complacency; and at last, turning to me with the most satisfied smile, said she never could think she had been half so handsome.

Upon her dismission a lady of distinction was reluctantly hauled along to the glass by her husband. In bringing her forward, as he came first to the glass himself, his mind appeared tinctured with immoderate jealousy, and I was going to reproach him for using her with such severity; but when the lady came to present herself I immediately retracted; for, alas! it was seen that he had but too much reason for his suspicions.

The next was a lady who usually teased all her acquaintance in desiring to be told of her faults, and then never mended any. Upon approaching the glass I could readily perceive vanity, affectation, and some other ill-looking blots on her mind; wherefore, by my advice, she immediately set about mending. But I could easily find she was not earnest in the work; for as she repaired them on one side, they generally broke out on another. Thus, after three or four attempts, she began to make the ordinary use of the glass in settling her hair.

The company now made room for a woman of learning, who approached with a slow pace and a solemn countenance, which, for her own sake, I could wish had been cleaner. "Sir," cried the lady, flourishing her hand, which held a pinch of snuff, "I shall be enraptured by having presented to my view a mind with which I have so long studied to be acquainted; but, in order to give the sex a proper example, I must insist that all the company may be permitted to look over my shoulder." I bowed assent, and, presenting the glass, showed the lady a mind by no means so fair as she had expected to see. Ill-nature, ill-placed pride, and spleen were too legible to be mistaken. Nothing could be more amusing than the mirth of her female companions who had looked over. They had hated her from the beginning, and now the apartment echoed with a universal laugh. Nothing but a fortitude like hers could have withstood their raillery: she stood it, however; and when the burst was exhausted, with great tranquillity she assured the company that the whole was a *deceptio visûs*, and that she was too well acquainted with her own mind to believe any false representations from another. Thus saying, she retired with a sullen satisfaction, resolved not to mend her faults, but to write a criticism on the mental reflector.

I must own by this time I began myself to suspect the fidelity of my mirror; for, as the ladies appeared at least to have the merit of rising early, since they were up at five, I was amazed to find nothing of this good quality pictured upon their minds in the reflection: I was resolved, therefore, to communicate my suspicions to a lady whose intellectual countenance appeared more fair than any of the rest, not having above seventy-nine spots in all, besides slips and foibles. "I

II.—17

own, young woman," said I, "that there are some virtues upon that mind of yours, but there is still one which I do not see represented—I mean that of rising betimes in the morning. I fancy the glass false in that particular." The young lady smiled at my simplicity; and, with a blush, confessed that she and the whole company had been up all night gaming.

By this time all the ladies, except one, had seen themselves successively, and disliked the show or scolded the showman: I was resolved, however, that she who seemed to neglect herself and was neglected by the rest should take a view; and going up to a corner of the room where she still continued sitting, I presented my glass full in her face. Here it was that I exulted in my success; no blot, no stain appeared on any part of the faithful mirror. As when the large unwritten page presents its snowy spotless bosom to the writer's hand so appeared the glass to my view. "Here, O ye daughters of English ancestors," cried I, "turn hither and behold an object worthy imitation; look upon the mirror now, and acknowledge its justice, and this woman's pre-eminence!" The ladies, obeying the summons, came up in a group, and looking on, acknowledged there was some truth in the picture—as the person now represented had been deaf, dumb, and a fool from her cradle!

Thus much of my dream I distinctly remember; the rest was filled with chimeras, enchanted castles, and flying dragons, as usual. As you, my dear Fum Hoam, are particularly versed in the interpretation of those midnight warnings, what pleasure should I find in your explanation! But that our distance prevents: I make no doubt, however, but that, from my description, you will very much venerate the good qualities of the English ladies in general; since dreams, you know, go always by contraries. Adieu.

LETTER XLVII.

MISERY BEST RELIEVED BY DISSIPATION.

From Lien Chi Altangi to Hingpo, a Slave in Persia.[1]

YOUR last letters betray a mind seemingly fond of wisdom, yet tempested up by a thousand various passions. You would fondly persuade me that my former lessons still influence your conduct, and yet your mind seems not less enslaved than your body. Knowledge, wisdom, erudition, arts, and elegance, what are they but the mere trappings of the mind, if they do not serve to increase the happiness of the possessor? A mind rightly instituted in the school of philosophy acquires at once the stability of the oak, and the flexibility of the osier. The truest manner of lessening our agonies is to shrink from their pressure—is to confess that we feel them.

The fortitude of European sages is but a dream; for where lies the merit in being insensible to the strokes of fortune, or in dissembling our sensibility? If we are insensible, that arises only from a happy constitution: that is a blessing previously granted by Heaven, and which no art can procure, no institutions improve.

If we dissemble our feelings, we only artificially endeavor to persuade others that we enjoy privileges which we actually do not possess. Thus, while we endeavor to appear happy, we feel at once all the pangs of internal misery, and all the self-reproaching consciousness of endeavoring to deceive.

I know but of two sects of philosophers in the world that have endeavored to inculcate that fortitude is but an imaginary virtue—I mean the followers of Confucius, and those who profess the doctrines of Christ. All other sects teach pride

---

[1] This letter appears to be little more than a rhapsody of sentiments from Confucius. *Vide* the Latin translation.—GOLDSMITH.

under misfortunes; they alone teach humility. "Night" says our Chinese philosopher, "not more surely follows day, than groans and tears grow out of pain; when misfortunes therefore oppress, when tyrants threaten, it is our interest, it is our duty to fly even to dissipation for support, to seek redress from friendship, or from that best of friends who loved us into being."

Philosophers, my son, have long declaimed against the passions, as being the source of all our miseries: they are the source of all our misfortunes, I own; but they are the source of our pleasures, too; and every endeavor of our lives, and all the institutions of philosophy, should tend to this—not to dissemble an absence of passion, but to repel those which lead to vice by those which direct to virtue.

The soul may be compared to a field of battle, where two armies are ready every moment to encounter; not a single vice but has a more powerful opponent, and not one virtue but may be overborne by a combination of vices. Reason guides the hands of either host; nor can it subdue one passion but by the assistance of another. Thus as a bark on every side beset with storms enjoys a state of rest, so does the mind, when influenced by a just equipoise of the passions, enjoy tranquillity.

I have used such means as my little fortune would admit to procure your freedom. I have lately written to the governor of Argun to pay your ransom, though at the expense of all the wealth I brought with me from China. If we become poor, we shall at least have the pleasure of bearing poverty together; for what is fatigue or famine when weighed against friendship and freedom? Adieu.

LETTER XLVIII.

THE ABSURDITY OF PERSONS IN HIGH STATION PURSUING EM-
PLOYMENTS BENEATH THEM EXEMPLIFIED IN A FAIRY TALE.

From Lien Chi Altangi to ——, Merchant in Amsterdam.

HAPPENING some days ago to call at a painter's to amuse
myself in examining some pictures (I had no design to buy),
it surprised me to see a young prince in the working-room,
dressed in a painter's apron, and assiduously learning the
trade. We instantly remembered to have seen each other ;
and, after the usual compliments, I stood by while he continued to paint on. As everything done by the rich is praised ;
as princes here, as well as in China, are never without followers, three or four persons, who had the appearance of gentlemen, were placed behind to comfort and applaud him at
every stroke.

Need I tell that it struck me with very disagreeable sensations to see a youth, who, by his station in life, had it in his
power to be useful to thousands, thus letting his mind run to
waste upon canvas, at the same time fancying himself improving in taste, and filling his rank with proper decorum ?

As seeing an error, and attempting to redress it, are only
one and the same with me, I took occasion, upon his lordship's
desiring my opinion of a Chinese scroll intended for the
frame of a picture, to assure him that a mandarin of China
thought a minute acquaintance with such mechanical trifles
below his dignity.

This reply raised the indignation of some and the contempt
of others. I could hear the names of Vandal, Goth, taste,
polite arts, delicacy, and fire repeated in tones of ridicule or
resentment. But—considering that it was in vain to argue
against people who had so much to say—without contradicting
them, I begged leave to repeat a fairy tale. This request re-

doubled their laughter; but, not easily abashed at the raillery of boys, I persisted, observing that it would set the absurdity of placing our affections upon trifles in the strongest point of view, and adding that it was hoped the moral would compensate for its stupidity. "For Heaven's sake," cried the great man, washing his brush in water, "let us have no morality at present; if we·must have a story let it be without any moral." I pretended not to hear, and while he handled the brush proceeded as follows:

"In the kingdom of Bonbobbin, which, by the Chinese annals, appears to have flourished twenty thousand years ago, there reigned a prince endowed with every accomplishment which generally distinguishes the sons of kings. His beauty was brighter than the sun. The sun, to which he was nearly related, would sometimes stop his course in order to look down and admire him.

"His mind was not less perfect than his body: he knew all things without having ever read; philosophers, poets, and historians submitted their works to his decision; and so penetrating was he that he could tell the merit of a book by looking on the cover. He made epic poems, tragedies, and pastorals with surprising facility; song, epigram, or rebus was all one to him, though it is observed he could never finish an acrostic. In short, the fairy who presided at his birth had endowed him with almost every perfection, or what was just the same, his subjects were ready to acknowledge he possessed them; and, for his own part, he knew nothing to the contrary. A prince so accomplished received a name suitable to his merit; and he was called Bonbenin-bonbobbin-bonbobbinet, which signifies Enlightener of the Sun.

"As he was very powerful, and yet unmarried, all the neighboring kings earnestly sought his alliance. Each sent his daughter dressed out in the most magnificent manner, and with the most sumptuous retinue imaginable, in order to allure the prince; so that at one time there were seen at his court not less than seven hundred foreign princesses of exquisite sentiment and beauty, each alone sufficient to make seven hundred ordinary men happy.

"Distracted in such a variety, the generous Bonbenin, had he not been obliged by the laws of the empire to make choice of one, would very willingly have married them all, for none understood gallantry better. He spent numberless hours of solicitude in endeavoring to determine whom he should choose : one lady was possessed of every perfection, but he disliked her eyebrows ; another was brighter than the morning-star, but he disapproved her fong-whang.[1] A third did not lay white enough on her cheek ; and a fourth did not sufficiently blacken her nails. At last, after numberless disappointments on the one side and the other, he made choice of the incomparable Nanhoa, queen of the scarlet dragons.

"The preparations for the royal nuptials, or the envy of the disappointed ladies, needs no description ; both the one and the other were as great as they could be ; the beautiful princess was conducted amid admiring multitudes to the royal couch, where, after being divested of every encumbering ornament, she was placed, in expectance of the youthful bridegroom, who did not keep her long in expectation. He came more cheerful than the morning, and, printing on her lips a burning kiss, the attendants took this as a proper signal to withdraw.

"Perhaps I ought to have mentioned in the beginning that, among several other qualifications, the prince was fond of collecting and breeding mice, which, being a harmless pastime, none of his counsellors thought proper to dissuade him from ; he therefore kept a variety of these pretty little animals in the most beautiful cages enriched with diamonds, rubies, emeralds, pearls, and other precious stones : thus he innocently spent four hours each day in contemplating their innocent little pastimes.

"But to proceed. The prince and princess were now in bed : one with all the love and expectation, the other with all the modesty and fear which is natural to suppose—both willing, yet afraid to begin ; when the prince, happening to look towards the outside of the bed, perceived one of the most

---

[1] See page 232.

beautiful animal in the world, a white mouse with green eyes, playing about the floor and performing a hundred pretty tricks. He was already master of blue mice, red mice, and even white mice with yellow eyes; but a white mouse with green eyes was what he had long endeavored to possess: wherefore, leaping from bed with the utmost impatience and agility, the youthful prince attempted to seize the little charmer, but it was fled in a moment; for, alas! the mouse was sent by a discontented princess, and was itself a fairy.

"It is impossible to describe the agony of the prince upon this occasion; he sought round and round every part of the room, even the bed where the princess lay was not exempt from the inquiry: he turned the princess on one side and the other, stripped her quite naked, but no mouse was to be found. The princess herself was kind enough to assist, but still to no purpose.

"'Alas,' cried the young prince, in an agony, 'how unhappy am I to be thus disappointed! never, sure, was so beautiful an animal seen! I would give half my kingdom and my princess to him that would find it.' The princess, though not much pleased with the latter part of his offer, endeavored to comfort him as well as she could; she let him know that he had a hundred mice already, which ought to be at least sufficient to satisfy any philosopher like him. Though none of them had green eyes, yet he should learn to thank Heaven that they had eyes. She told him (for she was a profound moralist) that incurable evils must be borne, and that useless lamentations were vain, and that man was born to misfortunes; she even entreated him to return to bed, and she would endeavor to lull him on her bosom to repose; but still the prince continued inconsolable; and, regarding her with a stern air, for which his family was remarkable, he vowed never to sleep in the royal palace, or indulge himself in the innocent pleasures of matrimony, till he had found the white mouse with the green eyes."

"Prithee, Colonel Leech," cried his lordship, interrupting me, "how do you like that nose? don't you think there is something of the manner of Rembrandt in it? A prince in all this agony for a white mouse, oh, ridiculous! Don't you think, Major Vampyre, that eyebrow stippled very prettily? But pray what are the green eyes to the purpose, except to amuse children? I would give a thousand guineas to lay on the coloring of this cheek more smoothly. But I ask pardon; pray, sir, proceed."

LETTER XLIX.

THE FAIRY TALE CONTINUED.

From the Same.

"Kings," continued I, "at that time were different from what they are now; they then never engaged their word for anything which they did not rigorously intend to perform. This was the case of Bonbenin, who continued all night to lament his misfortunes to the princess who echoed groan for groan. When morning came he published an edict, offering half his kingdom and his princess to the person who should catch and bring him the white mouse with the green eyes.

"The edict was scarcely published when all the traps in the kingdom were baited with cheese: numberless mice were taken and destroyed; but still the much-wished-for mouse was not among the number. The privy-council was assembled more than once to give their advice; but all their deliberations came to nothing; even though there were two complete vermin-killers, and three professed rat-catchers of the number. Frequent addresses, as is usual on extraordinary occasions, were sent from all parts of the empire; but though these promised well, though in them he received an assurance that his faithful subjects would assist in his search with their lives and fortunes, yet, with all their loyalty, they failed when the time came that the mouse was to be caught.

"The prince, therefore, was resolved to go himself in search, determined never to lie two nights in one place, till he had found what he sought for. Thus, quitting his palace without attendants, he set out upon his journey, and travelled through many a desert, and crossed many a river, high over hills and down long vales, still restless, still inquiring wherever he came; but no white mouse was to be found.

"As one day, fatigued with his journey, he was shading himself from the heat of the mid-day sun, under the arching branches of a banana-tree, meditating on the object of his pursuit, he perceived an old woman, hideously deformed, approaching him; by her stoop, and the wrinkles of her visage, she seemed at least five hundred years old; and the spotted toad was not more freckled than was her skin. 'Ah! Prince Bonbenin-bonbobbin-bonbobbinet,' cried the creature, 'what has led you so many thousand miles from your own kingdom? what is it you look for, and what induces you to travel into the kingdom of Emmets?' The prince, who was excessively complaisant, told her the whole story three times over; for she was hard of hearing. 'Well,' says the old fairy, for such she was, 'I promise to put you in possession of the white mouse with green eyes, and that immediately too, upon one condition.' 'One condition!' cried the prince, in a rapture, 'name a thousand; I shall undergo them all with pleasure.' 'Nay,' interrupted the old fairy, 'I ask but one, and that not very mortifying neither; it is only that you instantly consent to marry me.'

"It is impossible to express the prince's confusion at this demand; he loved the mouse, but he detested the bride: he hesitated; he desired time to think upon the proposal; he would have been glad to consult his friends upon such an occasion. 'Nay, nay,' cried the odious fairy, 'if you demur, I retract my promise; I do not desire to force my favors on any man. Here, you my attendants,' cried she, stamping with her foot, 'let my machine be driven up. Barbacela, Queen of Emmets, is not used to contemptuous treatment.' She had no sooner spoken than her fiery chariot appeared in the air, drawn by two snails; and she was just going to step in, when the prince reflected that now or never was the time to be possessed of the white mouse; and, quite forgetting his lawful princess Nanhoa, falling on his knees, he implored forgiveness for having rashly rejected so much beauty. This well-timed compliment instantly appeased the angry fairy. She affected a hideous leer of approbation, and, taking the young prince by the hand, conducted him to a neighboring church, where they were married together in a moment. As soon as the ceremony was performed the prince, who was to the last degree desirous of seeing his favorite mouse, reminded the bride of her promise. 'To confess a truth, my prince,' cried she, 'I myself am that very white mouse you saw on your wedding night in the royal apartment. I now, therefore, give you the choice whether you would have me a mouse by day and a woman by night, or a mouse by night and a woman by day.' Though the prince was an excellent casuist he was quite at a loss how to determine, but at last thought it most prudent to have recourse to a blue cat that had followed him from his own dominions, and frequently amused him with its conversation, and assisted him with its advice; in fact, this cat was no other than the faithful princess Nanhoa herself, who had shared with him all his hardships in this disguise.

"By her instructions he was determined in his choice, and returning to the old fairy, prudently observed, that as she must have been sensible he had married her only for the sake of what she had, and not for her personal qualifications, he thought it would for several reasons be most convenient if she continued a woman by day and appeared a mouse by night.

"The old fairy was a good deal mortified at her husband's want of gallantry, though she was reluctantly obliged to comply: the day was therefore spent in the most polite amusements—the gentlemen talked smut, the ladies laughed and were angry. At last the happy night drew near; the blue cat still stuck by the side of its master, and even followed him to the bridal apartment. Barbacela entered the chamber, wearing a train fifteen yards long, supported by porcupines, and all over beset with jewels, which served to render her more detestable. She was just stepping into bed to the prince, forgetting her promise, when he insisted upon seeing her in the shape of a mouse. She had promised, and no fairy can break her word; wherefore, assuming the figure of the most beautiful mouse in the world, she skipped and played about with an infinity of amusement. The prince, in an agony of rapture, was desirous of seeing his pretty playfellow move a slow dance about the floor to his own singing; he began to sing, and the mouse immediately to perform with the most perfect knowledge of time, and the finest grace and greatest gravity imaginable. It only began, for Nanhoa, who had long waited for the opportunity in the shape of a cat, flew upon it instantly without remorse, and eating it up in the hundredth part of a moment, broke the charm, and then resumed her natural figure.

"The prince now found that he had all along been under the power of enchantment, that his passion for the white mouse was entirely fictitious, and not the genuine complexion of his soul; he now saw that his earnestness after mice was an illiberal amusement, and much more becoming a rat-catcher than a prince. All his meannesses now stared him in the face; he begged the discreet princess's pardon a hundred times. The princess very readily forgave him; and, both returning to their palace in Bonbobbin, lived very happily together, and reigned many years with all that wisdom which, by the story, they appear to have been possessed of; perfectly convinced by their former adventures that they who place their affections on trifles at first for amusement will find those trifles at last become their most serious concern." Adieu.

LETTER L.

AN ATTEMPT TO DEFINE WHAT IS MEANT BY ENGLISH LIBERTY.

From Lien Chi Altangi to Fum Hoam, first President of the Ceremonial Academy at Pekin, in China.

Ask an Englishman what nation in the world enjoys most freedom, and he immediately answers his own. Ask him in what that freedom principally consists, and he is instantly silent. This happy pre-eminence does not arise from the people's enjoying a larger share in legislation than elsewhere;

for in this particular several states in Europe excel them;
nor does it arise from a greater exemption from taxes, for few
countries pay more; it does not proceed from their being
restrained by fewer laws, for no people are burdened with so
many; nor does it particularly consist in the security of their
property, for property is pretty well secured in every polite
state of Europe.

How then are the English more free—for more free they
certainly are—than the people of any other country, or under
any other form of government whatever? Their freedom
consists in their enjoying all the advantages of democracy,
with this superior prerogative borrowed from monarchy, that
the severity of their laws may be relaxed without endanger-
ing the constitution.

In a monarchical state, in which the constitution is strongest, the laws may be relaxed without danger; for though the
people should be unanimous in the breach of any one in particular, yet still there is an effective power superior to the
people, capable of enforcing obedience, whenever it may be
proper to inculcate the law either towards the support or welfare of the community.

But in all those governments, where laws derive their sanction from the people alone, transgressions cannot be overlooked without bringing the constitution into danger. They
who transgress the law in such a case are those who prescribe it, by which means it loses not only its influence but its
sanction. In every republic the laws must be strong, because
the constitution is feeble; they must resemble an Asiatic husband, who is justly jealous, because he knows himself impotent. Thus, in Holland, Switzerland, and Genoa new laws are
not frequently enacted, but the old ones are observed with
unremitting severity. In such republics, therefore, the people
are slaves to laws of their own making little less than in unmixed monarchies, where they are slaves to the will of one,
subject to frailties like themselves.

In England, from a variety of happy accidents, their constitution is just strong enough, or, if you will, monarchical
enough, to permit a relaxation of the severity of laws, and yet

those laws still to remain sufficiently strong to govern the people. This is the most perfect state of civil liberty of which we can form any idea; here we see a greater number of laws than in any other country, while the people at the same time obey only such as are immediately conducive to the interests of society; several are unnoticed, many unknown; some kept to be revived and enforced upon proper occasions, others left to grow obsolete, even without the necessity of abrogation.

There is scarce an Englishman who does not almost every day of his life offend with impunity against some express law, and for which, in a certain conjuncture of circumstances, he would not receive punishment. Gaming-houses, preaching at prohibited places, assembled crowds, nocturnal amusements, public shows, and a hundred other instances are forbidden, and frequented. These prohibitions are useful; though it be prudent in their magistrates, and happy for the people, that they are not enforced, and none but the venal or mercenary attempt to enforce them.

The law in this case, like an indulgent parent, still keeps the rod, though the child is seldom corrected. Were those pardoned offences to rise into enormity, were they likely to obstruct the happiness of society, or endanger the state, it is then that Justice would resume her terrors, and punish those faults she had so often overlooked with indulgence. It is to this ductility of the laws that an Englishman owes the freedom he enjoys superior to others in a more popular government: every step, therefore, the constitution takes towards a democratic form, every diminution of the legal authority, is, in fact, a diminution of the subject's freedom; but every attempt to render the government more popular not only impairs natural liberty, but even will at last dissolve the political constitution.

Every popular government seems calculated to last only for a time; it grows rigid with age, new laws are multiplying, and the old continue in force; the subjects are oppressed, burdened with a multiplicity of legal injunctions; there are none from whom to expect redress, and nothing but a strong convulsion in the state can vindicate them into former liberty: thus, the people of Rome, a few great ones excepted, found more real freedom under their emperors, though tyrants, than they had experienced in the old age of the commonwealth, in which their laws were become numerous and painful, in which new laws were every day enacting, and the old ones executed with rigor. They even refused to be reinstated in their former prerogatives, upon an offer made them to this purpose; for they actually found emperors the only means of softening the rigors of their constitution.

The constitution of England is at present possessed of the strength of its native oak and the flexibility of the bending tamarisk; but should the people at any time, with a mistaken zeal, pant after an imaginary freedom, and fancy that abridging monarchy was increasing their privileges, they would be very much mistaken, since every jewel plucked from the crown of majesty would only be made use of as a bribe to corruption; it might enrich the few who shared it among them, but would in fact impoverish the public.

As the Roman senators, by slow and imperceptible degrees, became masters of the people, yet still flattered them with a show of freedom, while themselves only were free,[1] so is it possible for a body of men, while they stand up for privileges, to grow into an exuberance of power themselves, and the public become actually dependent, while some of its individuals only governed.

If then, my friend, there should in this country ever be on the throne a king who, through good-nature or age, should give up the smallest part of his prerogative to the people; if there should come a minister of merit and popularity— But I have room for no more. Adieu.

---

[1] " But when contending chiefs blockade the throne,
    Contracting regal power to stretch their own;
    When I behold a factious band agree
    To call it freedom when themselves are free," etc.— *The Traveller.*

LETTER LI.

A BOOKSELLER'S VISIT TO THE CHINESE.

To the Same.

As I was yesterday seated at breakfast over a pensive dish of tea my meditations were interrupted by my old friend and companion, who introduced a stranger, dressed pretty much like himself. The gentleman made several apologies for his visit—begged of me to impute his intrusion to the sincerity of his respect and the warmth of his curiosity.

As I am very suspicious of my company when I find them very civil without any apparent reason, I answered the stranger's caresses at first with reserve; which my friend perceiving, instantly let me into my visitant's trade and character, asking Mr. Fudge whether he had lately published anything new. I now conjectured that my guest was no other than a bookseller, and his answer confirmed my suspicions.

"Excuse me, sir," says he, "it is not the season; books have their time as well as cucumbers. I would no more bring out a new work in summer than I would sell pork in the dog-days. Nothing in my way goes off in summer, except very light goods indeed. A review, a magazine, or a sessions paper may amuse a summer reader; but all our stock of value we reserve for a spring and winter trade." "I must confess, sir," says I, "a curiosity to know what you call a valuable stock, which can only bear a winter perusal." "Sir," replied the bookseller, "it is not my way to cry up my own goods; but, without exaggeration, I will venture to show with any of the trade. My books at least have the peculiar advantage of being always new; and it is my way to clear off my old to the trunk-makers every season. I have ten new title-pages now about me, which only want books to be added to make them the finest things in nature. Others may pretend to direct the vulgar, but that is not my way; I always let the vulgar direct me; wherever popular clamor arises, I always echo the

million. For instance, should the people in general say that
such a man is a rogue, I instantly give orders to set him down
in print a villain; thus every man buys the book, not to learn
new sentiments, but to have the pleasure of seeing his own
reflected." "But, sir," interrupted I, "you speak as if you
yourself wrote the books you publish; may I be so bold as to
ask a sight of some of those intended publications which are
shortly to surprise the world?" "As to that, sir," replied the
talkative bookseller, "I only draw out the plans myself; and
though I am very cautious of communicating them to any,
yet, as in the end I have a favor to ask, you shall see a few of
them. Here, sir—here they are, diamonds of the first water,
I assure you. *Imprimis*, a translation of several medical
precepts, for the use of such physicians as do not understand
Latin. *Item*, the young clergyman's art of placing patches
regularly, with a dissertation on the different manner of smiling without distorting the face. *Item*, the whole art of love
made perfectly easy, by a broker of 'Change Alley. *Item*,
the proper manner of cutting black-lead pencils and making
crayons, by the Right Hon. the Earl of ——. *Item*, the
muster-master-general, or the review of reviews—" "Sir,"
cried I, interrupting him, "my curiosity with regard to title-
pages is satisfied; I should be glad to see some longer manuscript, a history, or an epic poem." "Bless me!" cries the
man of industry, "now you speak of an epic poem, you shall
see an excellent farce. Here it is; dip into it where you will,
it will be found replete with true modern humor. Strokes,
sir; it is filled with strokes of wit and satire in every line."
"Do you call these dashes of the pen strokes," replied I, "for
I must confess I can see no other?" "And pray, sir," returned he, "what do you call them? Do you see anything
good nowadays that is not filled with strokes—and dashes?
Sir, a well-placed dash makes half the wit of our writers
of modern humor.[1] I bought last season a piece that had

---

[1] "A prologue, interdash'd with many a stroke—
  An art contriv'd to advertise a joke,
  So that the jest is clearly to be seen,
  Not in the words—but in the gap between."—COWPER.

no other merit upon earth than nine hundred and ninety-five breaks, seventy-two ha-ha's,[1] three good things, and a garter. And yet it played off, and bounced, and cracked, and made more sport than a firework." "I fancy, then, sir, you were a considerable gainer?" "It must be owned the piece did pay; but, upon the whole, I cannot much boast of last winter's success; I gained by two murders, but then I lost by an ill-timed charity sermon. I was a considerable sufferer by my 'Direct Road to an Estate,' but the 'Infernal Guide' brought me up again. Ah, sir, that was a piece touched off by the hand of a master, filled with good things from one end to the other. The author had nothing but the jest in view; no dull moral lurking beneath, nor ill-natured satire to sour the reader's good-humor; he wisely considered that moral and humor at the same time were quite overdoing the business." "To what purpose was the book, then, published?" cried I. "Sir, the book was published in order to be sold; and no book sold better, except the criticisms upon it, which came out soon after: of all kinds of writings that goes off best at present; and I generally fasten a criticism upon every selling book that is published.

"I once had an author who never left the least opening for the critics; close was the word, always very right, and very dull—ever on the safe side of an argument; yet, with all his qualifications, incapable of coming into favor. I soon perceived that his bent was for criticism; and, as he was good for nothing else, supplied him with pens and paper, and planted him at the beginning of every month as a censor on the works of others. In short, I found him a treasure; no merit could escape him; but what is most remarkable of all, he ever wrote best and bitterest when drunk." "But are there not some works," interrupted I, "that from the very manner of their composition must be exempt from criticism, particularly such as profess to disregard its laws?" "There is no work

---

[1] Alluding, as I see reason to believe, to Townley's farce of "High Life Below Stairs," in which the *ha-ha's* are indeed numerous enough. Goldsmith had already referred to this popular farce in No. 5 of *The Bee:* "A word or two on the late farce called 'High Life Below Stairs.'" See Vol. III.

whatsoever but he can criticise," replied the bookseller; "even though you wrote in Chinese he would have a pluck at you. Suppose you should take it into your head to publish a book, let it be a volume of Chinese Letters, for instance; write how you will, he shall show the world you could have written better. Should you, with the most local exactness, stick to the manners and customs of the country from whence you come— should you confine yourself to the narrow limits of Eastern knowledge, and be perfectly simple and perfectly natural— he has then the strongest reason to exclaim. He may, with a sneer, send you back to China for readers. He may observe that, after the first or second letter, the iteration of the same simplicity is insupportably tedious; but the worst of all is, the public in such a case will anticipate his censures, and leave you with all your instructive simplicity to be mauled at discretion."

"Yes," cried I, "but in order to avoid his indignation, and what I should fear more, that of the public, I would in such a case write with all the knowledge I was master of. As I am not possessed of much learning, at least I would not suppress what little I had; nor would I appear more stupid than nature made me." "Here, then," cries the bookseller, "we should have you entirely in our power; unnatural, uneastern, quite out of character, erroneously sensible, would be the whole cry; sir, we should then hunt you down like a rat."[1] "Head of my father!" said I, "sure there are but two ways: the door must either be shut or it must be open. I must either be natural or unnatural." "Be what you will, we shall criticise you," returned the bookseller, "and prove you a dunce in spite of your teeth. But, sir, it is time that I should come to business. I have just now in the press a history of China; and if you will but put your name to it as the author I shall repay the obligation with gratitude." "What, sir," replied I, "put my name to a work which I have not written! Never,

---

[1] Introduced as an indirect mode of reply to occasional objectors in the newspapers, that the character of a Chinese was not sufficiently preserved—that the letter-writer was too observant or too well-informed upon English matters for the country to which he assumed to belong.

while I retain a proper respect for the public and myself." The bluntness of my reply quite abated the ardor of the bookseller's conversation; and, after about half an hour's disagreeable reserve, he, with some ceremony, took his leave and withdrew. Adieu.[1]

LETTER LII.

THE IMPOSSIBILITY OF DISTINGUISHING MEN IN ENGLAND BY THEIR DRESS.—TWO INSTANCES OF THIS.

To the Same.

In all other countries, my dear Fum Hoam, the rich are distinguished by their dress. In Persia, China, and most parts of Europe, those who are possessed of much gold or silver put some of it upon their clothes; but in England those who carry much upon their clothes are remarked for having but little in their pockets. A tawdry outside is regarded as a badge of poverty; and those who can sit at home and gloat over their thousands in silent satisfaction are generally found to do it in plain clothes.

This diversity of thinking from the rest of the world which prevails here I was first at a loss to account for; but am since informed that it was introduced by an intercourse between them and their neighbors, the French; who, whenever they came in order to pay those islanders a visit, were generally very well dressed and very poor—daubed with lace, but all the gilding on the outside. By this means laced clothes have been brought so much into contempt that at present even their mandarins are ashamed of finery.

I must own myself a convert to English simplicity. I am no more for ostentation of wealth than of learning; the person who in company should pretend to be wiser than others I am apt to regard as illiterate and ill-bred; the person whose

---

[1] This admirable letter is built on Pope's still more admirable description of his ride to Oxford in company with Lintot, the bookseller. Lintot, in an unpublished letter to Broome, the poet, now before me, calls it a *merry* letter.

clothes are extremely fine I am too apt to consider as not being possessed of any superiority of fortune, but resembling those Indians who are found to wear all the gold they have in the world in a bob at the nose.

I was lately introduced into a company of the best-dressed men I have seen since my arrival. Upon entering the room I was struck with awe at the grandeur of the different dresses. "That personage," thought I, "in blue and gold must be some emperor's son; that in green and silver a prince of the blood; he in embroidered scarlet a prime-minister—all first-rate noblemen, I suppose, and well-looking noblemen too." I sat for some time, with that uneasiness which conscious inferiority produces in the ingenuous mind, all attention to their discourse. However, I found their conversation more vulgar than I could have expected from personages of such distinction. "If these," thought I to myself, "be princes, they are the most stupid princes I have ever conversed with;" yet still I continued to venerate their dress; for dress has a kind of mechanical influence on the mind.

My friend in black, indeed, did not behave with the same deference, but contradicted the finest of them all in the most peremptory tones of contempt. But I had scarcely time to wonder at the imprudence of his conduct, when I found occasion to be equally surprised at the absurdity of theirs; for upon the entry of a middle-aged man, dressed in a cap, dirty shirt, and boots, the whole circle seemed diminished of their former importance, and contended who should be first to pay their obeisance to the stranger. They somewhat resembled a circle of Calmucks offering incense to a bear.

Eager to know the cause of so much seeming contradiction, I whispered my friend out of the room, and found that the august company consisted of no other than a dancing-master, two fiddlers, and a third-rate actor, all assembled in order to make a set at country-dances—as the middle-aged gentleman whom I saw enter was a squire from the country, and desirous of learning the new manner of footing, and smoothing up the rudiments of his rural minuet.

I was no longer surprised at the authority which my friend

assumed among them; nay, was even displeased (pardon my Eastern education) that he had not kicked every creature of them down-stairs. "What!" said I, "shall a set of such paltry fellows dress themselves up like sons of kings, and claim even the transitory respect of half an hour? There should be some law to restrain so manifest a breach of privilege; they should go from house to house, as in China, with the instruments of their profession strung round their necks; by this means we might be able to distinguish and treat them in a style of becoming contempt." "Hold, my friend," replied my companion, "were your reformation to take place, as dancing-masters and fiddlers now mimic gentlemen in appearance, we should then find our fine gentlemen conforming to theirs. A beau might be introduced to a lady of fashion with a fiddle-case hanging at his neck by a red ribbon, and, instead of a cane, might carry a fiddle-stick. Though to be as dull as a first-rate dancing-master might be used with proverbial justice; yet, dull as he is, many a fine gentleman sets him up as the proper standard of politeness; copies not only the pert vivacity of his air, but the flat insipidity of his conversation. In short, if you make a law against dancing-masters imitating the fine gentleman, you should with as much reason enact that no fine gentleman shall imitate the dancing-master."

After I had left my friend I made toward home, reflecting as I went upon the difficulty of distinguishing men by their appearance. Invited, however, by the freshness of the evening, I did not return directly, but went to ruminate on what had passed in a public garden belonging to the city. Here, as I sat upon one of the benches, and felt the pleasing sympathy which nature in bloom inspires, a disconsolate figure, who sat on the other end of the seat, seemed no way to enjoy the serenity of the season. His dress was miserable beyond description: a threadbare coat of the rudest materials; a shirt, though clean, yet extremely coarse; hair that seemed to have been long unconscious of the comb; and all the rest of his equipage impressed with the marks of genuine poverty.

As he continued to sigh, and testify every symptom of despair, I was naturally led, from a motive of humanity, to offer comfort and assistance.   You know my heart, and that all who are miserable may claim a place there.   The pensive stranger at first declined my conversation; but at last, perceiving a peculiarity in my accent and manner of thinking, he began to unfold himself by degrees.

I now found that he was not so very miserable as he at first appeared: upon my offering him a small piece of money he refused my favor, yet without appearing displeased at my intended generosity.   It is true he sometimes interrupted the conversation with a sigh, and talked pathetically of neglected merit; yet still I could perceive a benignity in his countenance that, upon a closer inspection, bespoke inward content.

Upon a pause in the conversation I was going to take my leave, when he begged I would favor him with my company home to supper.   I was surprised at such a demand from a person of his appearance; but willing to indulge curiosity, I accepted his invitation, and, though I felt some repugnance at being seen with one who appeared so very wretched, went along with seeming alacrity.

Still, as he approached nearer home his good-humor proportionably seemed to increase.   At last he stopped, not at the gate of a hovel, but of a magnificent palace!   When I cast my eyes upon all the sumptuous elegance which everywhere presented upon entering, and then when I looked at my seemingly miserable conductor, I could scarcely think that all this finery belonged to him; yet in fact it did.   Numerous servants ran through the apartments with silent assiduity; several ladies of beauty, and magnificently dressed, came to welcome his return; a most elegant supper was provided: in short, I found the person, whom a little before I had sincerely pitied, to be in reality a most refined epicure—one who courted contempt abroad, in order to feel with keener gust the pleasures of pre-eminence at home.   Adieu.

LETTER LIII.

THE ABSURD TASTE FOR OBSCENE AND PERT NOVELS, SUCH AS
"TRISTRAM SHANDY," RIDICULED.[1]

From the Same.

How often have we admired the eloquence of Europe! that strength of thinking, that delicacy of imagination, even beyond the efforts of the Chinese themselves. How were we enraptured with those bold figures which sent every sentiment with force to the heart! How have we spent whole days together in learning those arts by which European writers got within the passions, and led the reader as if by enchantment!

But though we have learned most of the rhetorical figures of the last age, yet there seems to be one or two of great use here which have not yet travelled to China. The figures I mean are called bawdy and pertness: none are more fashionable; none so sure of admirers; they are of such a nature that the merest blockhead, by a proper use of them, shall have the reputation of a wit; they lie level to the meanest capacities, and address those passions which all have, or would be ashamed to disown.

It has been observed, and I believe with some truth, that it is very difficult for a dunce to obtain the reputation of a wit;

---

[1] "Until 1759, Sterne had only printed two sermons; but in this year he surprised the world by publishing the first and second volumes of 'Tristram Shandy.' He went to London to enjoy his fame, and met with all that attention which the public gives to men of notoriety. He boasts of being engaged fourteen dinners deep, and received this hospitality as a tribute; while his contemporaries saw the festivity in a very different light. 'Any man who has a name, or who has the power of pleasing,' said Johnson, 'will be very generally invited in London. The man Sterne, I am told, has had engagements for three months.' Johnson's feelings of morality, and respect for the priesthood, led him to speak of Sterne with contempt; but when Goldsmith added, 'And a very dull fellow,' he replied with his emphatic 'Why, no, sir.'"—SIR WALTER SCOTT, *Prose Works*, vol. iii. p. 282.

yet, by the assistance of the figure bawdy, this may be easily effected, and a bawdy blockhead often passes for a fellow of smart parts and pretensions. Every object in nature helps the jokes forward, without scarce any effort of the imagination. If a lady stands, something very good may be said upon that; if she happens to fall, with the help of a little fashionable pruriency, there are forty sly things ready on the occasion. But a prurient jest has always been found to give most pleasure to a few very old gentlemen, who, being in some measure dead to other sensations, feel the force of the allusion with double violence on the organs of risibility.

An author who writes in this manner is generally sure, therefore, of having the very old and the impotent among his admirers; for these he may properly be said to write, and from these he ought to expect his reward; his works being often a very proper succedaneum to cantharides, or an assafœtida pill. His pen should be considered in the same light as the squirt of an apothecary, both being directed at the same generous end.

But though this manner of writing be perfectly adapted to the taste of gentlemen and ladies of fashion here, yet still it deserves greater praise in being equally suited to the most vulgar apprehensions. The very ladies and gentlemen of Benin or Caffraria are in this respect tolerably polite, and might relish a prurient joke of this kind with critical propriety; probably, too, with higher gust, as they wear neither breeches nor petticoats to intercept the application.

It is certain I never could have expected the ladies here, biassed as they are by education, capable at once of bravely throwing off their prejudices, and not only applauding books in which this figure makes the only merit, but even adopting it in their own conversation. Yet so it is; the pretty innocents now carry those books openly in their hands which formerly were hid under the cushion; they now lisp their double meanings with so much grace, and talk over the raptures they bestow with such little reserve, that I am sometimes reminded of a custom among the entertainers in China, who think it a piece of necessary breeding to whet the appetites of their guests, by letting them smell dinner in the kitchen before it is served up to table.[1]

The veneration we have for many things entirely proceeds from their being carefully concealed. Were the idolatrous Tartar permitted to lift the veil which keeps his idol from view, it might be a certain method to cure his future superstition: with what a noble spirit of freedom, therefore, must that writer be possessed who bravely paints things as they are, who lifts the veil of modesty, who displays the most hidden recesses of the temple, and shows the erring people that the object of their vows is either, perhaps, a mouse or a monkey.

However, though this figure be at present so much in fashion; though the professors of it are so much caressed by the great, those perfect judges of literary excellence; yet it is confessed to be only a revival of what was once fashionable here before. There was a time when, by this very manner of writing, the gentle Tom D'Urfey,[2] as I read in English authors, acquired his great reputation, and became the favorite of a king.[3]

---

[1] "The following anecdote we have from a sure source: Soon after 'Tristram' had appeared, Sterne asked a Yorkshire lady of fortune and condition whether she had read his book. 'I have not, Mr. Sterne,' was the answer; 'and, to be plain with you, I am informed it is not proper for female perusal.' 'My dear good lady,' replied the author, 'do not be gulled by such stories; the book is like your young heir there' (pointing to a child of three years old, who was rolling on the carpet in his white tunics), 'he shows at times a good deal that is usually concealed, but it is all in perfect innocence!' This witty excuse may be so far admitted; for it cannot be said that the licentious humor of 'Tristram Shandy' is of the kind which applies itself to the passions, or is calculated to corrupt society. But it is a sin against taste, if allowed to be harmless as to morals. A handful of mud is neither a firebrand nor a stone; but to fling it about in sport, argues coarseness of mind and want of common manners."—SIR WALTER SCOTT, *Prose Works*, vol. iii. p. 290.

[2] Tom D'Urfey, as he was generally called, was descended from an ancient family in France. He wrote a number of ballads, songs, etc., which were published in six volumes 12mo, under the title of "Wit and Mirth, or Pills to Purge Melancholy;" besides more than thirty dramatic pieces, none of which are now on the muster-roll of acting plays. He was buried in the church-yard of St. James's, Westminster; against the outer wall of the south-west angle of which church is a stone inscribed, "Tom D'Urfey, died Feb. 26, 1723."

[3] "I myself remember King Charles the Second leaning on Tom D'Urfey's

The works of this original genius, though they never travelled abroad to China, and scarce have reached posterity at home, were once found upon every fashionable toilet, and made the subject of polite—I mean very polite—conversation. "Has your grace seen Mr. D'Urfey's last new thing, the 'Oylet Hole?' A most facetious piece!" "Sure, my lord, all the world must have seen it; D'Urfey is certainly the most comical creature alive. It is impossible to read his things and live. Was there ever anything so natural and pretty, as when the squire and Bridget meet in the cellar? And then the difficulties they both find in broaching the beer barrel are so arch and so ingenious! We have certainly nothing of this kind in the language."[1] In this manner they spoke then, and in this manner they speak now; for though the successor of D'Urfey does not excel him in wit, the world must confess he outdoes him in obscenity.

There are several very dull fellows, who, by a few mechanical helps, sometimes learn to become extremely brilliant and pleasing, with a little dexterity in the management of the eyebrows, fingers, and nose. By imitating a cat, a sow and pigs; by a loud laugh, and a slap on the shoulder; the most ignorant are furnished out for conversation. But the writer finds it impossible to throw his winks, his shrugs, or his attitudes upon paper; he may borrow some assistance, indeed, by printing his face at the title-page; but, without wit, to pass for a man of ingenuity, no other mechanical help but

---

shoulder more than once, and humming over a song with him."—*The Guardian*, No. 67. King William had him one night to sing to him, and Queen Anne gave him fifty guineas for singing a song to her, beginning,

> "The crown is too weighty
> For shoulders of eighty,"

written in ridicule of the Princess Sophia, electress-dowager of Hanover.

[1] "I have not quoted one Latin author since I came down, but have learned without book a song of Mr. Thomas D'Urfey's, who is your only poet of tolerable reputation in this country. He makes all the merriment in our entertainments, and but for him there would be so miserable a dearth of catches, that I fear they would put either the parson or me upon making some for 'em. Any man, of any quality, is heartily welcome to the best toping table of our gentry, who can roar out some rhapsodies of his works."—POPE *to Henry Cromwell*, April, 1710.

downright obscenity will suffice. By speaking to some peculiar sensations we are always sure of exciting laughter, for the jest does not lie in the writer, but in the subject.

But bawdy is often helped on by another figure, called pertness; and few indeed are found to excel in one that are not possessed of the other. As in common conversation the best way to make the audience laugh is by first laughing yourself, so in writing the properest manner is to show an attempt at humor, which will pass upon most for humor in reality. To effect this, readers must be treated with the most perfect familiarity: in one page the author is to make them a low bow, and in the next to pull them by the nose; he must talk in riddles, and then send them to bed in order to dream for the solution. He must speak of himself, and his chapters, and his manner, and what he would be at, and his own importance, and his mother's importance, with the most unpitying prolixity; now and then testifying his contempt for all but himself, smiling without a jest, and without wit professing vivacity. Adieu.

LETTER LIV.

THE CHARACTER OF AN IMPORTANT TRIFLER.[1]

From the Same.

THOUGH naturally pensive, yet I am fond of gay company, and take every opportunity of thus dismissing the mind from duty. From this motive, I am often found in the centre of a crowd; and wherever pleasure is to be sold am always a purchaser. In those places, without being remarked by any, I join in whatever goes forward, work my passions into a similitude of frivolous earnestness, shout as they shout, and condemn as they happen to disapprove. A mind thus sunk for a while below its natural standard is qualified for stronger

---

[1] Reprinted by Goldsmith, in 1765, as Essay X.

flights, as those first retire who would spring forward with greater vigor.

Attracted by the serenity of the evening, my friend and I lately went to gaze upon the company in one of the public walks near the city. Here we sauntered together for some time, either praising the beauty of such as were handsome, or the dresses of such as had nothing else to recommend them. We had gone thus deliberately forward for some time, when, stopping on a sudden, my friend caught me by the elbow and led me out of the public walk. I could perceive by the quickness of his pace, and by his frequently looking behind, that he was attempting to avoid somebody who followed: we now turned to the right, then to the left; as we went forward he still went faster, but in vain; the person whom he attempted to escape hunted us through every doubling, and gained upon us each moment; so that at last we fairly stood still, resolving to face what we could not avoid.

Our pursuer soon came up, and joined us with all the familiarity of an old acquaintance. "My dear Drybone,"[1] cries he, shaking my friend's hand, "where have you been hiding this half a century? Positively I had fancied you were gone down to cultivate matrimony and your estate in the country." During the reply I had an opportunity of surveying the appearance of our new companion: his hat was pinched up with peculiar smartness; his looks were pale, thin, and sharp; round his neck he wore a broad black ribbon, and in his bosom a buckle studded with glass; his coat was trimmed with tarnished twist; he wore by his side a sword with a black hilt, and his stockings of silk, though newly washed, were grown yellow by long service. I was so much engaged with the peculiarity of his dress, that I attended only to the latter part of my friend's reply, in which he complimented Mr. Tibbs on the taste of his clothes and the bloom in his countenance. "Pshaw, pshaw, Will,"[2] cried the figure, "no more of that if you love me: you know I hate flattery, on my soul

---

[1] *My dear Charles*, when reprinted, in 1765, as Essay X.

[2] *Charles*, when reprinted, in 1765, as Essay X.

I do; and yet, to be sure, an intimacy with the great will improve one's appearance, and a course of venison will fatten;
and yet, faith, I despise the great as much as you do: but
there are a great many damned honest fellows among them;
and we must not quarrel with one half because the other wants
breeding. If they were all such as my Lord Mudler, one of
the most good-natured creatures that ever squeezed a lemon,
I should myself be among the number of their admirers. I
was yesterday to dine at the Duchess of Piccadilly's. My
lord was there. 'Ned,' says he to me—'Ned,' says he, 'I'll
hold gold to silver I can tell where you were poaching last
night.' 'Poaching, my lord,' says I; 'faith, you have missed
already; for I stayed at home, and let the girls poach for me.
That's my way; I take a fine woman as some animals do their
prey—stand still, and, swoop, they fall into my mouth.' "

"Ah, Tibbs, thou art a happy fellow," cried my companion,
with looks of infinite pity; "I hope your fortune is as much
improved as your understanding in such company?" "Improved," replied the other; "you shall know—but let it go
no farther—a great secret—five hundred a year to begin with.
My lord's word of honor for it—his lordship took me down
in his own chariot yesterday, and we had a *tête-à-tête* dinner
in the country, where we talked of nothing else." "I fancy
you forget, sir," cried I, "you told us but this moment of your
dining yesterday in town." "Did I say so?" replied he, coolly; "to be sure, if I said so, it was so—dined in town: egad,
now I do remember, I did dine in town; but I dined in the
country, too; for you must know, my boys, I eat two dinners.
By-the-bye, I am grown as nice as the devil in my eating.
I'll tell you a pleasant affair about that: we were a select
party of us to dine at Lady Grogram's, an affected piece, but
let it go no farther; a secret: well, there happened to be no
assafœtida in the sauce to a turkey, upon which[1] says I, 'I'll
hold a thousand guineas, and say done first, that—' But, dear
Drybone, you are an honest creature, lend me half a crown for

---

[1] The words *there happened to be no assafœtida in the sauce to a turkey, upon
which*, were omitted when the paper was reprinted, in 1765, as Essay X.

a minute or two or so, just till—but, harkee, ask me for it the next time we meet, or it may be twenty to one but I forget to pay you."

When he left us our conversation naturally turned upon so extraordinary a character. "His very dress," cries my friend, "is not less extraordinary than his conduct. If you meet him this day you will find him in rags, if the next, in embroidery. With those persons of distinction, of whom he talks so familiarly, he has scarce a coffee-house acquaintance. However, both for the interests of society, and perhaps for his own, Heaven has made him poor, and while all the world perceive his wants, he fancies them concealed from every eye. An agreeable companion, because he understands flattery; and all must be pleased with the first part of his conversation, though all are sure of its ending with a demand on their purse. While his youth countenances the levity of his conduct he may thus earn a precarious subsistence, but when age comes on, the gravity of which is incompatible with buffoonery, then will he find himself forsaken by all; condemned in the decline of life to hang upon some rich family whom he once despised, there to undergo all the ingenuity of studied contempt, to be employed only as a spy upon the servants, or a bugbear to fright the children into obedience.[1]   Adieu.

LETTER LV.

HIS CHARACTER CONTINUED ; WITH THAT OF HIS WIFE, HIS HOUSE, AND FURNITURE.[2]

To the Same.

I AM apt to fancy I have contracted a new acquaintance whom it will be[3] no easy matter to shake off. My little beau yesterday overtook me again in one of the public walks, and

---

[1] *Duty*, Essay X., 1765.   [2] Reprinted by its author in 1765, as Essay XI.

[3] Altered in 1765 to *There are some acquaintances whom it is*, when reprinted as Essay XI.

slapping me on the shoulder, saluted me with an air of the most perfect familiarity. His dress was the same as usual, except that he had more powder in his hair, wore a dirtier shirt, a pair of temple spectacles, and his hat under his arm.

As I knew him to be a harmless, amusing little thing, I could not return his smiles with any degree of severity; so we walked forward on terms of the utmost intimacy, and in a few minutes discussed all the usual topics preliminary to particular conversation.

The oddities that marked his character, however, soon began to appear; he bowed to several well-dressed persons, who, by their manner of returning the compliment, appeared perfect strangers. At intervals he drew out a pocket-book, seeming to take memorandums before all the company, with much importance and assiduity. In this manner he led me through the length of the whole walk, fretting at his absurdities, and fancying myself laughed at not less than him[1] by every spectator.

When we were got to the end of our procession, "Blast me," cries he, with an air of vivacity, "I never saw the park so thin in my life before! there's no company at all to-day; not a single face to be seen." "No company!" interrupted I, peevishly; "no company where there is such a crowd? why man, there's too much. What are the thousand that have been laughing at us but company?" "Lord, my dear," returned he, with the utmost good-humor, "you seem immensely chagrined; but, blast me, when the world laughs at me I laugh at the world, and so we are even. My Lord Trip, Bill Squash the Creolian, and I sometimes make a party at being ridiculous; and so we say and do a thousand things for the joke's sake. But I see you are grave, and if you are for a fine grave sentimental companion, you shall dine with me and my wife to-day; I must insist on't: I'll introduce you to Mrs. Tibbs, a lady of as elegant qualifications as any in nature; she was bred—but that's between ourselves—under the inspection of the Countess of All-night.[2] A charming body of voice; but

---

[1] Altered in 1765 to *as well as he*, Essay XI.   [2] *Shoreditch*, Essay XI.

no more of that; she shall give us a song.   You shall see my little girl too, Carolina Wilhelmina Amelia Tibbs, a sweet pretty creature!   I design her for my Lord Drumstick's eldest son; but that's in friendship—let it go no farther: she's but six years old, and yet she walks a minuet, and plays on the guitar immensely already.   I intend she shall be as perfect as possible in every accomplishment.   In the first place, I'll make her a scholar; I'll teach her Greek myself, and learn that language purposely to instruct her; but let that be a secret."

Thus saying, without waiting for a reply, he took me by the arm and hauled me along.   We passed through many dark alleys and winding ways; for, from some motives to me unknown, he seemed to have a particular aversion to every frequented street; at last, however, we got to the door of a dismal-looking house in the outlets of the town, where he informed me he chose to reside for the benefit of the air.

We entered the lower door, which ever seemed to lie most hospitably open; and I began to ascend an old and creaking staircase, when, as he mounted to show me the way, he demanded whether I delighted in prospects; to which, answering in the affirmative, " Then," says he, " I shall show you one of the most charming in the world, out of my windows; we shall see the ships sailing, and the whole country for twenty miles round, tip-top, quite high.   My Lord Swamp would give ten thousand guineas for such a one; but, as I sometimes pleasantly tell him, I always love to keep my prospects at home, that my friends may come to see me the oftener."

By this time we were arrived as high as the stairs would permit us to ascend, till we came to what he was facetiously pleased to call the first floor down the chimney; and knocking at the door, a voice from within demanded, who's there? My conductor answered that it was him.   But this was not satisfying the querist, the voice again repeated the demand: to which he answered louder than before; and now the door was opened by an old woman[1] with cautious reluctance.

---

[1] *Maid-servant,* Essay XI.

When we were got in he welcomed me to his house with great ceremony, and, turning to the old woman, asked where was her lady? "Good troth," replied she, in a peculiar dialect, "she's washing your twa shirts at the next door, because they have taken an oath against lending out the tub any longer." "My two shirts!" cries he, in a tone that faltered with confusion, "what does the idiot mean?" "I ken what I mean weel enough," replied the other; "she's washing your twa shirts at the next door, because—" "Fire and fury! no more of thy stupid explanations!" cried he; "go and inform her we have got company. Were that Scotch hag to be forever in my family she would never learn politeness, nor forget that absurd poisonous accent of hers, or testify the smallest specimen of breeding or high life; and yet it is very surprising too, as I had her from a Parliament man, a friend of mine from the Highlands, one of the politest men in the world; but that's a secret."

We waited some time for Mrs. Tibbs's arrival, during which interval I had a full opportunity of surveying the chamber and all its furniture; which consisted of four chairs with old wrought bottoms, that he assured me were his wife's embroidery; a square table that had been once japanned; a cradle in one corner, a lumbering cabinet in the other; a broken shepherdess and a mandarin without a head were stuck over the chimney; and round the walls several paltry unframed pictures, which, he observed, were all his own drawing. "What do you think, sir, of that head in the corner, done in the manner of Grisoni? there's the true keeping in it; it's my own face, and though there happens to be no likeness, a countess offered me a hundred for its fellow: I refused her, for, hang it, that would be mechanical, you know."

The wife at last made her appearance, at once a slattern and a coquette; much emaciated, but still carrying the remains of beauty. She made twenty apologies for being seen in such an odious dishabille, but hoped to be excused, as she had stayed out all night at the Gardens[1] with the countess, who

---

[1] *Vauxhall Gardens*, Essay XI.

was excessively fond of the horns. "And indeed, my dear," added she, turning to her husband, "his lordship drank your health in a bumper." "Poor Jack," cries he, "a dear good-natured creature, I know he loves me : but I hope, my dear, you have given orders for dinner; you need make no great preparations neither—there are but three of us; something elegant, and little will do; a turbot, an ortolan, or a—" "Or what do you think, my dear," interrupts the wife, "of a nice pretty bit of ox-cheek, piping hot, and dressed with a little of my own sauce?" "The very thing," replies he; "it will eat best with some smart bottled beer; but be sure to let's have the sauce his grace was so fond of. I hate your immense loads of meat; that is country all over; extreme disgusting to those who are in the least acquainted with high life."

By this time my curiosity began to abate, and my appetite to increase : the company of fools may at first make us smile, but at last never fails of rendering us melancholy; I there-fore pretended to recollect a prior engagement, and, after having shown my respect to the house, according to the fash-ion of the English, by giving the old servant a piece of money at the door, I took my leave; Mr. Tibbs assuring me that din-ner, if I stayed, would be ready at least in less than two hours.

LETTER LVI.

THE PRESENT SITUATION OF THE SEVERAL STATES OF EUROPE.

From Fum Hoam to Altangi, the discontented Wanderer.

THE distant sounds of music, that catch new sweetness as they vibrate through the long-drawn valley, are not more pleasing to the ear than the tidings of a far-distant friend. I have just received two hundred of thy letters by the Russian caravan, descriptive of the manners of Europe. You have left it to geographers to determine the site of their mountains and extent of their lakes, seeming only employed in discover-ing the genius, the government, and disposition of the people.

In those letters I perceive a journal of the operations of your mind upon whatever occurs, rather than a detail of your travels from one building to another; of your taking a draught of this ruin or that obelisk; of paying so many tomans for this commodity, or laying up a proper store for the passage of some new wilderness.

From your accounts of Russia I learn that this nation is again relaxing into pristine barbarity; that its great emperor wanted a life of a hundred years more to bring about his vast design. A savage people may be resembled to their own forests: a few years are sufficient to clear away the obstructions to agriculture; but it requires many ere the ground acquires a proper degree of fertility. The Russians, attached to their ancient prejudices, again renew their hatred to strangers, and indulge every former brutal excess. So true it is that the revolutions of wisdom are slow and difficult, the revolutions of folly or ambition precipitate and easy. "We are not to be astonished," says Confucius, "that the wise walk more slowly in their road to virtue than fools in their passage to vice, since passion drags us along, while wisdom only points out the way."[1]

The German Empire, that remnant of the majesty of ancient Rome, appears, from your accounts, on the eve of dissolution. The members of its vast body want every tie of government to unite them, and seem feebly held together only by their respect for ancient institutions. The very name of country and countrymen, which in other nations makes one of the strongest bonds of government, has been here for some time laid aside—each of its inhabitants seeming more proud of being called from the petty state which gives him birth than by the more well-known title of German.

This government may be regarded in the light of a severe master and a feeble opponent. The states which are now subject to the laws of the empire are only watching a proper occasion to fling off the yoke, and those which are become too

---

[1] Though this fine maxim be not found in the Latin edition of the morals of Confucius, yet we find it ascribed to him by Le Comte, "Etat présent de la Chine," vol. i. p. 348.—GOLDSMITH.

powerful to be compelled to obedience now begin to think of dictating in their turn. The struggles in this state are, there-fore, not in order to preserve but to destroy the ancient con-stitution : if one side succeeds, the government must become despotic ; if the other, several states will subsist without even nominal subordination ; but, in either case, the Germanic con-stitution will be no more.

Sweden, on the contrary, though now seemingly a strenu-ous assertor of its liberties, is probably only hastening on to despotism. Their senators, while they pretend to vindicate the freedom of the people, are only establishing their own in-dependence. The deluded people will, however, at last per-ceive the miseries of an aristocratical government; they will perceive that the administration of a society of men is ever more painful than that of one only. They will fly from this most oppressive of all forms, where one single member is capable of controlling the whole, to take refuge under the throne, which will ever be attentive to their complaints. No people long endure an aristocratical government when they can apply elsewhere for redress. The lower orders of people may be enslaved for a time by a number of tyrants, but upon the first opportunity they will ever take a refuge in despot-ism or democracy.

As the Swedes are making concealed approaches to despot-ism, the French, on the other hand, are imperceptibly vindi-cating themselves into freedom. When I consider that those parliaments (the members of which are all created by the court, the presidents of which can act only by immediate di-rection) presume even to mention privileges and freedom, who, till of late, received directions from the throne with im-plicit humility ; when this is considered, I cannot help fan-cying that the genius of freedom has entered that kingdom in disguise. If they have but three weak monarchs more suc-cessively on the throne, the mask will be laid aside, and the country will certainly once more be free.

When I compare the figure which the Dutch make in Eu-rope with that they assume in Asia, I am struck with surprise. In Asia I find them the great lords of all the Indian seas ; in

Europe, the timid inhabitants of a paltry state. No longer
the sons of freedom, but of avarice; no longer assertors of
their rights by courage, but by negotiations; fawning on those
who insult them, and crouching under the rod of every neighboring power. Without a friend to save them in distress, and
without virtue to save themselves; their government is poor,
and their private wealth will serve but to invite some neighboring invader.

I long with impatience for your letters from England,
Denmark, Holland, and Italy; yet why wish for relations
which only describe new calamities, which show that ambition
and avarice are equally terrible in every region? Adieu.

LETTER LVII.

THE DIFFICULTY OF RISING IN LITERARY REPUTATION WITHOUT
INTRIGUE OR RICHES.

*From Lien Chi Altangi to Fum Hoam, first President of the Ceremonial
Academy at Pekin, in China.*

I HAVE frequently admired the manner of criticising in
China, where the learned are assembled in a body to judge
of every new publication; to examine the merits of the work
without knowing the circumstances of the author; and then
to usher it into the world with the proper marks of respect
or reprobation.

In England there are no such tribunals erected; but if a
man thinks proper to be a judge of genius, few will be at the
pains to contradict his pretensions. If any choose to be
critics, it is but saying they are critics; and from that time
forward they become invested with full power and authority
over every caitiff who aims at their instruction or entertainment.

As almost every member of society has by this means a
vote in literary transactions, it is no way surprising to find
the rich leading the way here, as in other common concerns

of life, to see them either bribing the numerous herd of voters by their interest or browbeating them by their authority.

A great man says at his table that such a book is "no bad thing." Immediately the praise is carried off by five flatterers to be dispersed at twelve different coffee-houses,[1] from whence it circulates, still improving as it proceeds, through forty-five houses where cheaper liquors are sold; from thence it is carried away by the honest tradesman to his own fireside, where the applause is eagerly caught up by his wife and children, who have been long taught to regard his judgment as the standard of perfection. Thus, when we have traced a wide-extended literary reputation up to its original source, we shall find it derived from some great man, who has, perhaps, received all his education and English from a tutor of Berne or a dancing-master of Picardy.

The English are a people of good-sense; and I am the more surprised to find them swayed in their opinions by men who often, from their very education, are incompetent judges. Men who, being always bred in affluence, see the world only on one side are surely improper judges of human nature: they may, indeed, describe a ceremony, a pageant, or a ball; but how can they pretend to dive into the secrets of the human heart who have been nursed up only in forms, and daily behold nothing but the same insipid adulation smiling upon every face? Few of them have been bred in that best of schools, the school of adversity; and, by what I can learn, fewer still have been bred in any school at all.

From such a description one would think that a droning duke or a dowager duchess was not possessed of more just pretensions to taste than persons of less quality; and yet whatever the one or the other may write or praise shall pass for perfection without further examination. A nobleman has

---

[1] The influence of coffee-houses on the sale of books has now entirely changed. When Goldsmith wrote, every new poem and pamphlet of even ordinary importance was to be seen at a coffee-house. I have many quarto poems in my own possession bearing the inscription "Dick's Coffee House" in large written letters on their title-pages. The influence of what was said at Will's Coffee-house is almost proverbial.

but to take a pen, ink, and paper and write away through three large volumes, and then sign his name to the title-page; though the whole might have been before more disgusting than his own rent-roll, yet signing his name and title gives value to the deed; title being alone equivalent to taste, imagination, and genius.[1]

As soon as a piece, therefore, is published, the first questions are, " Who is the author? does he keep a coach? where lies his estate? what sort of a table does he keep?" If he happens to be poor and unqualified for such a scrutiny, he and his works sink into irremediable obscurity; and too late he finds that having fed upon turtle is a more ready way to fame than having digested Tully.

The poor devil against whom fashion has set its face vainly alleges that he has been bred in every part of Europe where knowledge was to be sold; that he has grown pale in the study of nature and himself; his works may please upon the perusal, but his pretensions to fame are entirely disregarded; he is treated like a fiddler, whose music, though liked, is not much praised, because he lives by it; while a gentleman performer, though the most wretched scraper alive, throws the audience into raptures. The fiddler, indeed, may in such a case console himself by thinking that, while the other goes off with all the praise, he runs away with all the money; but here the parallel drops: for while the nobleman triumphs in unmerited applause, the author by profession steals off with—nothing.

The poor, therefore, here, who draw their pens auxiliary to

---

[1] " Let but his lordship write some dull lampoon,
     He's *Horaced* up in doggrel like his own;
     But if to tragedy his lordship yields—
     False fame cries Athens; honest truth—Moorfields."—GARTH.

" What woful stuff this madrigal would be,
     In some starved hackney sonneteer, or me;
     But let a lord once own the happy lines,
     How the wit brightens! how the style refines!
     Before his sacred name flies every fault,
     And each exalted stanza teems with thought."—POPE.

the laws of their country, must think themselves very happy if they find, not fame, but forgiveness; and yet they are hardly treated; for as every country grows more polite the Press becomes more useful, and writers become more necessary as readers are supposed to increase. In a polished society that man, though in rags, who has the power of enforcing virtue from the Press is of more real use than forty stupid brachmans, or bonzes, or guebres, though they preached never so often, never so loud, or never so long. That man, though in rags, who is capable of deceiving even indolence into wisdom, and who professes amusement while he aims at reformation, is more useful in refined society than twenty cardinals, with all their scarlet, and tricked out in all the fopperies of scholastic finery.

LETTER LVIII.

A VISITATION DINNER DESCRIBED.

To the Same.

As the man in black takes every opportunity of introducing me to such company as may serve to indulge my speculative temper, or gratify my curiosity, I was by his influence lately invited to a *visitation* dinner. To understand this term you must know that it was formerly the custom here for the principal priests to go about the country once a year, and examine upon the spot whether those of subordinate orders did their duty or were qualified for the task; whether their temples were kept in proper repair or the laity pleased with their administration.

Though a visitation of this nature was very useful, yet it was found to be extremely troublesome, and for many reasons utterly inconvenient; for as the principal priests were obliged to attend at court, in order to solicit preferment, it was impossible they could at the same time attend in the country, which was quite out of the road of promotion; if we add to this the gout, which has been time immemorial a clerical disorder here, together with the bad wine and ill-dressed provisions that must infallibly be served up by the way, it was not strange that the custom has been long discontinued. At present, therefore, every head of the Church, instead of going about to visit his priests, is satisfied if his priests come in a body once a year to visit him ; by this means the duty of half a year is despatched in a day. When assembled he asks each in his turn how they have behaved, and are liked ; upon which those who have neglected their duty, or are disagreeable to their congregation, no doubt accuse themselves, and tell him all their faults ; for which he reprimands them most severely.

The thoughts of being introduced into a company of philosophers and learned men (for as such I conceived them) gave me no small pleasure. I expected our entertainment would resemble those sentimental banquets so finely described by Xenophon and Plato : I was hoping some Socrates would be brought in from the door, in order to harangue upon divine love ; but as for eating and drinking, I had prepared myself to be disappointed in that particular. I was apprised that fasting and temperance were tenets strongly recommended to the professors of Christianity, and I had seen the frugality and mortification of the priests of the East ; so that I expected an entertainment where we should have much reasoning and little meat.

Upon being introduced I confess I found no great signs of mortification in the faces or persons of the company. However, I imputed their florid look to temperance, and their corpulency to a sedentary way of living. I saw several preparations, indeed, for dinner, but none for philosophy. The company seemed to gaze upon the table with silent expectation : but this I easily excused. Men of wisdom, thought I, are ever slow of speech ; they deliver nothing unadvisedly. "Silence," says Confucius, "is a friend that will never betray." They are now probably inventing maxims or hard sayings for their mutual instruction, when some one shall think proper to begin.

My curiosity was now wrought up to the highest pitch ; I

impatiently looked round, to see if any were going to interrupt the mighty pause; when at last one of the company declared that there was a sow in his neighborhood that farrowed
fifteen pigs at a litter. This I thought a very preposterous
beginning; but just as another was going to second the remark dinner was served, which interrupted the conversation
for that time.

The appearance of dinner, which consisted of a variety of
dishes, seemed to diffuse new cheerfulness upon every face; so
that I now expected the philosophical conversation to begin,
as they improved in good-humor. The principal priest, however, opened his mouth with only observing that the venison
had not been kept enough, though he had given strict orders
for having it killed ten days before. "I fear," continued he,
"it will be found to want the true heathy flavor; you will
find nothing of the original wildness in it." A priest, who
sat next him, having smelled it and wiped his nose, "Ah, my
good lord," cries he, "you are too modest—it is perfectly fine;
everybody knows that nobody understands keeping venison
with your lordship." "Ay, and partridges too," interrupted
another; "I never find them right anywhere else." His lordship was going to reply, when a third took off the attention
of the company, by recommending the pig as inimitable. "I
fancy, my lord," continues he, "it has been smothered in its
own blood." "If it has been smothered in its own blood,"
cried a facetious member, helping himself, "we'll now smother it in egg-sauce." This poignant piece of humor produced
a long, loud laugh, which the facetious brother observing, and,
now that he was in luck, willing to second his blow, assured
the company he would tell them a good story about that:
"As good a story," cries he, bursting into a violent fit of
laughter himself, "as ever you heard in your lives. There
was a farmer in my parish who used to sup upon wild ducks
and flummery: so this farmer"—"Doctor Marrowfat," cries
his lordship, interrupting him, "give me leave to drink your
health"—"so being fond of wild ducks and flummery"—
"Doctor," adds a gentleman who sat next him, "let me advise
you to a wing of this turkey"—"so this farmer being fond"

—"Hob nob, doctor, which do you choose, white or red?"—
"so, being fond of wild ducks and flummery"—"Take care
of your band, sir, it may dip in the gravy." The doctor, now
looking round, found not a single *eye* disposed to listen;
wherefore, calling for a glass of wine, he gulped down the
disappointment and the tale in a bumper.[1]

The conversation now began to be little more than a rhapsody of exclamations: as each had pretty well satisfied his
own appetite he now found sufficient time to press others.
"Excellent! the very thing! let me recommend the pig: do
but taste the bacon; never eat a better thing in my life:
exquisite! delicious!" This edifying discourse continued
through three courses, which lasted as many hours, till every
one of the company were unable to swallow or utter anything more.

It is very natural for men who are abridged in one excess
to break into some other. The clergy here, particularly those
who are advanced in years, think, if they are abstemious with
regard to women and wine, they may indulge their other ap-

---

[1] "I would refer the reader to George Selwyn's 'Correspondence,' if he would
desire to study attentively one of the latest full-blown specimens of the breed of
clergymen engendered by this system, and introduce himself to by no means one
of the most objectionable of the smoking, reading, claret-drinking, toadying, gor-
mandizing, good-humored parsons of the time when Goldsmith lived and wrote.
He will find Doctor Warner quite an ornament to the Establishment throughout
that book, and only cursing, flinging, stamping, or gnashing when anything goes
amiss with Selwyn. He will observe that the reverend doctor is ready to wager
his best cassock against a dozen of claret any day; and that the holy man would
quote you even texts with the most pious of his cloth, 'if our friend the countess
had not blasted them.' In short, at whatever page he opens the 'Correspondence,'
he will find parson Warner in the highest possible spirits, whether quizzing 'cant-
ing pot-bellied justices,' contemplating with equanimity 'a fine corpse at Surgeons'
Hall,' or looking forward with hopeful vivacity to the time when he shall 'be a fine
gray-headed old jollocks of sixty-five.' They who would hastily accuse Fielding
of exaggeration in his portraitures taken from the Church should first contemplate
this. Goldsmith is less severe in his exposure, but it is efficient, too; and I confess I never read a letter of Doctor Warner's, or think of his guzzling, his telling
the same story over and over again, and his indifference to any kind of treatment
shown him or service exacted of him so long as his bumper of claret is well filled,
without being forcibly reminded of Doctor Marrowfat."—FORSTER's *Life of Goldsmith*, vol. i. p. 278.

petites without censure. Thus some are found to rise in the morning only to a consultation with their cook about dinner, and, when that has been swallowed, make no other use of their faculties (if they have any) but to ruminate on the succeeding meal.

A debauch of wine is even more pardonable than this, since one glass insensibly leads on to another, and instead of sating whets the appetite. The progressive steps to it are cheerful and seducing; the grave are animated, the melancholy relieved, and there is even classic authority to countenance the excess. But in eating, after nature is once satisfied, every additional morsel brings stupidity and distempers with it; and, as one of their own poets expresses it,

> " The soul subsides, and wickedly inclines
> To seem but mortal, e'en in sound divines." [1]

Let me suppose, after such a meal as this I have been describing, while all the company are sitting in lethargic silence round the table, groaning under a load of soup, pig, pork, and bacon—let me suppose, I say, some hungry beggar with looks of want peeping through one of the windows and thus addressing the assembly: " Prithee, pluck those napkins from your chins; after nature is satisfied, all that you eat extraordinary is my property, and I claim it as mine. It was given you in order to relieve me, and not to oppress yourselves. How can they comfort or instruct others who can scarce feel their own existence, except from the unsavory returns of an ill-digested meal? But though neither you nor the cushions you sit upon will hear me, yet the world regards the excesses of its teachers with a prying eye, and notes their conduct with double severity." I know no other answer any one of the company could make to such an expostulation but this:

---

[1] " How pale, each worshipful and reverend guest
Rise from a clergy or a City feast!
What life in all that ample body, say?
What heav'nly particle inspires the clay?
The soul subsides, and wickedly inclines
To seem but mortal, e'en in sound divines."—POPE.

" Friend, you talk of our losing a character, and being disliked by the world; well, and supposing all this to be true, what then? who cares for the world? We'll preach for the world, and the world shall pay us for preaching, whether we like each other or not."

LETTER LIX.

THE CHINESE PHILOSOPHER'S SON ESCAPES WITH THE BEAUTIFUL CAPTIVE FROM SLAVERY.

From Hingpo to Lien Chi Altangi, by the way of Moscow.

You will probably be pleased to see my letter dated from Terki, a city which lies beyond the bounds of the Persian Empire: here, blessed with security, with all that is dear, I double my raptures by communicating them to you; the mind sympathizing with the freedom of the body, my whole soul is dilated in gratitude, love, and praise.

Yet were my own happiness all that inspired my present joy, my raptures might justly merit the imputation of self-interest; but when I think that the beautiful Zelis is also free, forgive my triumph when I boast of having rescued from captivity the most deserving object upon earth.

You remember the reluctance she testified at being obliged to marry the tyrant she hated. Her compliance at last was only feigned, in order to gain time to try some future means of escape. During the interval between her promise and the intended performance of it, she came undiscovered one evening to the place where I generally retired after the fatigues of the day: her appearance was like that of an aerial genius, when it descends to minister comfort to undeserved distress; the mild lustre of her eye served to banish my timidity; her accents were sweeter than the echo of some distant symphony! "Unhappy stranger," said she, in the Persian language, "you here perceive one more wretched than thyself! All this solemnity of preparation, this elegance of dress, and the number of my attendants, serve but to increase my miseries; if you have courage to rescue an unhappy woman from approaching ruin and our detested tyrant you may depend upon my future gratitude." I bowed to the ground, and she left me filled with rapture and astonishment. Night brought no rest, nor could the ensuing morning calm the anxieties of my mind. I projected a thousand methods for her delivery; but each, when strictly examined, appeared impracticable: in this uncertainty the evening again arrived, and I placed myself on my former station in hopes of a repeated visit. After some short expectation the bright perfection again appeared: I bowed as before to the ground; when, raising me up, she observed that the time was not to be spent in useless ceremony; she observed that the day following was appointed for the celebration of her nuptials, and that something was to be done that very night for our mutual deliverance. I offered with the utmost humility to pursue whatever scheme she should direct: upon which she proposed that instant to scale the garden wall, adding that she had prevailed upon a female slave, who was now waiting at the appointed place, to assist her with a ladder.

Pursuant to this information, I led her trembling to the place appointed; but instead of the slave we expected to see, Mostadad himself was there awaiting our arrival: the wretch in whom we confided, it seems, had betrayed our design to her master, and he now saw the most convincing proofs of her information. He was just going to draw his sabre, when a principle of avarice repressed his fury, and he resolved, after a severe chastisement, to dispose of me to another master; in the mean time he ordered me to be confined in the strictest manner, and the next day to receive a hundred blows on the soles of my feet.

When the morning came I was led out in order to receive the punishment, which, from the severity with which it is generally inflicted upon slaves, is worse even than death.

A trumpet was to be the signal for the solemnization of the nuptials of Zelis, and for the infliction of my punishment. Each ceremony, to me equally dreadful, was just going to begin, when we were informed that a large body of Circassian

Tartars had invaded the town, and were laying all in ruin. Every person now thought only of saving himself. I instantly unloosed the cords with which I was bound, and seizing a cimeter from one of the slaves, who had not courage to resist me, flew to the women's apartment where Zelis was confined, dressed out for the intended nuptials. I bade her follow me without delay, and going forward, cut my way through eunuchs, who made but a faint resistance. The whole city was now a scene of conflagration and terror; every person was willing to save himself, unmindful of others. In this confusion, seizing upon two of the fleetest coursers in the stable of Mostadad, we fled northward towards the kingdom of Circassia. As there were several others flying in the same manner we passed without notice, and in three days arrived at Terki, a city that lies in a valley within the bosom of the frowning mountains of Caucasus. Here, free from every apprehension of danger, we enjoy all those satisfactions which are consistent with virtue; though I find my heart at intervals give way to unusual passions, yet such is my admiration for my fair companion that I lose even tenderness in distant respect. Though her person demands particular regard even among the beauties of Circassia, yet is her mind far more lovely. How very different is a woman who thus has cultivated her understanding, and been refined into delicacy of sentiment, from the daughters of the East, whose education is only formed to improve the person, and make them more tempting objects of prostitution. Adieu.

LETTER LX.

THE HISTORY OF THE BEAUTIFUL CAPTIVE.

From Hingpo to Lien Chi Altangi, by the way of Moscow.

WHEN sufficiently refreshed after the fatigues of our precipitate flight, my curiosity, which had been restrained by the appearance of immediate danger, now began to revive; I longed to know by what distressful accidents my fair fugitive became a captive, and could not avoid testifying a surprise how so much beauty could be involved in the calamities from whence she had been so lately rescued.

"Talk not of personal charms," cried she, with emotion, "since to them I owe every misfortune. Look round on the numberless beauties of the country where we are, and see how nature has poured its charms upon every face; and yet by this profusion Heaven would seem to show how little it regards such a blessing, since the gift is lavished upon a nation of prostitutes.

"I perceive you desire to know my story, and your curiosity is not so great as my impatience to gratify it. I find a pleasure in telling past misfortunes to any, but when my deliverer is pleased with the relation my pleasure is prompted by duty.

"I was born in a country far to the west, where the men are braver and the women more fair than those of Circassia; where the valor of the hero is guided by wisdom, and where delicacy of sentiment points the shafts of female beauty.[1] I was the only daughter of an officer in the army, the child of his age, and, as he used fondly to express it, the only chain that bound him to the world or made his life pleasing. His station procured him an acquaintance with men of greater rank and fortune than himself, and his regard for me induced him to bring me into every family where he was acquainted. Thus I was early taught all the elegancies and fashionable foibles of such as the world calls polite, and though without fortune myself, was taught to despise those who lived as if they were poor.

"My intercourse with the great, and my affectation of

---

[1] "This story bears a striking similitude to the real history of Miss S——d, who accompanied Lady W——e in her retreat near Florence, and which the editor had from her own mouth."—GOLDSMITH. This eccentric lady was the daughter of Samuel Rolle, Esq., of Haynton, Devon. She married in 1724 Robert, afterwards second Earl of Orford; and again, in 1751, Mr. Sewallis Shirley, son of Lord Ferrers, from whom she was parted, as she had been from her first husband. In 1742 Count Richecourt, the chief minister at Florence, was her lover. She died at Pisa in 1781, "leaving," says Lord Orford, "everything in her power to her *friend* cavalier Mozzif, at Florence." See WALPOLE'S *Correspondence*, vol. iv. p. 241.

grandeur, procured me many lovers; but want of fortune deterred them all from any other views than those of passing the present moment agreeably, or of meditating my future ruin. In every company I found myself addressed in a warmer strain of passion than other ladies who were superior in point of rank and beauty; and this I imputed to an excess of respect, which in reality proceeded from very different motives.

"Among the number of such as paid me their addresses was a gentleman, a friend of my father, rather in the decline of life, with nothing remarkable either in his person or address to recommend him. His age, which was about forty, his fortune, which was moderate and barely sufficient to support him, served to throw me off my guard, so that I considered him as the only sincere admirer I had.

"Designing lovers in the decline of life are ever most dangerous. Skilled in all the weaknesses of the sex, they seize each favorable opportunity; and by having less passion than youthful admirers, have less real respect, and therefore less timidity. This insidious wretch used a thousand arts to succeed in his base designs, all which I saw, but imputed to different views, because I thought it absurd to believe the real motives.

"As he continued to frequent my father's, the friendship between them became every day greater; and at last, from the intimacy with which he was received, I was taught to look upon him as a guardian and a friend. Though I never loved yet I esteemed him; and this was enough to make me wish for a union, for which he seemed desirous, but to which he feigned several delays; while in the mean time, from a false report of our being married, every other admirer forsook me.

"I was at last, however, awakened from the delusion by an account of his being just married to another young lady with a considerable fortune. This was no great mortification to me, as I had always regarded him merely from prudential motives; but it had a very different effect upon my father, who, rash and passionate by nature, and besides stimulated by

a mistaken notion of military honor, upbraided his friend in
such terms that a challenge was soon given and accepted.

"It was about midnight when I was awakened by a message from my father, who desired to see me that moment. I
rose with some surprise, and, following the messenger, attended only by another servant, came to a field not far from the
house, where I found him, the assertor of my honor, my only
friend and supporter, the tutor and companion of my youth,
lying on one side covered over with blood, and just expiring.
No tears streamed down my cheeks nor sigh escaped from
my breast at an object of such terror. I sat down, and, supporting his aged head in my lap, gazed upon the ghastly
visage with an agony more poignant even than despairing
madness. The servants were gone for more assistance. In
this gloomy stillness of the night no sounds were heard but
his agonizing respiration; no object was presented but his
wounds, which still continued to stream. With silent anguish I hung over his dear face, and with my hands strove to
stop the blood as it flowed from his wounds. He seemed at
first insensible, but at last turning his dying eyes upon me,
'My dear, dear child,' cried he—'dear, though you have forgotten your own honor and stained mine—I will yet forgive
you; by abandoning virtue you have undone me and yourself, yet take my forgiveness with the same compassion I
wish Heaven may pity me.' He expired. All my succeeding
happiness fled with him. Reflecting that I was the cause of
his death, whom only I loved upon earth; accused of betraying
the honor of his family with his latest breath; conscious of my
own innocence, yet without even a possibility of vindicating
it; without fortune or friends to relieve or pity me; abandoned to infamy and the wide, censuring world, I called out upon
the dead body that lay stretched before me, and in the agony
of my heart asked why he could have left me thus! 'Why,
my dear, my only papa—why could you ruin me thus and
yourself forever? Oh, pity and return, since there is none but
you to comfort me!'

"I soon found that I had real cause for sorrow; that I was
to expect no compassion from my own sex, nor assistance

from the other ; and that reputation was much more useful
in our commerce with mankind than really to deserve it.
Wherever I came, I perceived myself received either with
contempt or detestation ; or whenever I was civilly treated it
was from the most base and ungenerous motives.

"Thus driven from the society of the virtuous, I was at
last, in order to dispel the anxieties of insupportable solitude,
obliged to take up with the company of those whose characters were blasted like my own; but who, perhaps, deserved
their infamy. Among this number was a lady of the first
distinction, whose character the public thought proper to
brand even with greater infamy than mine. A similitude of
distress soon united us; I knew that general reproach had
made her miserable ; and I had learned to regard misery as an
excuse for guilt. Though this lady had not virtue enough to
avoid reproach, yet she had too much delicate sensibility not
to feel it. She therefore proposed our leaving the country
where we were born, and going to live in Italy, where our
characters and misfortunes would be unknown. With this I
eagerly complied, and we soon found ourselves in one of the
most charming retreats in the most beautiful province of that
enchanting country.

"Had my companion chosen this as a retreat for injured
virtue, a harbor where we might look with tranquillity on
the distant angry world, I should have been happy; but very
different was her design ; she had pitched upon this situation
only to enjoy those pleasures in private which she had not
sufficient effrontery to satisfy in a more open manner. A
nearer acquaintance soon showed me the vicious part of her
character ; her mind, as well as her body, seemed formed only
for pleasure ; she was sentimental only as it served to protract the immediate enjoyment. Formed for society alone,
she spoke infinitely better than she wrote, and wrote infinitely
better than she lived. A person devoted to pleasure often
leads the most miserable life imaginable ; such was her case ;
she considered the natural moments of languor as insupportable, passed all her hours between rapture and anxiety ; ever
in an extreme of agony or of bliss. She felt a pain as sincere

for want of appetite as the starving wretch who wants a meal. In those intervals she usually kept her bed, and rose only when in expectation of some new enjoyment. The luxuriant air of the country, the romantic situation of her palace, and the genius of a people whose only happiness lies in sensual refinement, all contributed to banish the remembrance of her native country.

"But though such a life gave her pleasure it had a very different effect upon me; I grew every day more pensive, and my melancholy was regarded as an insult upon her good-humor. I now perceived myself entirely unfit for all society; discarded from the good, and detesting the infamous, I seemed in a state of war with every rank of people; that virtue, which should have been my protection in the world, was here my crime: in short, detesting life, I was determined to become a recluse, to leave a world where I found no pleasure that could allure me to stay. Thus determined, I embarked in order to go by sea to Rome, where I intended to take the veil; but even in so short a passage my hard fortune still attended me: our ship was taken by a Barbary corsair—the whole crew, and I among the number, being made slaves. It carries too much the air of romance to inform you of my distresses or obstinacy in this miserable state; it is enough to observe that I have been bought by several masters, each of whom perceiving my reluctance, rather than use violence, sold me to another, till it was my happiness to be at last rescued by you."

Thus ended her relation, which I have abridged; but as soon as we are arrived at Moscow, for which we intend to set out shortly, you shall be informed of all more particularly. In the mean time the greatest addition to my happiness will be to hear of yours. Adieu.

LETTER LXI.[1]

PROPER LESSONS TO A YOUTH ENTERING THE WORLD, WITH
FABLES SUITED TO THE OCCASION.

From Lien Chi Altangi to Hingpo.

THE news of your freedom lifts the load of former anxiety
from my mind. I can now think of my son without regret,
applaud his resignation under calamities, and his conduct in
extricating himself from them.

You are now free, just let loose from the bondage of a
hard master. This is the crisis of your fate; and as you now
manage fortune, succeeding life will be marked with happiness or misery. A few years' perseverance in prudence, which
at your age is but another name for virtue, will insure comfort, pleasure, tranquillity, esteem; too eager an enjoyment of
every good that now offers will reverse the medal, and present you with poverty, anxiety, remorse, contempt.

[2]As it has been observed that none are better qualified to
give others advice than those who have taken the least of it
themselves, so in this respect I find myself perfectly authorized
to offer mine, even though I should waive my paternal authority upon this occasion.[3]

The most usual way among young men who have no resolution of their own is first to ask one friend's advice and follow it for some time; then to ask advice of another, and turn
to that; so of a third, still unsteady, always changing. However, be assured that every change of this nature is for the

---

[1] Partly reprinted in Essays, 1765, as Essay XII.

[2] With this sentence Essay XII. afterwards commenced.

[3] The words "even though I should waive my paternal authority upon this occasion" were altered in 1765 to "and must take leave to throw together a few observations upon that part of a young man's conduct on his entering into life, as it
is called"—and thus they stand in the second edition of the Essays, 1766.

worse: people may tell you of your being unfit for some peculiar occupations in life, but heed them not; whatever employment you follow with perseverance and assiduity will be found fit for you; it will be your support in youth and comfort in age. In learning the useful part of every profession very moderate abilities will suffice; even if the mind be a little balanced with stupidity, it may in this case be useful. Great abilities have always been less serviceable to the possessors than moderate ones.[1] Life has been compared to a race, but the allusion still improves by observing that the most swift are ever the least manageable.[2]

To know one profession only is enough for one man to know; and this (whatever the professors may tell you to the contrary) is soon learned. Be contented, therefore, with one good employment; for if you understand two at a time people will give you business in neither.

A conjurer and a tailor once happened to converse together. "Alas," cries the tailor, "what an unhappy poor creature am I! if people should ever take it in their heads to live without clothes I am undone; I have no other trade to have recourse to." "Indeed, friend, I pity you sincerely," replies the conjurer; "but, thank Heaven, things are not quite so bad with me; for if one trick should fail I have a hundred tricks more for them yet. However, if at any time you are reduced to beggary, apply to me and I will relieve you." A famine overspread the land; the tailor made a shift to live, because his customers could not be without clothes; but the poor conjurer, with all his hundred tricks, could find none that had money to throw away: it was in vain that he promised to eat fire, or to vomit pins; no single creature would relieve him, till he was at last obliged to beg from the very tailor whose calling he had formerly despised.

There are no obstructions more fatal to fortune than pride and resentment. If you must resent injuries at all, at least suppress your indignation until you become rich, and then

---

[1] "Great abilities are generally obnoxious to the possessors."—*Essays*, 1765 and 1766.

[2] "Most apt to stray from the course."—*Essays*, 1765 and 1766.

show away: the resentment of a poor man is like the efforts of a harmless insect to sting; it may get him crushed, but cannot defend him. Who values that anger which is consumed only in empty menaces?

Once upon a time a goose fed its young by a pond-side; and a goose in such circumstances is always extremely proud and excessive punctilious. If any other animal, without the least design to offend, happened to pass that way, the goose was immediately at him. The pond, she said, was hers, and she would maintain a right in it, and support her honor, while she had a bill to hiss or a wing to flutter. In this manner she drove away ducks, pigs, and chickens; nay, even the insidious cat was seen to scamper. A lounging mastiff, however, happened to pass by, and thought it no harm if he should lap a little of the water, as he was thirsty. The guardian goose flew at him like a fury, pecked at him with her beak, and sapped him with her feathers. The dog grew angry, had twenty times a good mind to give her a sly snap; but suppressing his indignation, because his master was nigh, "A pox take thee," cries he, "for a fool! sure, those who have neither strength nor weapons to fight at least should be civil, [that fluttering and hissing of thine may one day get thine head snapped off, but it can neither injure thy enemies or ever protect thee]."[1] So saying, he went forward to the pond, quenched his thirst in spite of the goose, and followed his master.

Another obstruction to the fortune of youth is that, while they are willing to take offence from none, they are also equally desirous of giving nobody offence. From hence they endeavor to please all, comply with every request, attempt to suit themselves to every company, have no will of their own, but like wax catch every contiguous impression. By thus attempting to give universal satisfaction, they at last find themselves miserably disappointed: to bring the generality of admirers on our side, it is sufficient to attempt pleasing a very few.

---

[1] The passage in brackets [ ] is not in the Essays, 1765 and 1766.

A painter of eminence was once resolved to finish a piece which should please the whole world. When, therefore, he had drawn a picture in which his utmost skill was exhausted, it was exposed in the public market-place, with directions at the bottom for every spectator to mark with a brush, which lay by, every limb and feature which seemed erroneous. The spectators came, and in general applauded; but each, willing to show his talent at criticism, marked whatever he thought proper. At evening, when the painter came, he was mortified to find the whole picture one universal blot; not a single stroke that was not stigmatized with marks of disapprobation. Not satisfied with this trial, the next day he was resolved to try them in a different manner, and, exposing his picture as before, desired that every spectator would mark those beauties he approved or admired. The people complied; and the artist returning found his picture replete with the marks of beauty; every stroke that had been yesterday condemned now received the character of approbation. "Well," cries the painter, "I now find that the best way to please one-half of the world is not to mind what the other half says; since what are faults in the eyes of these, shall be by those regarded as beauties."[1] Adieu.

LETTER LXII.

HISTORY OF CATHARINA ALEXOWNA, WIFE OF PETER THE GREAT.

From the Same.

A CHARACTER, such as you have represented that of your fair companion, which continues virtuous though loaded with infamy, is truly great. Many regard virtue because it is attended with applause; your favorite only for the internal pleasure it confers. I have often wished that ladies like her were proposed as models for female imitation, and not such

---

[1] "Well," cries the painter, "I now find that the best way to please all the world is to attempt pleasing one-half of it."—*Essays*, 1765 and 1766.

as have acquired fame by qualities repugnant to the natural softness of the sex.

Women famed for their valor, their skill in politics, or their learning, leave the duties of their own sex in order to invade the privileges of ours. I can no more pardon a fair one for endeavoring to wield the club of Hercules than I could him for attempting to twirl her distaff.

The modest virgin, the prudent wife, or the careful matron are much more serviceable in life than petticoated philosophers, blustering heroines, or virago queens. She who makes her husband and her children happy, who reclaims the one from vice and trains up the other to virtue, is a much greater character than ladies described in romance, whose whole occupation is to murder mankind with shafts from their quiver or their eyes.

Women, it has been observed, are not naturally formed for great cares themselves, but to soften ours. Their tenderness is the proper reward for the dangers we undergo for their preservation; and the ease and cheerfulness of their conversation, our desirable retreat from the fatigues of intense application. They are confined within the narrow limits of domestic assiduity; and when they stray beyond them, they move beyond their sphere, and consequently without grace.[1]

Fame, therefore, has been very unjustly dispensed among the female sex. Those who least deserved to be remembered meet our admiration and applause; while many, who have been an honor to humanity, are passed over in silence. Perhaps no age has produced a stronger instance of misplaced fame than the present: the Semiramis and the Thalestris of antiquity are talked of, while a modern character, infinitely greater than either, is unnoticed and unknown.

Catharina Alexowna,[2] born near Derpat, a little city in Livonia, was heir to no other inheritance than the virtues and frugality of her parents. Her father being dead, she lived with her aged mother in their cottage covered with straw;

---

[1] Compare Vol. III. p. 322.

[2] This account seems taken from the manuscript memoirs of H. Spilman, Esq.— GOLDSMITH.

and both, though very poor, were very contented. Here, retired from the gaze of the world, by the labor of her hands she supported her parent, who was now incapable of supporting herself. While Catharina spun, the old woman would sit by and read some book of devotion; thus, when the fatigues of the day were over, both would sit down contentedly by their fireside, and enjoy the frugal meal with vacant festivity.

Though her face and person were models of perfection, yet her whole attention seemed bestowed upon her mind; her mother taught her to read, and an old Lutheran minister instructed her in the maxims and duties of religion. Nature had furnished her not only with a ready but a solid turn of thought—not only with a strong but a right understanding. Such truly female accomplishments procured her several solicitations of marriage from the peasants of the country; but their offers were refused, for she loved her mother too tenderly to think of a separation.

Catharina was fifteen when her mother died; she now, therefore, left her cottage, and went to live with the Lutheran minister by whom she had been instructed from her childhood. In his house she resided in quality of governess to his children; at once reconciling in her character unerring prudence with surprising vivacity.

The old man, who regarded her as one of his own children, had her instructed in dancing and music by the masters who attended the rest of his family; thus she continued to improve till he died, by which accident she was once more reduced to pristine poverty. The country of Livonia was at this time wasted by war, and lay in a most miserable state of desolation. Those calamities are ever most heavy upon the poor; wherefore Catharina, though possessed of so many accomplishments, experienced all the miseries of hopeless indigence. Provisions becoming every day more scarce, and her private stock being entirely exhausted, she resolved at last to travel to Marienburg, a city of greater plenty.

With her scanty wardrobe packed up in a wallet, she set out on her journey on foot; she was to walk through a region miserable by nature, but rendered still more hideous by the Swedes and Russians, who, as each happened to become masters, plundered it at discretion ; but hunger had taught her to despise the dangers and fatigues of the way.

One evening upon her journey, as she had entered a cottage by the wayside, to take up her lodging for the night, she was insulted by two Swedish soldiers, who insisted upon qualifying her, as they termed it, to follow the camp. They might probably have carried their insults into violence, had not a subaltern officer, accidentally passing by, come in to her assistance ; upon his appearing, the soldiers immediately desisted ; but her thankfulness was hardly greater than her surprise when she instantly recollected in her deliverer the son of the Lutheran minister, her former instructor, benefactor, and friend.

This was a happy interview for Catharina : the little stock of money she had brought from home was by this time quite exhausted ; her clothes were gone, piece by piece, in order to satisfy those who had entertained her in their houses. Her generous countryman, therefore, parted with what he could spare to buy her clothes, furnished her with a horse, and gave her letters of recommendation to Mr. Gluck, a faithful friend of his father's and superintendent of Marienburg.

Our beautiful stranger had only to appear to be well received ; she was immediately admitted into the superintendent's family as governess to his two daughters ; and though yet but seventeen, showed herself capable of instructing her sex not only in virtue but politeness. Such was her good sense and beauty, that her master himself in a short time offered her his hand, which, to his great surprise, she thought proper to refuse. Actuated by a principle of gratitude, she was resolved to marry her deliverer only, even though he had lost an arm, and was otherwise disfigured by wounds in the service.

In order, therefore, to prevent further solicitations from others, as soon as the officer came to town upon duty she offered him her person, which he accepted with transport, and their nuptials were solemnized as usual. But all the lines of her fortune were to be striking : the very day on which they were married the Russians laid siege to Marienburg. The unhappy soldier had now no time to enjoy the well-earned pleasures of matrimony; he was called off before consummation to an attack, from which he was never after seen to return.

In the mean time the siege went on with fury, aggravated on one side by obstinacy, on the other by revenge. This war between the two Northern powers at that time was truly barbarous; the innocent peasant and the harmless virgin often shared the fate of the soldier in arms. Marienburg was taken by assault; and such was the fury of the assailants, that not only the garrison, but almost all the inhabitants—men, women, and children—were put to the sword. At length, when the carnage was pretty well over, Catharina was found hid in an oven.

She had been hitherto poor, but still was free; she was now to conform to her hard fate, and learn what it was to be a slave: in this situation, however, she behaved with piety and humility; and though misfortunes had abated her vivacity, yet she was cheerful. The fame of her merit and resignation reached even Prince Menzikoff, the Russian general: he desired to see her, was struck with her beauty, bought her from the soldier her master, and placed her under the direction of his own sister. Here she was treated with all the respect which her merit deserved, while her beauty every day improved with her good fortune.

She had not been long in this situation, when Peter the Great, paying the prince a visit, Catharina happened to come in with some dry fruits, which she served round with peculiar modesty. The mighty monarch saw and was struck with her beauty. He returned the next day, called for the beautiful slave, asked her several questions, and found her understanding even more perfect than her person.

He had been forced when young to marry from motives of interest; he was now resolved to marry pursuant to his own inclinations. He immediately inquired the history of the fair Livonian, who was not yet eighteen. He traced her through the vale of obscurity, through all the vicissitudes of her fortune, and found her truly great in them all. The meanness of her birth was no obstruction to his design; their nuptials were solemnized in private, the prince assuring his courtiers that virtue alone was the properest ladder to a throne.

We now see Catharina, from the low mud-walled cottage, empress of the greatest kingdom upon earth. The poor solitary wanderer is now surrounded by thousands who find happiness in her smile. She who formerly wanted a meal is now capable of diffusing plenty upon whole nations. To her fortune she owed a part of this pre-eminence, but to her virtues more.[1]

She ever after retained those great qualities which first placed her on a throne; and while the extraordinary prince, her husband, labored for the reformation of his male subjects, she studied in her turn the improvement of her own sex. She altered their dresses, introduced mixed assemblies, instituted an order of female knighthood; and at length, when she had greatly filled all the stations of empress, friend, wife, and mother, bravely died without regret, regretted by all. Adieu.

LETTER LXIII.

THE RISE OR THE DECLINE OF LITERATURE NOT DEPENDENT ON MAN, BUT RESULTING FROM THE VICISSITUDES OF NATURE.

From Lien Chi Altangi to Fum Hoam, first President of the Ceremonial Academy at Pekin, in China.

In every letter I expect accounts of some new revolutions in China, some strange occurrence in the state, or disaster among my private acquaintance. I open every packet with tremulous expectation, and am agreeably disappointed when I find my friends and my country continuing in felicity. I

---

[1] "There have been," says Voltaire, "instances, before this, of private persons being raised to the throne; but that a poor stranger, who had been discovered amid the ruins of a plundered town, should become the absolute sovereign of that very empire into which she was led captive, is an incident which fortune and merit have never before produced in the annals of the world."

wander, but they are at rest; they suffer few changes but what pass in my own restless imagination; it is only the rapidity of my own motion that gives an imaginary swiftness to objects which are in some measure immovable.[1]

Yet believe me, my friend, that even China itself is imperceptibly degenerating from her ancient greatness: her laws are now more venal, and her merchants are more deceitful than formerly; the very arts and sciences have run to decay. Observe the carvings on our ancient bridges; figures that add grace even to nature. There is not an artist now in all the empire that can imitate their beauty. Our manufactures in porcelain, too, are inferior to what we once were famous for; and even Europe now begins to excel us. There was a time when China was the receptacle of strangers; when all were welcome who either came to improve the state, or admire its greatness: now, the empire is shut up from every foreign improvement, and the very inhabitants discourage each other from prosecuting their own internal advantages.

Whence this degeneracy in a state so little subject to external revolutions? how happens it that China, which is now more powerful than ever, which is less subject to foreign invasions, and even assisted in some discoveries by her connections with Europe; whence comes it, I say, that the empire is thus declining so fast into barbarity?

This decay is surely from nature, and not the result of voluntary degeneracy. In a period of two or three thousand years she seems at proper intervals to produce great minds, with an effort resembling that which introduces the vicissitudes of seasons. They rise up at once, continue for an age, enlighten the world, fall like ripened corn, and mankind again gradually relapse into pristine barbarity. We little ones look around, are amazed at the decline, seek after the causes of this invisible decay, attribute to want of encouragement what really proceeds from want of power, are astonished to find

---

[1] " Before my brother Charles came hither, my thoughts sometimes found refuge from severe studies among my friends in Ireland. I fancied strange revolutions at home; but I find it was the rapidity of my own motion that gave an imaginary one to objects really at rest."—GOLDSMITH *to D. Hodson, Esq.*, Dec. 27, 1757.

every art and every science in the decline, not considering that autumn is over, and fatigued nature again begins to repose for some succeeding effort.

Some periods have been remarkable for the production of men of extraordinary stature, others for producing some particular animals in great abundance; some for excessive plenty, and others again for seemingly causeless famine. Nature, which shows herself so very different in her visible productions, must surely differ also from herself in the production of minds, and while she astonishes one age with the strength and stature of Milo or a Maximin, may bless another with the wisdom of a Plato, or the goodness of an Antonine.

Let us not, then, attribute to accident the falling off of every nation, but to the natural revolution of things. Often in the darkest ages there has appeared some one man of surprising abilities, who, with all his understanding, failed to bring his barbarous age into refinement: all mankind seemed to sleep till nature gave the general call, and then the whole world seemed at once roused at the voice; science triumphed in every country, and the brightness of a single genius seemed lost in a galaxy of contiguous glory.

Thus, the enlightened periods in every age have been universal. At the time when China first began to emerge from barbarity, the Western world was equally rising into refinement; when we had our Yaou,[1] they had their Sesostris. In succeeding ages Confucius[2] and Pythagoras seem born nearly

---

[1] Yaou, the pattern of all Chinese emperors, is said to have commenced his reign 2357 years before Christ. According to the Shoo-king (one of the five canonical works), he commissioned Hi and Ho, and other eminent astronomers, to observe the revolutions of the heavens, and to proclaim the periods of the different seasons. By the assistance of these learned men, he fixed the length of the year at $365\frac{1}{4}$ days, and at 366 in every fourth year.—See DAVIS's *Chinese*, vol. i. p. 171.

[2] "The family of Confucius is, in my opinion, the most illustrious in the world. After a painful ascent of eight or ten centuries, our barons and princes of Europe are lost in the darkness of the Middle Ages; but, in the vast equality of the empire of China, the posterity of Confucius have maintained, above two thousand two hundred years, this peaceful honor and perpetual succession. The chief of the family is still revered, by the sovereign and the people, as the lively image of the wisest of mankind."—GIBBON, *Miscellaneous Works*, vol. i. p. 3.

together, and a train of philosophers then sprung up as well in Greece as in China. The period of renewed barbarity began to have a universal spread much about the same time, and continued for several centuries, till, in the year of the Christian era 1400, the emperor Yong-lo [1] arose to revive the learning of the East; while, about the same time, the Medicean family labored in Italy to raise infant genius from the cradle.[2] Thus, we see politeness spreading over every part of the world in one age, and barbarity succeeding in another—at one period a blaze of light diffusing itself over the whole world, and at another all mankind wrapped up in the profoundest ignorance.

Such has been the situation of things in times past; and such probably it will ever be. China, I have observed, has evidently begun to degenerate from its former politeness; and, were the learning of the Europeans at present candidly considered, the decline would perhaps appear to have already taken place. We should find among the natives of the West the study of morality displaced for mathematical disquisition or metaphysical subtleties; we should find learning begin to separate from the useful duties and concerns of life, while none ventured to aspire after that character, but they who know much more than is truly amusing or useful. We should find every great attempt suppressed by prudence, and the rapturous sublimity in writing cooled by a cautious fear of offence. We should find few of those daring spirits, who bravely venture to be wrong, and who are willing to hazard much for the sake of great acquisitions. Providence has in-

---

[1] Yong-lo ascended the throne A.D. 1400. On his accession, the capital was transferred to Pekin; and in his reign Timour, or Tamerlane, died on his way to the conquest of China.

[2] "But see! each Muse, in Leo's golden days,
Starts from her trance, and trims her wither'd bays;
Rome's ancient Genius, o'er its ruins spread,
Shakes off the dust, and rears his rev'rend head.
Then Sculpture and her sister arts revive;
Stones leaped to form, and rocks began to live:
With sweeter notes each rising temple rung;
A Raphael painted, and a Vida sung."—POPE.

II.—21

dulged the world with a period of almost four hundred years' refinement: does it not now by degrees sink us into our former ignorance, leaving us only the love of wisdom, while it deprives us of its advantages? Adieu.

LETTER LXIV.

THE GREAT EXCHANGE HAPPINESS FOR SHOW.—THEIR FOLLY IN
THIS RESPECT OF USE TO SOCIETY.

From the Same.

THE princes of Europe have found out a manner of rewarding their subjects who have behaved well, by presenting them with about two yards of blue ribbon, which is worn about the shoulder. They who are honored with this mark of distinction are called knights, and the king himself is always the head of the order. This is a very frugal method of recompensing the most important services; and it is very fortunate for kings that their subjects are satisfied with such trifling rewards. Should a nobleman happen to lose his leg in a battle, the king presents him with two yards of ribbon, and he is paid for the loss of his limb. Should an ambassador spend all his paternal fortune in supporting the honor of his country abroad, the king presents him with two yards of ribbon, which is to be considered as an equivalent to his estate. In short, while a European king has a yard of blue or green ribbon left, he need be under no apprehension of wanting statesmen, generals, and soldiers.

I cannot sufficiently admire those kingdoms in which men with large patrimonial estates are willing thus to undergo real hardships for empty favors. A person already possessed of a competent fortune, who undertakes to enter the career of ambition, feels many real inconveniences from his station, while it procures him no real happiness that he was not possessed of before. He could eat, drink, and sleep before he became a courtier as well, perhaps better, than when invested with his authority. He could command flatterers in a private

station as well as in his public capacity, and indulge at home
every favorite inclination, uncensured and unseen by the
people.

What real good, then, does an addition to a fortune already
sufficient procure? Not any. Could the great man, by having his fortune increased, increase also his appetites, then precedence might be attended with real amusement.

Was he, by having his one thousand made two, thus enabled
to enjoy two wives or eat two dinners, then, indeed, he might
be excused for undergoing some pain in order to extend the
sphere of his enjoyments. But, on the contrary, he finds his
desire for pleasure often lessen as he takes pains to be able
to improve it; and his capacity of enjoyment diminishes as
his fortune happens to increase.

Instead, therefore, of regarding the great with envy, I generally consider them with some share of compassion. I look
upon them as a set of good-natured, misguided people, who
are indebted to us and not to themselves for all the happiness
they enjoy. For our pleasure, and not their own, they sweat
under a cumbrous heap of finery; for our pleasure the lack-
eyed train, the slow parading pageant, with all the gravity of
grandeur, moves in review; a single coat, or a single footman,
answers all the purposes of the most indolent refinement as
well; and those who have twenty may be said to keep one for
their own pleasure, and the other nineteen merely for ours.
So true is the observation of Confucius, that " we take greater
pains to persuade others that we are happy than in endeavoring to think so ourselves."

But though this desire of being seen, of being made the
subject of discourse, and of supporting the dignities of an exalted station be troublesome enough to the ambitious, yet it is
well for society that there are men thus willing to exchange
ease and safety for danger and a ribbon. We lose nothing by
their vanity, and it would be unkind to endeavor to deprive a
child of its rattle. If a duke or a duchess are willing to carry
a long train for our entertainment, so much the worse for themselves; if they choose to exhibit in public, with a hundred
lackeys and Mamelukes in their equipage, for our entertain-

ment, still so much the worse for themselves; it is the spectators alone who give and receive the pleasure; they only are the sweating figures that swell the pageant.

A mandarin, who took much pride in appearing with a number of jewels on every part of his robe, was once accosted by an old sly bonze, who, following him through several streets, and bowing often to the ground, thanked him for his jewels. "What does the man mean?" cried the mandarin. "Friend, I never gave thee any of my jewels." "No," replied the other; "but you let me look at them, and that is all the use you can make of them yourself; so there is no difference between us, except that you have the trouble of watching them, and that is an employment I don't much desire." Adieu.

LETTER LXV.

THE HISTORY OF A PHILOSOPHIC COBBLER.

From the Same.

THOUGH not very fond of seeing a pageant myself, yet I am generally pleased with being in the crowd which sees it; it is amusing to observe the effect which such a spectacle has upon the variety of faces—the pleasure it excites in some, the envy in others, and the wishes it raises in all. With this design I lately went to see the entry of a foreign ambassador, resolved to make one in the mob, to shout as they shouted, to fix with earnestness upon the same frivolous objects, and participate for a while the pleasures and the wishes of the vulgar.

Struggling here for some time, in order to be first to see the cavalcade as it passed, some one of the crowd unluckily happened to tread upon my shoe, and tore it in such a manner that I was utterly unqualified to march forward with the main body, and obliged to fall back in the rear. Thus rendered incapable of being a spectator of the show myself, I was at least willing to observe the spectators, and limped behind like one of the invalids which follow the march of an army.

In this plight, as I was considering the eagerness that appeared on every face—how some bustled to get foremost, and others contented themselves with taking a transient peep when they could; how some praised the four black servants that were stuck behind one of the equipages, and some the ribbons that decorated the horses' necks in another—my attention was called off to an object more extraordinary than any that I had yet seen: a poor cobbler sat in his stall by the wayside, and continued to work while the crowd passed by, without testifying the smallest share of curiosity. I own his want of attention excited mine; and as I stood in need of his assistance, I thought it best to employ a philosophic cobbler on this occasion. Perceiving my business, therefore, he desired me to enter and sit down, took my shoe in his lap, and began to mend it with his usual indifference and taciturnity.

"How, my friend," said I to him, "can you continue to work while all those fine things are passing by your door?" " Very fine they are, master," returned the cobbler, "for those that like them, to be sure; but what are all those fine things to me? You don't know what it is to be a cobbler, and so much the better for yourself. Your bread is baked; you may go and see sights the whole day, and eat a warm supper when you come home at night; but for me, if I should run hunting after all these fine folk, what should I get by my journey but an appetite?—and, God help me! I have too much of that at home already, without stirring out for it. Your people who may eat four meals a day and a supper at night are but a bad example to such a one as I. No, master; as God has called me into this world in order to mend old shoes, I have no business with fine folk, and they no business with me." I here interrupted him with a smile. "See this last, master," continues he, "and this hammer; this last and hammer are the two best friends I have in this world; nobody else will be my friend, because I want a friend. The great folks you saw pass by just now have five hundred friends, because they have no occasion for them; now, while I stick to my good friends here, I am very contented; but when I ever so little run after sights and fine things, I begin to hate my work, I grow sad, and have no heart to mend shoes any longer."

This discourse only served to raise my curiosity to know more of a man whom nature had thus formed into a philosopher. I therefore insensibly led him into a history of his adventures. "I have lived," said he, "a wandering sort of a life now five-and-fifty years—here to-day, and gone to-morrow; for it was my misfortune, when I was young, to be fond of changing." "You have been a traveller, then, I presume?" interrupted I. "I cannot boast much of travelling," continued he, "for I have never left the parish in which I was born but three times in my life, that I can remember; but then there is not a street in the whole neighborhood that I have not lived in, at some time or another. When I began to settle, and to take to my business in one street, some unforeseen misfortune, or a desire of trying my luck elsewhere, has removed me perhaps a whole mile away from my former customers, while some more lucky cobbler would come into my place, and make a handsome fortune among friends of my making: there was one who actually died in a stall that I had left, worth seven pounds seven shillings, all in hard gold, which he had quilted into the waistband of his breeches."

I could not but smile at these migrations of a man by the fireside, and continued to ask if he had ever been married. "Ay, that I have, master," replied he, "for sixteen long years; and a weary life I had of it, Heaven knows. My wife took it into her head that the only way to thrive in this world was to save money; so, though our comings-in was but about three shillings a week, all that ever she could lay her hands upon she used to hide away from me, though we were obliged to starve the whole week after for it.

"The first three years we used to quarrel about this every day, and I always got the better; but she had a hard spirit, and still continued to hide as usual: so that I was at last tired of quarrelling and getting the better, and she scraped and scraped at pleasure, till I was almost starved to death. Her conduct drove me at last in despair to the alehouse: here I used to sit with people who hated home like myself, drank while I had money left, and run in score when anybody would trust me; till at last the landlady, coming one day with a long bill when I was from home, and putting it into my wife's hands, the length of it effectually broke her heart. I searched the whole stall after she was dead for money, but she had hidden it so effectually that, with all my pains, I could never find a farthing."

By this time my shoe was mended, and satisfying the poor artist for his trouble, and rewarding him besides for his information, I took my leave, and returned home to lengthen out the amusement his conversation afforded, by communicating it to my friend. Adieu.

LETTER LXVI.

THE DIFFERENCE BETWEEN LOVE AND GRATITUDE. — MENCIUS
AND THE HERMIT. — STORY OF THE FIDDLE-CASE.

From Lien Chi Altangi to Hingpo, by the way of Moscow.

GENEROSITY, properly applied, will supply every other external advantage in life but the love of those we converse with: it will procure esteem and a conduct resembling real affection; but actual love is the spontaneous production of the mind; no generosity can purchase, no rewards increase, nor no liberality continue it: the very person who is obliged has it not in his power to force his lingering affections upon the object he should love, and voluntarily mix passion with gratitude.

Imparted fortune, and well-placed liberality, may procure the benefactor good-will, may load the person obliged with the sense of the duty he lies under to retaliate: this is gratitude; and simple gratitude, untinctured with love, is all the return an ingenuous mind can bestow for former benefits.

But gratitude and love are almost opposite affections; love is often an involuntary passion, placed upon our companions without our consent, and frequently conferred without our previous esteem. We love some men, we know not why; our tenderness is naturally excited in all their concerns; we excuse their faults with the same indulgence, and approve their virtues with the same applause, with which we consider our own.   While we entertain the passion, it pleases us; we cherish it with delight, and give it up with reluctance; and love for love is all the reward we expect or desire.

Gratitude, on the contrary, is never conferred but where there have been previous endeavors to excite it; we consider it as a debt, and our spirits wear a load till we have discharged the obligation.   Every acknowledgment of gratitude is a circumstance of humiliation; and some are found to submit to frequent mortifications of this kind, proclaiming what obligations they owe, merely because they think it in some measure cancels the debt.

Thus love is the most easy and agreeable, and gratitude the most humiliating affection of the mind: we never reflect on the man we *love* without exulting in our choice; while he who has bound us to him by *benefits* alone rises to our idea as a person to whom we have in some measure forfeited our freedom.   Love and gratitude are seldom, therefore, found in the same breast without impairing each other; we may tender the one or the other singly to those we converse with, but cannot command both together.   By attempting to increase, we diminish them; the mind becomes bankrupt under too large obligations; all additional benefits lessen every hope of future return, and shut up every avenue that leads to tenderness.

In all our connections with society, therefore, it is not only generous but prudent to appear insensible of the value of those favors we bestow, and endeavor to make the obligation seem as slight as possible.   Love must be taken by stratagem, and not by open force: we should seem ignorant that we oblige, and leave the mind at full liberty to give or refuse its affections; for constraint may, indeed, leave the receiver still grateful, but it will certainly produce disgust.

If to procure gratitude be our only aim, there is no great art in making the acquisition—a benefit conferred demands a just acknowledgment, and we have a right to insist upon our due.

But it were much more prudent to forego our right on such

an occasion, and exchange it, if we can, for love. We receive but little advantage from repeated protestations of gratitude, but they cost him very much from whom we exact them in return; exacting a grateful acknowledgment is demanding a debt by which the creditor is not advantaged, and the debtor pays with reluctance.

As Mencius the philosopher was travelling in pursuit of wisdom, night overtook him at the foot of a gloomy mountain, remote from the habitations of men. Here, as he was straying, while rain and thunder conspired to make solitude still more hideous, he perceived a hermit's cell, and approaching, asked for shelter. "Enter," cries the hermit, in a severe tone; "men deserve not to be obliged, but it would be imitating their ingratitude to treat them as they deserve. Come in. Examples of vice may sometimes strengthen us in the ways of virtue."

After a frugal meal, which consisted of roots and tea, Mencius could not repress his curiosity to know why the hermit had retired from mankind, the actions of whom taught the truest lessons of wisdom. "Mention not the name of man," cries the hermit, with indignation; "here let me live retired from a base, ungrateful world; here among the beasts of the forest I shall find no flatterers; the lion is a generous enemy, and the dog a faithful friend; but man, base man, can poison the bowl and smile while he presents it." "You have been used ill by mankind?" interrupted the philosopher, shrewdly. "Yes," returned the hermit, "on mankind I have exhausted my whole fortune, and this staff and that cup and those roots are all that I have in return." "Did you bestow your fortune, or did you only lend it?" returned Mencius. "I bestowed it, undoubtedly," replied the other; "for where were the merit of being a money-lender?" "Did they ever own that they received it?" still adds the philosopher. "A thousand times," cries the hermit; "they every day loaded me with professions of gratitude for obligations received, and solicitations for future favors." "If, then," says Mencius, smiling, "you did not lend your fortune in order to have it returned, it is unjust to accuse them of ingratitude; they owned themselves obliged—you expected no more—and they certainly earned each favor by frequently acknowledging the obligation." The hermit was struck with the reply, and, surveying his guest with emotion, "I have heard of the great Mencius, and you certainly are the man; I am now fourscore years old, but still a child in wisdom; take me back to the school of man, and educate me as one of the most ignorant and the youngest of your disciples!"

Indeed, my son, it is better to have friends in our passage through life than grateful dependents; and as love is a more willing so it is a more lasting tribute, than extorted obligation. As we are uneasy when greatly obliged, gratitude once refused can never after be recovered; the mind that is base enough to disallow the just return, instead of feeling any uneasiness upon recollection, triumphs in its new-acquired freedom, and in some measure is pleased with conscious baseness.

Very different is the situation of disagreeing friends; their separation produces mutual uneasiness; like that divided being in fabulous creation, their sympathetic souls once more desire their former union; the joys of both are imperfect; their gayest moments tinctured with uneasiness, each seeks for the smallest concessions to clear the way to a wished-for explanation; the most trifling acknowledgment, the slightest accident serves to effect a mutual reconciliation.

But, instead of pursuing the thought, permit me to soften the severity of advice by a European story which will fully illustrate my meaning.

A fiddler and his wife, who had rubbed through life as most couples usually do—sometimes good friends, at others not quite so well—one day happened to have a dispute, which was conducted with becoming spirit on both sides. The wife was sure she was right, and the husband was resolved to have his own way. What was to be done in such a case? The quarrel grew worse by explanations, and at last the fury of both rose to such a pitch that they made a vow never to sleep together in the same bed for the future. This was the most rash vow that could be imagined, for they still were friends at bottom, and besides, they had but one bed in the house; however, resolved they were to go through with it, and at night the fiddle-case was laid in bed between them, in order to make a separation. In this manner they continued for three weeks, every night the fiddle-case being placed as a barrier to divide them.

"By this time, however, each heartily repented of their vow; their resentment was at an end, and their love began to return; they wished the fiddle-case away, but both had too much spirit to begin. One night, however, as they were both lying awake, with the detested fiddle-case between them, the husband happened to sneeze; to which the wife, as is usual in such cases, bid God bless him.[1]   "Ay, but," returns the husband, "woman, do you say that from your heart?" "Indeed I do, my poor Nicholas," cries his wife; "I say it with all my heart." "If so, then," says the husband, "we had as good remove the fiddle-case."

LETTER LXVII.

THE FOLLY OF ATTEMPTING TO LEARN WISDOM BY BEING A RECLUSE.[2]

From the Same.

BOOKS, my son, while they teach us to respect the interests of others, often make us unmindful of our own: while they instruct the youthful reader to grasp at social happiness, he grows miserable in detail, and, attentive to universal harmony, often forgets that he himself has a part to sustain in the concert. I dislike, therefore, the philosopher who describes the inconveniences of life in such pleasing colors that the pupil

---

[1] " As much as to say, 'May God so bless you as that portends;' for as sneezing is beneficial to the head, and an effort of nature to remove an obstruction, or to throw off anything that either clogs or stimulates, so it was anciently reckoned a good omen."—XENOPHON, *Cyrop.* iii. c. 2.   *Anonymiana*, p. 262.

[2] Many of the observations in this paper are to be found in Goldsmith's letters and in others of his writings, and allude, as he indeed admits, to his own outset in life.

grows enamored of distress, longs to try the charms of poverty, meets it without dread, nor fears its inconveniences till he severely feels them.

A youth who has thus spent his life among books, new to the world, and unacquainted with man but by philosophic information, may be considered as a being whose mind is filled with the vulgar errors of the wise: utterly unqualified for a journey through life, yet confident of his own skill in the direction, he sets out with confidence, blunders on with vanity, and finds himself at last undone.

He first has learned from books, and then lays it down as a maxim, that all mankind are virtuous or vicious in excess; and he has been long taught to detest vice and love virtue: warm, therefore, in attachments, and steadfast in enmity, he treats every creature as a friend or foe; expects from those he loves unerring integrity, and consigns his enemies to the reproach of wanting every virtue. On this principle he proceeds; and here begin his disappointments. Upon a closer inspection of human nature he perceives that he should have moderated his friendship, and softened his severity; for he often finds the excellences of one part of mankind clouded with vice, and the faults of the other brightened with virtue; he finds no character so sanctified that has not its failings, none so infamous but has somewhat to attract our esteem; he beholds impiety in lawn, and fidelity in fetters.

He now, therefore, but too late, perceives that his regards should have been more cool, and his hatred less violent; that the truly wise seldom court romantic friendships with the good, and avoid, if possible, the resentment even of the wicked: every moment gives him fresh instances that the bonds of friendship are broken if drawn too closely, and that those whom he has treated with disrespect more than retaliate the injury. At length, therefore, he is obliged to confess that he has declared war upon the vicious half of mankind, without being able to form an alliance among the virtuous to espouse his quarrel.

Our book-taught philosopher, however, is now too far advanced to recede; and though poverty be the just consequence of the many enemies his conduct has created, yet he is resolved to meet it without shrinking. Philosophers have described poverty in most charming colors, and even his vanity is touched in thinking that he shall show the world in himself one more example of patience, fortitude, and resignation. "Come then, O Poverty! for what is there in thee dreadful to the wise? Temperance, health, and frugality walk in thy train; cheerfulness and liberty are ever thy companions. Shall any be ashamed of thee, of whom Cincinnatus was not ashamed? The running brook, the herbs of the field, can amply satisfy nature; man wants but little, nor that little long.[1] Come, then, O Poverty, while kings stand by and gaze with admiration at the true philosopher's resignation."

The goddess appears; for Poverty ever comes at the call: but, alas! he finds her by no means the charming figure books and his warm imagination had painted. As when an Eastern bride, whom her friends and relations had long described as a model of perfection, pays her first visit, the longing bridegroom lifts the veil to see a face he had never seen before; but, instead of a countenance blazing with beauty like the sun, he beholds deformity shooting icicles to his heart; such appears Poverty to her new entertainer; all the fabric of enthusiasm is at once demolished, and a thousand miseries rise upon its ruins, while Contempt, with pointing finger, is foremost in the hideous procession.

The poor man now finds that he can get no kings to look at him while he is eating; he finds that, in proportion as he grows poor, the world turns its back upon him, and gives him leave to act the philosopher in all the majesty of solitude. It might be agreeable enough to play the philosopher while we are conscious that mankind are spectators; but what signifies wearing the mask of sturdy contentment, and mounting the stage of restraint, when not one creature will assist at the exhibition?[2] Thus is he forsaken of men, while his fortitude

---

[1] "Man wants but little here below,
    Nor wants that little long."—GOLDSMITH, *Edwin and Angelina*.
[2] A similar train of thought will be found in Letter CXIX.—On the Distresses

wants the satisfaction even of self-applause; for either he does not feel his present calamities, and that is natural insensibility, or he disguises his feelings, and that is dissimulation.

Spleen now begins to take up the man: not distinguishing in his resentments, he regards all mankind with detestation; and, commencing man-hater, seeks solitude to be at liberty to rail.

It has been said that he who retires to solitude is either a beast or an angel. The censure is too severe, and the praise unmerited: the discontented being who retires from society is generally some good-natured man, who has begun life without experience, and knew not how to gain it in his intercourse with mankind. Adieu.

LETTER LXVIII.

QUACKS RIDICULED.—SOME PARTICULARLY MENTIONED.

From Lien Chi Altangi to Fum Hoam, first President of the Ceremonial Academy, at Pekin.

I FORMERLY acquainted thee, most grave Fum, with the excellence of the English in the art of healing. The Chinese boast their skill in pulses, the Siamese their botanical knowledge, but the English advertising physicians alone of being the great restorers of health, the dispensers of youth, and the insurers of longevity. I can never enough admire[1] the sagacity of this country for the encouragement given to the professors of this art: with what indulgence does she foster up those of her own growth, and kindly cherish those that come from abroad! Like a skilful gardener, she invites them from every foreign climate to herself. Here every great exotic strikes root as soon as imported, and feels the genial beam of

---

of the Poor: "Where is the magnanimity of bearing misfortunes when the whole world is looking on? Men, in such circumstances, can act bravely, even from motives of vanity."

[1] The passage commencing "I can never enough admire," etc., was reprinted in part by its author in his Essays, 1765, as Essay No. XX.

favor; while the mighty metropolis, like one vast munificent dunghill, receives them indiscriminately to her breast, and supplies each with more than native nourishment.

In other countries the physician pretends to cure disorders in the lump: the same doctor who combats the gout in the toe shall pretend to prescribe for a pain in the head, and he who at one time cures a consumption shall at another give drugs for a dropsy. How absurd and ridiculous! this is being a mere jack-of-all-trades. Is the animal machine less complicated than a brass pin? Not less than ten different hands are required to make a pin; and shall the body be set right by one single operator?

The English are sensible of the force of this reasoning; they have, therefore, one doctor for the eyes, another for the toes; they have their sciatica doctors, and inoculating doctors; they have one doctor who is modestly content with securing them from bug-bites, and five hundred who prescribe for the bite of mad dogs.

The learned are not here retired, with vicious modesty, from public view; for every dead wall is covered with their names, their abilities, their amazing cures, and places of abode. Few patients can escape falling into their hands, unless blasted by lightning or struck dead with some sudden disorder. It may sometimes happen that a stranger who does not understand English, or a countryman who cannot read, dies without ever hearing of the vivifying drops or restorative electuary; but, for my part, before I was a week in town I had learned to bid the whole catalogue of disorders defiance, and was perfectly acquainted with the names and the medicines of every great man or great woman of them all.

But as nothing pleases curiosity more than anecdotes of the great, however minute or trifling, I must present you, inadequate as my abilities are to the subject, with some account of those personages who lead in this honorable profession.

The first upon this list of glory is Doctor Richard Rock, F.U.N. This great man, short of stature, is fat, and waddles as he walks. He always wears a white, three-tailed wig, nicely combed and frizzed upon each cheek; sometimes he car-

ries a cane, but a hat never. It is, indeed, very remarkable
that this extraordinary personage should never wear a hat,
but so it is—he never wears a hat. He is usually drawn, at the
top of his own bills, sitting in his arm-chair, holding a little
bottle between his finger and thumb, and surrounded with
rotten teeth, nippers, pills, packets, and gallipots. No man
can promise fairer nor better than he; for, as he observes,
" Be your disorder never so far gone, be under no uneasiness,
make yourself quite easy; I can cure you."

The next in fame, though by some reckoned of equal pretensions, is Doctor Timothy Franks, F.O.G.H., living in a
place called the Old Bailey. As Rock is remarkably squab,
his great rival Franks is as remarkably tall. He was born in
the year of the Christian era 1692, and is, while I now write,
exactly sixty-eight years three months and four days old.
Age, however, has no way impaired his usual health and
vivacity : I am told he generally walks with his breast open.
This gentleman, who is of a mixed reputation, is particularly
remarkable for a becoming assurance, which carries him gen-
tly through life; for, except Doctor Rock, none are more
blessed with the advantages of face than Doctor Franks.

And yet the great have their foibles as well as the little.
I am almost ashamed to mention it—let the foibles of the
great rest in peace — yet I must impart the whole to my
friend. These two great men are actually now at variance;
yes, my dear Fum Hoam, by the head of our grandfather, they
are now at variance like mere men, mere common mortals.
The champion Rock advises the world to beware of bog-
trotting quacks, while Franks retorts the wit and the sarcasm
(for they have both a world of wit) by fixing on his rival the
odious appellation of Dumplin Dick.[1] He calls the serious

---

[1] When these letters were written the contentions of Rock and Dick for employment furnished the public with occasional amusement. Franks cautioned the
town by public advertisements against Rock : " Be not *Rocked* into eternity by that
vain and impudent pretender, *Dumpling Dick*, who still lives at the gate of the
inn where he was once porter." To which Rock rejoined : " If you would avoid
destruction, avoid the Old Bailey; for there lives an old soldier discharged by the
beat of drum, who has killed his thousands, but not in battle; his pills are much
more fatal than were his *bullets*."

Doctor Rock, Dumplin Dick! Head of Confucius, what profanation! Dumplin Dick! What a pity, ye powers, that the learned, who were born mutually to assist in enlightening the world, should thus differ among themselves and make even the profession ridiculous! Sure the world is wide enough, at least, for two great personages to figure in. Men of science should leave controversy to the little world below them; and then we might see Rock and Franks walking together hand-in-hand, smiling onward to immortality.

Next to these is Doctor Walker, preparator of his own medicines. This gentleman is remarkable for an aversion to quacks; frequently cautioning the public to be careful into what hands they commit their safety; by which he would insinuate that if they do not employ him alone they must be undone. His public spirit is equal to his success. Not for himself, but his country, is the gallipot prepared, and the drops sealed up with proper directions, for any part of the town or country. All this is for his country's good; so that he is now grown old in the practice of physic and virtue; and, to use his own elegance of expression, "There is not such another medicine as his in the world again."

This, my friend, is a formidable triumvirate; and yet, formidable as they are, I am resolved to defend the honor of Chinese physic against them all. I have made a vow to summon Doctor Rock to a solemn disputation in all the mysteries of the profession before the face of every philomath, student in astrology, and member of the learned societies. I adhere to and venerate the doctrines of old Wang-shu-ho. In the very teeth of opposition I will maintain, "that the heart is the son of the liver, which has the kidneys for its mother, and the stomach for its wife."[1] I have, therefore, drawn up

---

[1] See Du Halde, vol. ii. fol. p. 185.—GOLDSMITH.—"A physician whom Dr. Abel saw at Canton was entirely destitute of anatomical knowledge. He appeared to be aware that there were such viscera as the heart, lungs, and liver, but had no notion of their real situation, or, like the Mock Doctor in Molière, placed them on the wrong sides of the body. The Chinese do not even know the distinction between arteries and veins, and not a syllable of the function of the lungs in oxygenizing the blood and getting rid of its superfluous carbon. Of the existence of certain sympathies between the different viscera, and of derangement being commu-

a disputation challenge, which is to be sent speedily, to this effect:

"I, Lien Chi Altangi, 𝕯.𝕹.𝕽.𝕻., native of Honan, in China, to Richard Rock, F.U.N., native of Garbage Alley, in Wapping, *defiance.*—Though, sir, I am perfectly sensible of your importance, though no stranger to your studies in the paths of nature, yet there may be many things in the art of physic with which you are yet unacquainted. I know full well a doctor thou art, great Rock, and so am I. Wherefore, I challenge, and do hereby invite you to a trial of learning upon hard problems and knotty physical points. In this debate we will calmly investigate the whole theory and practice of medicine, botany, and chemistry; and I invite all the philomaths, with many of the lecturers in medicine, to be present at the dispute; which, I hope, will be carried on with due decorum, with proper gravity, and as befits men of erudition and science among each other. But, before we meet face to face, I would thus publicly, and in the face of the whole world, desire you to answer me one question; I ask it with the same earnestness with which you have often solicited the public; answer me, I say, at once, without having recourse to your physical dictionary, which of those three disorders incident to the human body is the most fatal, the syncope, parenthesis, or apoplexy? I beg your reply may be as public as this my demand.[1] I am, as hereafter may be, your admirer or your rival." Adieu.

---

nicated to one by the disorders of another, they might seem to have some glimmering, and to express it strangely by calling the heart 'the husband,' and the lungs 'the wife,' etc."—DAVIS's *Chinese*, vol. ii. p. 284.

[1] The day after this was published the editor received an answer, in which the Doctor seems to be of opinion that the apoplexy is most fatal.—GOLDSMITH.

LETTER LXIX.[1]

THE FEAR OF MAD DOGS RIDICULED.

To the Same.

INDULGENT nature seems to have exempted this island from many of those epidemic evils which are so fatal in other parts of the world. A want of rain but for a few days beyond the expected season in China spreads famine, desolation, and terror over the whole country [the winds that blow from the brown bosom of the Western Desert are impregnated with death in every gale[2]]; but in this fortunate land of Britain the inhabitant courts health in every breeze, and the husbandman ever sows in joyful expectation.

But though the nation be exempt from real evils, think not, my friend, that it is more happy on this account than others. They are afflicted, it is true, with neither famine nor pestilence, but then there is a disorder peculiar to the country, which every season makes strange ravages among them; it spreads with pestilential rapidity, and infects almost every rank of people; what is still more strange, the natives have no name for this peculiar malady, though well known to foreign physicians by the appellation of *epidemic terror*.

A season is never known to pass in which the people are not visited by this cruel calamity in one shape or another, seemingly different though ever the same: one year it issues from a baker's shop in the shape of a sixpenny loaf; the next it takes the appearance of a comet with a fiery tail; a third, it threatens like a flat-bottomed boat; and a fourth, it carries consternation at the bite of a mad dog. The people, when once infected, lose their relish for happiness, saunter

---

[1] Reprinted by its author in 1765, with verbal alterations, as Essay XIII.

[2] The words in brackets are not in Essay XIII.

about with looks of despondence, ask after the calamities of
the day, and receive no comfort but in heightening each
other's distress. It is insignificant how remote or near, how
weak or powerful the object of terror may be, when once they
resolve to fright and be frightened; the merest trifles sow
consternation and dismay; each proportions his fears, not to
the object, but to the dread he discovers in the countenance
of others; for when once the fermentation is begun it goes
on of itself, though the original cause be discontinued which
first set it in motion.

A dread of mad dogs is the *epidemic terror* which now
prevails; and the whole nation is at present actually groaning
under the malignity of its influence. The people sally from
their houses with that circumspection which is prudent in
such as expect a mad dog at every turning. The physician
publishes his prescription, the beadle prepares his halter, and
a few of unusual bravery arm themselves with boots and buff
gloves, in order to face the enemy if he should offer to attack
them. In short, the whole people stand bravely upon their
defence, and seem by their present spirit to show a resolution
of not being tamely bit by mad dogs any longer.

Their manner of knowing whether a dog be mad or no
somewhat resembles the ancient European custom of trying
witches. The old woman suspected was tied hand and foot, and
thrown into the water. If she swum, then she was instantly
carried off to be burnt for a witch; if she sunk, then indeed
she was acquitted of the charge, but drowned in the experiment. In the same manner a crowd gather round a dog suspected of madness, and they begin by teasing the devoted
animal on every side; if he attempts to stand upon the de-
fensive and bite, then he is unanimously found guilty, for "a
mad dog always snaps at everything;" if, on the contrary, he
strives to escape by running away, then he can expect no
compassion, "for mad dogs always run straight forward before them."

It is pleasant enough for a neutral being like me, who have
no share in these ideal calamities, to mark the stages of this
national disease. The terror at first feebly enters with a dis-

regarded story of a little dog, that had gone through a neighboring village, that was thought to be mad by several that
had seen him. The next account comes, that a mastiff ran
through a certain town, and had bit five geese, which immediately ran mad, foamed at the bill, and died in great agonies
soon after. Then comes an affecting history of a little boy
bit in the leg, and gone down to be dipped in the salt-water.
When the people have sufficiently shuddered at that, they are
next congealed with a frightful account of a man who was said
lately to have died from a bite he had received some years
before. This relation only prepares the way for another still
more hideous, as how the master of a family, with seven small
children, were all bit by a mad lapdog; and how the poor
father first perceived the infection by calling for a draught
of water, where he saw the lapdog swimming in the cup.

When epidemic terror is thus once excited, every morning
comes loaded with some new disaster. As in stories of ghosts,
each loves to hear the account, though it only serves to make
him uneasy, so here each listens with eagerness, and adds to
the tidings new circumstances of peculiar horror, A lady, for
instance, in the country, of very weak nerves has been frightened by the barking of a dog; and this, alas! too frequently
happens. The story soon is improved and spreads that a mad
dog had frightened a lady of distinction. These circumstances
begin to grow terrible before they have reached the neighboring village, and there the report is that a lady of quality was
bit by a mad mastiff. This account every moment gathers
new strength, and grows more dismal as it approaches the
capital; and by the time it has arrived in town the lady is
described, with wild eyes, foaming mouth, running mad upon
all-fours, barking like a dog, biting her servants, and at last
smothered between two beds by the advice of her doctors;
while the mad mastiff is in the mean time ranging the whole
country over, slavering at the mouth and seeking whom he
may devour.

My landlady, a good-natured woman, but a little credulous,
waked me some mornings ago before the usual hour, with horror and astonishment in her looks. She desired me, if I had

any regard for my safety, to keep within; for a few days ago
so dismal an accident had happened as to put all the world
upon their guard. A mad dog down in the country, she assured me, had bit a farmer, who, soon becoming mad, ran into
his own yard and bit a fine brindled cow; the cow quickly
became as mad as the man, began to foam at the mouth, and,
raising herself up, walked about on her hind legs, sometimes
barking like a dog and sometimes attempting to talk like the
farmer. Upon examining the grounds of this story I found
my landlady had it from one neighbor, who had it from another neighbor, who heard it from very good authority.

Were most stories of this nature thoroughly examined, it
would be found that numbers of such as have been said to
suffer were no way injured; and that of those who have been
actually bitten, not one in a hundred was bit by a mad dog.
Such accounts in general, therefore, only serve to make the
people miserable by false terrors, and sometimes frighten the
patient into actual frenzy, by creating those very symptoms
they pretended to deplore.

But even allowing three or four to die in a season of this
terrible death (and four is probably too large a concession),
yet still it is not considered how many are preserved in their
health and in their property by this devoted animal's services. The midnight robber is kept at a distance; the insidious thief is often detected; the healthful chase repairs many
a worn constitution; and the poor man finds in his dog a
willing assistant, eager to lessen his toil, and content with
the smallest retribution.

"A dog," says one of the English poets, "is an honest
creature, and I am a friend to dogs."[1] Of all the beasts that
graze the lawn or hunt the forest, a dog is the only animal
that, leaving his fellows, attempts to cultivate the friendship
of man;[2] to man he looks in all his necessities with a speak-

---

[1] "A friend to dogs, for they are honest creatures,
   And ne'er betray their masters; never fawn
   On any that they love not."—OTWAY, *Venice Preserved*, act ii. sc. 1.

[2] "The dog alone, of all brute animals, has a στοργή, or affection upward to
man."—COLERIDGE, *Table Talk*, vol. i. p. 111.

ing eye for assistance; exerts for him all the little service in his power with cheerfulness and pleasure; for him bears famine and fatigue with patience and resignation; no injuries can abate his fidelity, no distress induce him to forsake his benefactor; studious to please, and fearing to offend, he is still a humble, steadfast dependant, and in him alone fawning is not flattery. How unkind, then, to torture this faithful creature, who has left the forest to claim the protection of man! how ungrateful a return to the trusty animal for all his services! Adieu.

LETTER LXX.

FORTUNE PROVED NOT TO BE BLIND. — THE STORY OF THE AVARICIOUS MILLER.

From Lien Chi Altangi to Hingpo, by the way of Moscow.

THE Europeans are themselves blind who described Fortune without sight. No first-rate beauty ever had finer eyes, or saw more clearly: they who have no other trade but seeking their fortune need never hope to find her; coquet-like, she flies from her close pursuers, and at last fixes on the plodding mechanic who stays at home and minds his business.

I am amazed how men can call her blind, when, by the company she keeps, she seems so very discerning. Wherever you see a gaming-table, be very sure Fortune is not there; wherever you see a house with the doors open, be very sure Fortune is not there; when you see a man whose pocket-holes are laced with gold, be satisfied Fortune is not there; wherever you see a beautiful woman good-natured and obliging, be convinced Fortune is never there. In short, she is ever seen accompanying industry, and as often trundling a wheelbarrow as lolling in a coach-and-six.

If you would make Fortune your friend, or, to personize her no longer, if you desire, my son, to be rich and have money, be more eager to save than to acquire. When people say, "Money is to be got here, and money is to be got there," take no notice: mind your own business; stay where you are, and secure all you can get, without stirring. When you hear that your neighbor has picked up a purse of gold in the street, never run out into the same street looking about you in order to pick up such another; or when you are informed that he has made a fortune in one branch of business, never change your own in order to be his rival. Do not desire to be rich all at once, but patiently add farthing to farthing. Perhaps you despise the petty sum; and yet they who want a farthing, and have no friend that will lend them it, think farthings very good things. Whang, the foolish miller, when he wanted a farthing in his distress, found that no friend would lend, because they knew he wanted. Did you ever read the story of Whang in our books of Chinese learning—he who, despising small sums, and grasping at all, lost even what he had?

Whang, the miller, was naturally avaricious; nobody loved money better than he, or more respected those that had it. When people would talk of a rich man in company, Whang would say, I know him very well; he and I have been long acquainted; he and I are intimate; he stood for a child of mine. But if ever a poor man was mentioned, he had not the least knowledge of the man; he might be very well for aught he knew; but he was not fond of many acquaintances, and loved to choose his company.

Whang, however, with all his eagerness for riches, was in reality poor; he had nothing but the profits of his mill to support him; but though these were small, they were certain: while his mill stood and went he was sure of eating; and his frugality was such that he every day laid some money by, which he would at intervals count and contemplate with much satisfaction. Yet still his acquisitions were not equal to his desires; he only found himself above want, whereas he desired to be possessed of affluence.

One day, as he was indulging these wishes, he was informed that a neighbor of his had found a pan of money underground, having dreamed of it three nights running before. These tidings were daggers to the heart of poor Whang.

"Here am I," says he, "toiling and moiling from morning till night for a few paltry farthings, while neighbor Hunks only goes quietly to bed and dreams himself into thousands before morning. Oh that I could dream like him! With what pleasure would I dig round the pan; how slyly would I carry it home; not even my wife should see me: and then, oh the pleasure of thrusting one's hand into a heap of gold up to the elbow!"

Such reflections only served to make the miller unhappy: he discontinued his former assiduity; he was quite disgusted with small gains, and his customers began to forsake him. Every day he repeated the wish, and every night laid himself down in order to dream. Fortune, that was for a long time unkind, at last, however, seemed to smile upon his distresses, and indulged him with the wished-for vision. He dreamed that under a certain part of the foundation of his mill there was concealed a monstrous pan of gold and diamonds, buried deep in the ground, and covered with a large flat stone. He rose up, thanked the stars, that were at last pleased to take pity on his sufferings, and concealed his good luck from every person, as is usual in money dreams, in order to have the vision repeated the two succeeding nights, by which he should be certain of its veracity. His wishes in this also were answered: he still dreamed of the same pan of money, in the very same place.

Now, therefore, it was past a doubt; so, getting up early the third morning, he repairs alone, with a mattock in his hand, to the mill, and began to undermine that part of the wall to which the vision directed. The first omen of success that he met was a broken mug; digging still deeper, he turns up a house-tile, quite new and entire. At last, after much digging, he came to the broad flat stone, but then so large that it was beyond one man's strength to remove it. "Here," cried he in raptures to himself, "here it is! under this stone there is room for a very large pan of diamonds indeed. I must e'en go home to my wife and tell her the whole affair, and get her to assist me in turning it up." Away therefore he goes, and acquaints his wife with every circumstance of their good fortune. Her raptures on this occasion easily may be imagined; she flew round his neck, and embraced him in an agony of joy; but those transports, however, did not delay their eagerness to know the exact sum: returning, therefore, speedily together to the place where Whang had been digging, there they found—not, indeed, the expected treasure, but the mill, their only support, undermined and fallen. Adieu.

LETTER LXXI.

THE SHABBY BEAU, THE MAN IN BLACK, THE CHINESE PHILOSOPHER, ETC., AT VAUXHALL.

From Lien Chi Altangi to Fum Hoam, first President of the Ceremonial Academy, at Pekin, in China.

THE people of London are as fond of walking as our friends at Pekin of riding: one of the principal entertainments of the citizens here in summer is to repair about nightfall to a garden[1] not far from town, where they walk about, show their best clothes and best faces, and listen to a concert provided for the occasion.

I accepted an invitation a few evenings ago from my old friend, the man in black, to be one of a party that was to sup there, and at the appointed hour waited upon him at his lodgings. There I found the company assembled and expecting my arrival. Our party consisted of my friend in superla-

---

[1] Vauxhall Gardens, at this time the property of Jonathan Tyers, Esq. (died 1767), father of "Tom Tyers," the friend of Johnson and Goldsmith. "Tyers was a worthy man, but indulged himself a little too much in a querulous strain when anything went amiss, insomuch that he said if he had been brought up a hatter, he believed people would have been born without heads. A farmer once gave him a humorous reproof for this kind of reproach of Heaven: he stepped up to him very respectfully, and asked him when he meant to open his gardens. Mr. Tyers replied, 'the next Monday fortnight.' The man thanked him repeatedly, and was going away; but Mr. Tyers asked him, in return, what made him so anxious to know. 'Why, sir,' said the farmer, 'I think of sowing my turnips on that day, for you know we shall *be sure to have rain*.'"—*Brasbridge's Memoir*, p. 134.—See art. "Vauxhall Gardens," in Cunningham's Hand-book of London, 2d edition, 1850.

tive finery, his stockings rolled, a black velvet waistcoat which was formerly new, and his gray wig combed down in imitation of hair; a pawnbroker's widow, of whom, by-the-bye, my friend was a professed admirer, dressed out in green damask, with three gold rings on every finger; Mr. Tibbs, the second-rate beau I have formerly described, together with his lady, in flimsy silk, dirty gauze instead of linen, and a hat as big as an umbrella.

Our first difficulty was in settling how we should set out. Mrs. Tibbs had a natural aversion to the water, and the widow, being a little in flesh, as warmly protested against walking; a coach was therefore agreed upon; which being too small to carry five, Mr. Tibbs consented to sit in his wife's lap.

In this manner, therefore, we set forward, being entertained by the way with the bodings of Mr. Tibbs, who assured us he did not expect to see a single creature for the evening above the degree of a cheese-monger; that this was the last night of the Gardens, and that consequently we should be pestered with the nobility and gentry from Thames Street and Crooked Lane, with several other pathetic ejaculations, probably inspired by the uneasiness of his situation.

The illuminations began before we arrived, and I must confess that upon entering the Gardens I found every sense overpaid with more than expected pleasure; the lights everywhere glimmering through the scarcely-moving trees—the full-bodied concert bursting on the stillness of the night—the natural concert of the birds in the more retired part of the grove, vying with that which was formed by art—the company gayly dressed, looking satisfaction, and the tables spread with various delicacies—all conspired to fill my imagination with the visionary happiness of the Arabian law-giver, and lifted me into an ecstasy of admiration.[1]   "Head of Con-

---

[1] "In the midst of the garden is a superb orchestra, containing a fine organ, with a band of music and some of the best voices. In most of the boxes are pictures painted from the designs of Hayman [and Hogarth] on subjects of humor well adapted to the place. The trees are scattered with a pleasing confusion; there are several noble vistas through very tall trees, the spaces between being filled up with neat hedges; and on the inside are planted flowers and sweet-smell-

fucius," cried I to my friend, "this is fine! this unites rural
beauty with courtly magnificence. If we except the virgins
of immortality that hang on every tree, and may be plucked
at every desire, I do not see how this falls short of Mohammed's paradise!"[1] "As for virgins," cries my friend, " it is
true they are a fruit that do not much abound in our gardens
here; but if ladies, as plenty as apples in autumn, and as complying as any houri of them all, can content you, I fancy we
have no need to go to heaven for paradise."

I was going to second his remarks, when we were called to
a consultation by Mr. Tibbs and the rest of the company, to
know in what manner we were to lay out the evening to the
greatest advantage. Mrs. Tibbs was for keeping the genteel
walk of the garden, where, she observed, there was always the
very best company; the widow, on the contrary, who came
but once a season, was for securing a good standing-place to
see the water-works, which she assured us would begin in less
than an hour at farthest; a dispute, therefore, began, and as
it was managed between two of very opposite characters, it
threatened to grow more bitter at every reply. Mrs. Tibbs
wondered how people could pretend to know the polite world
who had received all their rudiments of breeding behind a
counter; to which the other replied that, though some people
sat behind counters, yet they could sit at the head of their
own tables too, and carve three good dishes of hot meat whenever they thought proper; which was more than some people
could say for themselves, that hardly knew a rabbit and onions
from a green goose and gooseberries.

It is hard to say where this might have ended, had not the

---

ing shrubs. Some terminate by paintings representing ruins of buildings, others
a prospect of a distant country, and some of triumphal arches. There are several
statues, particularly a good one in marble, by Roubiliac, of Handel in the character
of Orpheus, playing on a lyre."—Dodsley's *London*, 1760. The price of admission
at this time was one shilling.

[1] "We were now arrived at Spring Garden [Vauxhall], which is exquisitely
pleasant at this time of the year. When I consider the fragrancy of the walks
and bowers, with the choir of birds that sung upon the trees, and the loose tribe
of people that walked under their shades, I could not but look on the place as a
kind of Mohammedan paradise."—Addison, *The Spectator*, No. 383.

husband, who probably knew the impetuosity of his wife's disposition, proposed to end the dispute by adjourning to a box, and try if there was anything to be had for supper that was supportable. To this we all consented; but here a new distress arose: Mr. and Mrs. Tibbs would sit in none but a genteel box, a box where they might see and be seen—one, as they expressed it, in the very focus of public view; but such a box was not easy to be obtained; for though we were perfectly convinced of our own gentility and the gentility of our appearance, yet we found it a difficult matter to persuade the keepers of the boxes to be of our opinion: they chose to reserve genteel boxes for what they judged more genteel company.

At last, however, we were fixed, though somewhat obscurely, and supplied with the usual entertainment of the place. The widow found the supper excellent, but Mrs. Tibbs thought everything detestable. "Come, come, my dear," cries the husband, by way of consolation, "to be sure we can't find such dressing here as we have at Lord Crump's, or Lady Crimp's; but for Vauxhall dressing it is pretty good; it is not their victuals, indeed, I find fault with, but their wine; their wine," cries he, drinking off a glass, "indeed, is most abominable."

By this last contradiction the widow was fairly conquered in point of politeness. She perceived now that she had no pretensions in the world to taste; her very senses were vulgar, since she had praised detestable custard and smacked at wretched wine; she was therefore content to yield the victory, and for the rest of the night to listen and improve. It is true, she would now and then forget herself, and confess she was pleased, but they soon brought her back again to miserable refinement. She once praised the painting of the box in which we were sitting, but was soon convinced that such paltry pieces ought rather to excite horror than satisfaction; she ventured again to commend one of the singers, but Mrs. Tibbs soon let her know, in the style of a connoisseur, that the singer in question had neither ear, voice, nor judgment.

Mr. Tibbs, now willing to prove that his wife's pretensions to music were just, entreated her to favor the company with a song; but to this she gave a positive denial: "For you know very well, my dear," says she, "that I am not in voice to-day, and when one's voice is not equal to one's judgment what signifies singing? Besides, as there is no accompaniment, it would be but spoiling music." All these excuses, however, were overruled by the rest of the company, who, though one would think they already had music enough, joined in the entreaty. But particularly the widow, now willing to convince the company of her breeding, pressed so warmly that she seemed determined to take no refusal. At last, then, the lady complied, and after humming for some minutes, began with such a voice and such affectation as I could perceive gave but little satisfaction to any except her husband. He sat with rapture in his eye, and beat time with his hand on the table.

You must observe, my friend, that it is the custom of this country, when a lady or gentleman happens to sing, for the company to sit as mute and motionless as statues. Every feature, every limb must seem to correspond in fixed attention; and while the song continues they are to remain in a state of universal petrifaction. In this mortifying situation we had continued for some time, listening to the song and looking with tranquillity, when the master of the box came to inform us that the water-works were going to begin. At this information I could instantly perceive the widow bounce from her seat; but, correcting herself, she sat down again, repressed by motives of good-breeding. Mrs. Tibbs, who had seen the water-works a hundred times, resolving not to be interrupted, continued her song without any share of mercy, nor had the smallest pity on our impatience. The widow's face, I own, gave me high entertainment; in it I could plainly read the struggle she felt between good-breeding and curiosity; she talked of the water-works the whole evening before, and seemed to have come merely in order to see them; but then she could not bounce out in the very middle of a song, for that would be forfeiting all pretensions to high life or high-lived company ever after. Mrs. Tibbs, therefore, kept on singing, and we continued to listen, till at last, when the song was just concluded, the waiter came to inform us that the water-works were over.

" The water-works over !" cried the widow; " the water-works over already ! that's impossible ; they can't be over so soon !"   " It is not my business," replied the fellow, " to contradict your ladyship ; I'll run again and see."   He went, and soon returned with a confirmation of the dismal tidings.   No ceremony could now bind my friend's disappointed mistress ; she testified her displeasure in the openest manner ; in short, she now began to find fault in turn, and at last insisted upon going home just at the time that Mr. and Mrs. Tibbs assured the company that the polite hours were going to begin, and that the ladies would instantaneously be entertained with the horns.   Adieu.

LETTER LXXII.

THE MARRIAGE ACT CENSURED.

From the Same.

Not far from the city lives a poor tinker, who has educated seven sons, all at this very time in arms and fighting for their country ; and what reward, do you think, has the tinker from the state for such important services ?   None in the world ; his sons, when the war is over, may probably be whipped from parish to parish as vagabonds, and the old man, when past labor, may die a prisoner in some house of correction.

Such a worthy subject in China would be held in universal reverence ; his services would be rewarded, if not with dignities, at least with an exemption from labor ; he would take the left hand at feasts, and mandarins themselves would be proud to show their submission.   The English laws punish vice ; the Chinese laws do more, they reward virtue.

Considering the little encouragement given to matrimony here, I am not surprised at the discouragements given to propagation.   Would you believe it, my dear Fum Hoam, there are laws made which even forbid the people's marrying each other ! By the head of Confucius, I jest not ; there are such laws in being here ; and yet their law-givers have neither been instructed among the Hottentots, nor imbibed their principles of equity from the natives of Anamaboe.

There are laws which ordain that no man shall marry a woman against her own consent. This, though contrary to what we are taught in Asia, and though in some measure a clog upon matrimony, I have no great objection to. There are laws which ordain that no woman shall marry against her father and mother's consent, unless arrived at an age of maturity; by which is understood those years when women with us are generally past child-bearing. This must be a clog upon matrimony, as it is more difficult for the lover to please three than one, and much more difficult to please old people than young ones. The laws ordain that the consenting couple shall take a long time to consider before they marry ; this is a very great clog, because people love to have all rash actions done in a hurry. It is ordained that all marriages shall be proclaimed before celebration. This is a severe clog, as many are ashamed to have their marriage made public from motives of vicious modesty, and many afraid from views of temporal interest. It is ordained that there is nothing sacred in the ceremony, but that it may be dissolved, to all intents and purposes, by the authority of any civil magistrate. And yet, opposite to this, it is ordained that the priest shall be paid a large sum of money for granting his sacred permission.

Thus you see, my friend, that matrimony here is hedged round with so many obstructions that those who are willing to break through or surmount them must be contented if at last they find it a bed of thorns. The laws are not to blame, for they have deterred the people from engaging as much as they could. It is, indeed, become a very serious affair in England, and none but serious people are generally found willing to engage. The young, the gay, and the beautiful, who have motives of passion only to induce them, are seldom found to embark, as those inducements are taken away ; and none but the old, the ugly, and the mercenary are seen to unite, who, if they have any posterity at all, will probably be an ill-favored race like themselves.

What gave rise to those laws might have been some such accidents as these: It sometimes happened that a miser, who had spent all his youth in scraping up money to give his daughter such a fortune as might get her a mandarin husband, found his expectations disappointed at last by her running away with his footman. This must have been a sad shock to the poor, disconsolate parent, to see his poor daughter in a one-horse chaise, when he had designed her for a coach-and-six. What a stroke from Providence! to see his dear money go to enrich a beggar! All nature cried out at the profanation.

It sometimes happened, also, that a lady, who had inherited all the titles and all the nervous complaints of nobility, thought fit to impair her dignity and mend her constitution by marrying a farmer. This must have been a sad shock to her inconsolable relations, to see so fine a flower snatched from a flourishing family and planted in a dunghill; this was an absolute inversion of the first principles of things.

In order, therefore, to prevent the great from being thus contaminated by vulgar alliances, the obstacles to matrimony have been so contrived that the rich only can marry among the rich, and the poor, who would leave celibacy, must be content to increase their poverty with a wife. Thus have their laws fairly inverted the inducements to matrimony. Nature tells us that beauty is the proper allurement of those who are rich, and money of those who are poor; but things here are so contrived that the rich are invited to marry by that fortune which they do not want, and the poor have no inducement but that beauty which they do not feel.

An equal diffusion of riches through any country ever constitutes its happiness. Great wealth in the possession of one stagnates, and extreme poverty with another keeps him in unambitious indigence; but the moderately rich are generally active: not too far removed from poverty to fear its calamities, nor too near extreme wealth to slacken the nerve of labor, they remain still between both in a state of continual

II.—23

fluctuation. How impolitic, therefore, are those laws which promote the accumulation of wealth among the rich; more impolitic still, in attempting to increase the depression on poverty.

Bacon, the English philosopher, compares money to manure. "If gathered in heaps," says he, "it does no good; on the contrary, it becomes offensive; but being spread, though never so thinly, over the surface of the earth, it enriches the whole country." Thus, the wealth a nation possesses must expatiate, or it is of no benefit to the public; it becomes rather a grievance, where matrimonial laws thus confine it to a few.

But this restraint upon matrimonial community, even considered in a physical light, is injurious. As those who rear up animals take all possible pains to cross the strain in order to improve the breed, so in those countries where marriage is most free, the inhabitants are found every age to improve in stature and in beauty; on the contrary, where it is confined to a caste, a tribe, or a horde, as among the Giaours, the Jews, or the Tartars, each division soon assumes a family likeness, and every tribe degenerates into peculiar deformity. Hence it may be easily inferred that if the mandarins here are resolved only to marry among each other, they will soon produce a posterity with mandarin faces; and we shall see the heir of some honorable family scarce equal to the abortion of a country farmer.

These are a few of the obstacles to marriage here; and it is certain they have in some measure answered the end, for celibacy is both frequent and fashionable. Old bachelors appear abroad without a mask, and old maids, my dear Fum Hoam, have been absolutely known to ogle. To confess in friendship, if I were an Englishman, I fancy I should be an old bachelor myself; I should never find courage to run through all the adventures prescribed by the law. I could submit to court my mistress herself upon reasonable terms; but to court her father, her mother, and a long tribe of cousins, aunts, and relations, and then stand the butt of a whole country church! I would as soon turn tail and make love to her grandmother.

I can conceive no other reason for thus loading matrimony with so many prohibitions, unless it be that the country was thought already too populous, and this was found to be the most effectual means of thinning it.   If this was the motive, I cannot but congratulate the wise projectors on the success of their scheme.   "Hail, O ye dim-sighted politicians, ye weeders of men! 'Tis yours to clip the wing of industry and convert Hymen to a broker. 'Tis yours to behold small objects with a microscopic eye, but to be blind to those which require an extent of vision. 'Tis yours, O ye discerners of mankind! to lay the line between society, and weaken that force by dividing, which should bind with united vigor. 'Tis yours to introduce national real distress, in order to avoid the imaginary distresses of a few.   Your actions can be justified by a hundred reasons like truth; they can be opposed by but a few reasons, and those reasons are true."   Farewell.

LETTER LXXIII.

LIFE ENDEARED BY AGE.[1]

From Lien Chi Altangi to Hingpo, by the way of Moscow.

AGE, that lessens the enjoyment of life, increases our desire of living.   Those dangers which, in the vigor of youth, we had learned to despise, assume new terrors as we grow old. Our caution increasing as our years increase, fear becomes at last the prevailing passion of the mind; and the small remainder of life is taken up in useless efforts to keep off our end, or provide for a continued existence.

Strange contradiction in our nature, and to which even the wise are liable! If I should judge of that part of life which lies before me by that which I have already seen, the prospect is hideous.[2] Experience tells me that my past enjoy-

---

[1] Reprinted in the Essays, 1765, as Essay XIV.

[2] "*Honeywood:* To say truth, if we compare that part of life which is to come by that which is past, the prospect is hideous."—GOLDSMITH, *The Good-Natured Man*, act i. sc. 2.

ments have brought no real felicity; and sensation assures
me that those I have felt are stronger than those which are
yet to come. Yet experience and sensation in vain persuade;
hope, more powerful than either, dresses out the distant prospect in fancied beauty, some happiness in long perspective
still beckons me to pursue, and, like a losing gamester, every new disappointment increases my ardor to continue the
game.

Whence, my friend, this increased love of life, which grows
upon us with our years? whence comes it that we thus make
greater efforts to preserve our existence at a period when it
becomes scarce worth the keeping? Is it that Nature, attentive to the preservation of mankind, increases our wishes to
live while she lessens our enjoyments; and, as she robs the
senses of every pleasure, equips imagination in the spoil?
Life would be insupportable to an old man who, loaded with
infirmities, feared death no more than when in the vigor of
manhood; the numberless calamities of decaying nature, and
the consciousness of surviving every pleasure, would at once
induce him, with his own hand, to terminate the scene of misery; but happily the contempt of death forsakes him at a
time when it could only be prejudicial; and life acquires an
imaginary value, in proportion as its real value is no more.

Our attachment to every object around us increases, in general, from the length of our acquaintance with it. "I would
not choose," says a French philosopher, "to see an old post
pulled up with which I had been long acquainted." A mind
long habituated to a certain set of objects insensibly becomes
fond of seeing them; visits them from habit, and parts from
them with reluctance:[1] from hence proceeds the avarice of
the old in every kind of possession. They love the world and

---

[1] When Cardinal Richelieu built his magnificent palace on the site of the old
family château at Richelieu, he sacrificed its symmetry to preserve the room in which
he was born. (See *Mém. de Montpensier*, t. i. p. 27.) When the Duke of Lenox
wished to buy, or obtain by exchange, York House, in the Strand, Lord Bacon, to
whom it belonged, replied: "For this you will pardon me; York House still is the
house where my father died, and where I first breathed, and there will I yield my
last breath, if so please God and the king.—See CUNNINGHAM'S *Hand-Book of London*, ed. 1850, p. 560.

all that it produces; they love life and all its advantages; not because it gives them pleasure, but because they have known it long.

Chinvang the Chaste, ascending the throne of China, commanded that all who were unjustly detained in prison during the preceding reigns should be set free.   Among the number who came to thank their deliverer on this occasion there appeared a majestic old man, who, falling at the emperor's feet, addressed him as follows: "Great father of China, behold a wretch now eighty-five years old, who was shut up in a dungeon at the age of twenty-two.   I was imprisoned, though a stranger to crime, or without being even confronted by my accusers.   I have now lived in solitude and in darkness for more than fifty years, and am grown familiar with distress. As yet, dazzled with the splendor of that sun to which you have restored me, I have been wandering the streets to find some friend that would assist, or relieve, or remember me; but my friends, my family, and relations are all dead, and I am forgotten.   Permit me, then, O Chinvang, to wear out the wretched remains of life in my former prison: the walls of my dungeon are to me more pleasing than the most splendid palace; I have not long to live, and shall be unhappy except I spend the rest of my days where my youth was passed—in that prison from whence you were pleased to release me."

The old man's passion for confinement is similar to that we all have for life.   We are habituated to the prison; we look round with discontent, are displeased with the abode, and yet the length of our captivity only increases our fondness for the cell.   The trees we have planted, the houses we have built, or the posterity we have begotten, all serve to bind us closer to earth, and embitter our parting.   Life sues the young like a new acquaintance: the companion, as yet unexhausted, is at once instructive and amusing; its company pleases; yet, for all this, it is but little regarded.   To us, who are declined in years, life appears like an old friend; its jests have been anticipated in former conversation; it has no new story to make us smile, no new improvement with which to surprise: yet still we love it: destitute of every agreement, still we love it, husband the wasting treasure with increased frugality, and feel all the poignancy of anguish in the fatal separation.[1]

Sir Philip Mordaunt was young, beautiful, sincere, brave, an Englishman. He had a complete fortune of his own, and the love of the king his master, which was equivalent to riches. Life opened all her treasure before him, and promised a long succession of future happiness. He came, tasted of the entertainment, but was disgusted even in the beginning. He professed an aversion to living; was tired of walking round the same circle; had tried every enjoyment, and found them all grow weaker at every repetition. "If life be in youth so displeasing," cried he to himself, "what will it appear when age comes on? if it be at present indifferent, sure it will then be execrable." This thought embittered every reflection; till at last, with all the serenity of perverted reason, he ended the debate with a pistol! Had this self-deluded man been apprised that existence grows more desirable to us the longer we exist, he would have then faced old age without shrinking; he would have boldly dared to live, and served that society by his future assiduity which he basely injured by his desertion. Adieu.

---

[1] "I have heard Mr. Burke make use of a very ingenious and plausible argument on this subject: 'Every man,' said he, 'would lead his life over again; for every man is willing to go on and take an addition to his life, which, as he grows older, he has no reason to think will be better, or even so good as what has preceded.' I imagine, however, the truth is that there is a deceitful hope that the next part of life will be free from the pains, and anxieties, and sorrows which we have already felt. We are for wise purposes 'condemned to Hope's delusive mine,' as Johnson finely says; and I may also quote the celebrated lines of Dryden, equally philosophical and poetical:

"'When I consider life, 'tis all a cheat;
Yet, fool'd with hope, men favor the deceit—
Trust on, and think to-morrow will repay:
To-morrow's falser than the former day;
Lies worse; and, while it says we shall be blessed
With some new joys, cuts off what we possessed.
Strange cozenage! none would live past years again;
Yet all hope pleasure in what yet remain;
And from the dregs of life think to receive
What the first sprightly running could not give.'"
BOSWELL'S *Life of Johnson*, ed. Croker, p. 764.

LETTER LXXIV.

THE DESCRIPTION OF A LITTLE GREAT MAN.

From Lien Chi Altangi to Fum Hoam, first President of the Ceremonial Academy at Pekin, in China.

IN reading the newspapers here, I have reckoned up not less than twenty-five great men, seventeen very great men, and nine very extraordinary men, in less than the compass of half a year. "These," say the gazettes, "are the men that posterity are to gaze at with admiration; these the names that fame will be employed in holding up for the astonishment of succeeding ages." Let me see—forty-six great men in half a year amount just to ninety-two in a year. I wonder how posterity will be able to remember them all, or whether the people, in future times, will have any other business to mind but that of getting the catalogue by heart?

Does the mayor of a corporation make a speech? he is instantly set down for a great man. Does a pedant digest his commonplace-book into a folio? he quickly becomes great. Does a poet string up trite sentiments in rhyme? he also becomes the great man of the hour. How diminutive soever the object of admiration, each is followed by a crowd of still more diminutive admirers. The shout begins in his train; onward he marches toward immortality; looks back at the pursuing crowd with self-satisfaction—catching all the oddities, the whimsies, the absurdities, and the littlenesses of conscious greatness by the way.

I was yesterday invited by a gentleman to dinner, who promised that our entertainment should consist of a haunch of venison, a turtle, and a great man. I came according to appointment. The venison was fine, the turtle good, but the great man insupportable. The moment I ventured to speak I was at once contradicted with a snap. I attempted by a second and a third assault to retrieve my lost reputation, but was still beat back with confusion. I was resolved to attack him once more from intrenchment, and turned the conversation upon the government of China; but even here he asserted, snapped, and contradicted as before. "Heavens," thought I, "this man pretends to know China even better than myself!" I looked round to see who was on my side, but every eye was fixed in admiration on the great man; I therefore at last thought proper to sit silent, and act the pretty gentleman during the ensuing conversation.

When a man has once secured a circle of admirers he may be as ridiculous here as he thinks proper; and it all passes for elevation of sentiment or learned absence. If he transgresses the common forms of breeding, mistakes even a tea-pot for a tobacco-box, it is said that his thoughts are fixed on more important objects; to speak and to act like the rest of mankind is to be no greater than they. There is something of oddity in the very idea of greatness; for we are seldom astonished at a thing very much resembling ourselves.

When the Tartars make a Lama, their first care is to place him in a dark corner of the temple; here he is to sit half-concealed from view, to regulate the motion of his hands, lips, and eyes; but, above all, he is enjoined gravity and silence. This, however, is but the prelude to his apotheosis; a set of emissaries are despatched among the people to cry up his piety, gravity, and love of raw flesh; the people take them at their word, approach the Lama, now become an idol, with the most humble prostration. He receives their addresses without motion, commences a god, and is ever after fed by his priests with the spoon of immortality. The same receipt in this country serves to make a great man. The idol only keeps close, sends out his little emissaries to be hearty in his praise; and straight, whether statesman or author, he is set down in the list of fame, continuing to be praised while it is fashionable to praise, or while he prudently keeps his minuteness concealed from the public.

I have visited many countries, and have been in cities without number, yet never did I enter a town which could not produce ten or twelve of those little great men; all fancying themselves known to the rest of the world, and complimenting each other upon their extensive reputation.   It is amusing enough when two of those domestic prodigies of learning mount the stage of ceremony, and give and take praise from each other.   I have been present when a German doctor, for having pronounced a panegyric upon a certain monk, was thought the most ingenious man in the world; till the monk soon after divided this reputation by returning the compliment; by which means they both marched off with universal applause.

The same degree of undeserved adulation that attends our great man while living often also follows him to the tomb. It frequently happens that one of his little admirers sits down big with the important subject, and is delivered of the history of his life and writings.   This may probably be called the revolutions of a life between the fireside and the easy-chair. In this we learn the year in which he was born, at what an early age he gave symptoms of uncommon genius and application, together with some of his smart sayings, collected by his aunt and mother, while yet but a boy.   The next book introduces him to the university, where we are informed of his amazing progress in learning, his excellent skill in darning stockings, and his new invention for papering books to save the covers.   He next makes his appearance in the republic of letters, and publishes his folio.   Now the colossus is reared, his works are eagerly bought up by all the purchasers of scarce books.   The learned societies invite him to become a member; he disputes against some foreigner with a long Latin name, conquers in the controversy, is complimented by several authors of gravity and importance, is excessively fond of egg-sauce with his pig, becomes president of a literary club, and dies in the meridian of his glory.   Happy they who thus have some little faithful attendant, who never forsakes them, but prepares to wrangle and to praise against every opposer; at once ready to increase their pride while living, and their character when dead.   For you and I, my friend, who have no humble admirer thus to attend us, we, who neither are, nor ever will be, great men, and who do not much care whether we are great men or no, at least let us strive to be honest men, and to have common-sense. Adieu.

LETTER LXXV.

THE NECESSITY OF AMUSING EACH OTHER WITH NEW BOOKS INSISTED UPON.

To the Same.

THERE are numbers in this city who live by writing new books; and yet there are thousands of volumes in every large library unread and forgotten. This, upon my arrival, was one of those contradictions which I was unable to account for. "Is it possible," said I, "that there should be any demand for new books, before those already published are read? Can there be so many employed in producing a commodity with which the market is already overstocked, and with goods also better than any of modern manufacture?"

What at first view appeared an inconsistence is a proof at once of this people's wisdom and refinement. Even allowing the works of their ancestors better written than theirs, yet those of the moderns acquire a real value by being marked with the impression of the times. Antiquity has been in the possession of others; the present is our own: let us first, therefore, learn to know what belongs to ourselves, and then, if we have leisure, cast our reflections back to the reign of Shonou, who governed twenty thousand years' before the creation of the moon.

The volumes of antiquity, like medals, may very well serve to amuse the curious; but the works of the moderns, like the current coin of a kingdom, are much better for immediate use: the former are often prized above their intrinsic value, and kept with care; the latter seldom pass for more than they are worth, and are often subject to the merciless hands of sweating critics and clipping compilers; the works of antiquity were ever praised, those of the moderns read; the treasures of our ancestors have our esteem, and we boast the passion; those of contemporary genius engage our heart, although we blush to own it. The visits we pay the former resemble those we pay the great; the ceremony is troublesome, and yet such as we would not choose to forego; our acquaintance with modern books is like sitting with a friend; our pride is not flattered in the interview, but it gives more internal satisfaction.

In proportion as society refines, new books must ever become more necessary. Savage rusticity is reclaimed by oral admonition alone; but the elegant excesses of refinement are best corrected by the still voice of a studious inquiry. In a polite age almost every person becomes a reader, and receives more instruction from the Press than the Pulpit. The preaching bonze may instruct the illiterate peasant; but nothing less than the insinuating address of a fine writer can win its way to a heart already relaxed in all the effeminacy of refinement. Books are necessary to correct the vices of the polite; but those vices are ever changing, and the antidote should be changed accordingly—should still be new.

Instead, therefore, of thinking the number of new publications here too great, I could wish it still greater, as they are the most useful instruments of reformation. Every country must be instructed either by writers or preachers; but as the number of readers increases, the number of hearers is proportionably diminished; the writer becomes more useful, and the preaching bonze less necessary.

Instead, therefore, of complaining that writers are overpaid when their works procure them a bare subsistence, I should imagine it the duty of a state not only to encourage their numbers but their industry. A bonze is rewarded with immense riches for instructing only a few, even of the most ignorant of the people; and sure the poor scholar should not beg his bread who is capable of instructing a million.

Of all rewards, I grant, the most pleasing to a man of real merit is fame; but a polite age, of all times, is that in which scarcely any share of merit can acquire it. What numbers of fine writers in the latter empire of Rome, when refinement was carried to the highest pitch, have missed that fame and immortality which they had fondly arrogated to themselves! How many Greek authors, who wrote at that period when Constantinople was the refined mistress of the empire, now rest, either not printed or not read, in the libraries of Europe! Those who came first, while either state as yet was barbarous, carried all the reputation away. Authors, as the age refined, became more numerous, and their numbers destroyed their fame. It is but natural, therefore, for the writer, when conscious that his works will not produce him fame hereafter, to endeavor to make them turn out to his temporal interest here.

Whatever be the motives which induce men to write, whether avarice or fame, the country becomes most wise and happy in which they most serve for instructors. The countries where sacerdotal instruction alone is permitted remain in ignorance, superstition, and hopeless slavery. In England, where there are as many new books published as in all the rest of Europe together, a spirit of freedom and reason reigns among the people: they have been often known to act like fools, they are generally found to think like men.

The only danger that attends a multiplicity of publications is that some of them may be calculated to injure rather than benefit society. But where writers are numerous, they also serve as a check upon each other; and perhaps a literary inquisition is the most terrible punishment that can be conceived to a literary transgressor.

But, to do the English justice, there are but few offenders of this kind; their publications in general aim at mending either the heart or improving the common weal. The dullest writer talks of virtue, and liberty, and benevolence with esteem; tells his true story, filled with good and wholesome advice; warns against slavery, bribery, or the bite of a mad dog; and dresses up his little useful magazine of knowledge and entertainment at least with a good intention. The dunces of France, on the other hand, who have less encouragement, are more vicious. Tender hearts, languishing eyes, Leonora in love at thirteen, ecstatic transports, stolen blisses, are the frivolous subjects of their frivolous memoirs. In England, if a bawdy blockhead thus breaks in on the community, he sets his whole fraternity in a roar; nor can he escape, even though he should fly to nobility for shelter.

Thus even dunces, my friend, may make themselves useful. But there are others whom nature has blessed with talents above the rest of mankind: men capable of thinking with precision and impressing their thoughts with rapidity; beings who diffuse those regards upon mankind which others contract and settle upon themselves. These deserve every honor from that community of which they are more peculiarly the children; to such I would give my heart, since to them I am indebted for its humanity! Adieu.

LETTER LXXVI.

THE PREFERENCE OF GRACE TO BEAUTY: AN ALLEGORY.

From Hingpo to Lien Chi Altangi, by the way of Moscow.

I STILL remain at Terki, where I have received that money which was remitted here in order to release me from captivity. My fair companion still improves in my esteem; the more I know her mind, her beauty becomes more poignant: she appears charming, even among the daughters of Circassia.

Yet, were I to examine her beauty with the art of a statuary, I should find numbers here that far surpass her: nature has not granted her all the boasted Circassian regularity of feature, and yet she greatly exceeds the fairest of the country in the art of seizing the affections. "Whence," have I often said to myself, "this resistless magic that attends even moderate charms? Though I regard the beauties of the country with admiration, every interview weakens the impression, but the form of Zelis grows upon my imagination; I never behold her without an increase of tenderness and respect. Whence this injustice of the mind, in preferring imperfect beauty to that which Nature seems to have finished with care? Whence the infatuation that he whom a comet could not amaze should be astonished at a meteor?" When reason was thus fatigued to find an answer, my imagination pursued the subject, and this was the result:

I fancied myself placed between two landscapes—this called the Region of Beauty, and that the Valley of the Graces. The one was adorned with all that luxuriant nature could bestow: the fruits of various climates adorned the trees, the grove resounded with music, the gale breathed perfume, every charm that could arise from symmetry and exact distribution was here conspicuous, the whole offering a prospect of pleasure without end. The Valley of the Graces, on the other hand, seemed by no means so inviting; the streams and the groves appeared just as they usually do in frequented countries: no magnificent parterres, no concert in the grove; the rivulet was edged with weeds, and the rook joined its voice to that of the nightingale. All was simplicity and nature.

The most striking objects ever first allure the traveller. I entered the Region of Beauty with increased curiosity, and promised myself endless satisfaction in being introduced to the presiding goddess. I perceived several strangers, who entered with the same design; and what surprised me not a little was to see several others hastening to leave this abode of seeming felicity.

After some fatigue, I had at last the honor of being introduced to the goddess who represented Beauty in person. She was seated on a throne, at the foot of which stood several strangers, lately introduced like me, all regarding her form in ecstasy. "Ah, what eyes! what lips! how clear her complexion! how perfect her shape!" At these exclamations Beauty, with downcast eyes, would endeavor to counterfeit modesty, but soon again looking round, as if to confirm every spectator in his favorable sentiments: sometimes she would attempt to allure us by smiles; and at intervals would bridle back, in order to inspire us with respect as well as tenderness.

This ceremony lasted for some time, and had so much employed our eyes that we had forgot all this while that the goddess was silent. We soon, however, began to perceive the defect. "What!" said we among each other, "are we to have nothing but languishing airs, soft looks, and inclinations of the head? will the goddess only deign to satisfy our eyes?" Upon this one of the company stepped up to present her with some fruits he had gathered by the way. She received the present most sweetly smiling, and with one of the whitest hands in the world, but still not a word escaped her lips.

I now found that my companions grew weary of their homage; they went off one by one, and, resolving not to be left behind, I offered to go in my turn; when, just at the door of the temple, I was called back by a female whose name was Pride, and who seemed displeased at the behavior of the company. "Where are you hastening?" said she to me, with an angry air; "the Goddess of Beauty is here." "I have been to visit her, madam," replied I, "and find her more beautiful even than report had made her." "And why, then, will you leave her?" added the female. "I have seen her long enough," returned I; "I have got all her features by heart. Her eyes are still the same. Her nose is a very fine one, but it is such a nose now as it was half an hour ago: could she throw a little more mind into her face, perhaps I should be for wishing to have more of her company." "What signifies," replied my female, "whether she has a mind or not? has she any occasion for a mind, so formed as she is by nature? If she had a common face, indeed, there might be some reason for thinking to improve it; but when features are already perfect every alteration would but impair them. A fine face is already at the point of perfection, and a fine lady should endeavor to keep it so: the impression it would receive from thought would but disturb its whole economy."

To this speech I gave no reply, but made the best of my way to the Valley of the Graces. Here I found all those who before had been my companions in the Region of Beauty, now upon the same errand.

As we entered the valley the prospect insensibly seemed to improve; we found everything so natural, so domestic and pleasing, that our minds, which before were congealed in admiration, now relaxed into gayety and good-humor. We had designed to pay our respects to the presiding goddess, but she was nowhere to be found. One of our companions asserted that her temple lay to the right; another, to the left; a third insisted that it was straight before us; and a fourth that we had left it behind. In short, we found everything familiar and charming, but could not determine where to seek for the Grace in person.

In this agreeable incertitude we passed several hours, and though very desirous of finding the goddess, by no means impatient of the delay. Every part of the valley presented some minute beauty, which, without offering itself, at once stole upon the soul, and captivated us with the charms of our retreat. Still, however, we continued to search, and might still have continued, had we not been interrupted by a voice which, though we could not see from whence it came, addressed us in this manner:

"If you would find the Goddess of Grace, seek her not under one form, for she assumes a thousand. Ever changing under the eye of inspection, her variety, rather than her figure, is pleasing. In contemplating her beauty, the eye glides over every perfection with giddy delight, and, capable of fixing nowhere, is charmed with the whole.[1] She is now Contemplation with solemn look, again Compassion with humid eye: she now sparkles with joy, soon every feature speaks distress; her looks at times invite our approach, at others repress our presumption. The goddess cannot be properly called beautiful under any one of these forms, but by combining them all she becomes irresistibly pleasing." Adieu.

---

[1] "Vultus nimium lubricus aspici."—*Hor.*—GOLDSMITH.

LETTER LXXVII.

THE BEHAVIOR OF A SHOPKEEPER AND HIS JOURNEYMAN.

From Lien Chi Altangi to Fum Hoam, first President of the Ceremonial Academy,
at Pekin, in China.

THE shops of London are as well furnished as those of
Pekin. Those of London have a picture hung at their door,[1]
informing the passengers what they have to sell, as those at
Pekin have a board to assure the buyer that they have no intention to cheat him.[2]

I was this morning to buy silk for a nightcap: immediately
upon entering the mercer's shop, the master and his two men,
with wigs plastered with powder, appeared to ask my commands. They were certainly the civilest people alive; if I
but looked, they flew to the place where I cast my eye; every motion of mine sent them running round the whole shop
for my satisfaction. I informed them that I wanted what
was good, and they showed me not less than forty pieces, and
each was better than the former, the prettiest pattern in nature, and the fittest in the world for nightcaps. "My very
good friend," said I to the mercer, "you must not pretend to
instruct me in silks; I know these in particular to be no better
than your mere flimsy bungees." "That may be," cried the
mercer, who I afterward found had never contradicted a man

---

[1] See Letter II. p. 98. The house or door signs of London were taken down
in 1766.

[2] "By the side of each shop is suspended from on high a huge ornamental label
of wood, varnished and gilded, on which are inscribed the particular calling of the
tenant, and the goods in which he deals. The inscriptions in the shops are sometimes amusing, and at the same time highly characteristic of the keenness and industry of the people as traders. We have seen the following: 'Goods genuine,
prices true.' 'Trade circling like a wheel,' etc. 'Former customers have inspired
caution—no credit given.' 'A small stream always flowing,' etc."—DAVIS's *Chinese*, vol. ii. p. 9.

in his life; "I cannot pretend to say but they may; but I can assure you my Lady Trail has had a sack from this piece this very morning." "But, friend," said I, "though my lady has chosen a sack from it, I see no necessity that I should wear it for a nightcap." "That may be," returned he again, "yet what becomes a pretty lady will at any time look well on a handsome gentleman." This short compliment was thrown in so very seasonably upon my ugly face, that, even though I disliked the silk, I desired him to cut me off the pattern of a nightcap.

While this business was consigned to his journeyman, the master himself took down some pieces of silk still finer than any I had yet seen, and spreading them before me, "There," cries he, "there's a beauty! my Lord Snakeskin has bespoke the fellow to this for the birth-night this very morning; it would look charmingly in waistcoats." "But I do not want a waistcoat," replied I. "Not want a waistcoat?" returned the mercer; "then I would advise you to buy one; when waistcoats are wanted, you may depend upon it they will come dear. Always buy before you want, and you are sure to be well used, as they say in Cheapside." There was so much justice in his advice that I could not refuse taking it; besides, the silk, which was really a good one, increased the temptation; so I gave orders for that too.

As I was waiting to have my bargains measured and cut, which, I know not how, they executed but slowly, during the interval the mercer entertained me with the modern manner of some of the nobility receiving company in their morning-gowns. "Perhaps, sir," adds he, "you have a mind to see what kind of silk is universally worn?" Without waiting for my reply, he spreads a piece before me which might be reckoned beautiful even in China. "If the nobility," continues he, "were to know I sold this to any under a Right Honorable I should certainly lose their custom; you see, my lord, it is at once rich, tasty, and quite the thing." "I am no lord," interrupted I. "I beg pardon," cried he; "but be pleased to remember, when you intend buying a morning-gown, that you had an offer from me of something worth money. Conscience, sir, conscience is my way of dealing: you may buy a morning-gown now, or you may stay till they become dearer and less fashionable; but it is not my business to advise." In short, most reverend Fum, he persuaded me to buy a morning-gown also, and would probably have persuaded me to have bought half the goods in his shop, if I had stayed long enough, or was furnished with sufficient money.

Upon returning home, I could not help reflecting with some astonishment how this very man, with such a confined education and capacity, was yet capable of turning me as he thought proper and moulding me to his inclinations. I knew he was only answering his own purposes, even while he attempted to appear solicitous about mine; yet, by a voluntary infatuation, a sort of passion, compounded of vanity and good-nature, I walked into the snare with my eyes open, and put myself to future pain in order to give him immediate pleasure. The wisdom of the ignorant somewhat resembles the instinct of animals; it is diffused in but a very narrow sphere, but within that circle it acts with vigor, uniformity, and success. Adieu.

LETTER LXXVIII.

THE FRENCH RIDICULED AFTER THEIR OWN MANNER.

From the Same.

From my former accounts, you may be apt to fancy the English the most ridiculous people under the sun. They are indeed ridiculous; yet every other nation in Europe is equally so; each laughs at each, and the Asiatic at all.

I may, upon another occasion, point out what is most strikingly absurd in other countries; I shall, at present, confine myself only to France. The first national peculiarity a traveller meets upon entering that kingdom is an odd sort of a staring vivacity in every eye, not excepting even the children; the people, it seems, have got into their heads that they have more wit than others, and so stare in order to look smart.

I know not how it happens, but there appears a sickly delicacy in the faces of their finest women. This may have introduced the use of paint, and paint produces wrinkles; so that a fine lady shall look like a hag at twenty-three. But as, in some measure, they never appear young, so it may be equally asserted that they actually think themselves never old: a gentle miss shall prepare for new conquests at sixty, shall hobble a rigadoon when she can scarce walk out without a crutch; she shall affect the girl, play her fan and her eyes, and talk of sentiments, bleeding hearts, and expiring for love, when actually dying with age. Like a departing philosopher, she attempts to make her last moments the most brilliant of her life.

Their civility to strangers is what they are chiefly proud of; and, to confess sincerely, their beggars are the very politest beggars I ever knew: in other places a traveller is addressed with a piteous whine or a sturdy solemnity, but a French beggar shall ask your charity with a very genteel bow, and thank you for it with a smile and a shrug.

Another instance of this people's breeding I must not forget. An Englishman would not speak his native language in a company of foreigners, where he was sure that none understood him; a travelling Hottentot himself would be silent if acquainted only with the language of his country; but a Frenchman shall talk to you whether you understand his language or not; never troubling his head whether you have learned French, still he keeps up the conversation, fixes his eye full in your face, and asks a thousand questions, which he answers himself for want of a more satisfactory reply.

But their civility to foreigners is not half so great as their admiration of themselves. Everything that belongs to them and their nation is great, magnificent beyond expression, quite romantic; every garden is a paradise, every hovel a palace, and every woman an angel. They shut their eyes close; throw their mouths wide open, and cry out in rapture, "*Sacre!* what beauty! *O Ciel!* what taste! *mort de ma vie!* what grandeur! Was ever any people like ourselves? We are the nation of men, and all the rest no better than two-legged barbarians."

I fancy the French would make the best cooks in the world, if they had but meat; as it is, they can dress you out five different dishes from a nettle-top, seven from a dock-leaf, and twice as many from a frog's haunches; these eat prettily enough when one is a little used to them, are easy of digestion, and seldom overload the stomach with crudities. They seldom dine under seven hot dishes. It is true, indeed, with all this magnificence they seldom spread a cloth before the guests; but in that I cannot be angry with them, since those who have no linen on their backs may very well be excused for wanting it upon their tables.

Even religion itself loses its solemnity among them. Upon their roads, at about every five miles' distance, you see an image of the Virgin Mary, dressed up in grim head-cloths, painted cheeks, and an old red petticoat; before her a lamp is often kept burning, at which, with the saint's permission, I have frequently lighted my pipe. Instead of the Virgin, you are sometimes presented with a crucifix, at other times with a wooden Saviour, fitted out in complete garniture, with sponge, spear, nails, pincers, hammer, beeswax, and vinegar-bottle. Some of those images, I have been told, came down from heaven; if so, in heaven they have but bungling workmen.

In passing through their towns you frequently see the men sitting at the doors knitting stockings, while the care of cultivating the ground and pruning the vines falls to the women. This is, perhaps, the reason why the fair sex are granted some peculiar privileges in this country; particularly, when they can get horses, of riding without a side-saddle.

But I begin to think you may find this description pert and dull enough; perhaps it is so, yet in general it is the manner in which the French usually describe foreigners; and it is but just to force a part of that ridicule back upon them which they attempt to lavish on others. Adieu.

LETTER LXXIX.

THE PREPARATIONS OF BOTH THEATRES FOR A WINTER CAMPAIGN.

From the Same.

THE two theatres[1] which serve to amuse the citizens here are opened for the winter. The mimetic troops, different from those of the State, begin their campaign when all the others quit the field; and, at a time when the Europeans cease to destroy each other in reality, they are entertained with mock battles upon the stage.

The dancing-master once more shakes his quivering feet; the carpenter prepares his paradise of pasteboard; the hero resolves to cover his forehead with brass, and the heroine begins to scour her copper tail, preparative to future operations; in short, all are in motion, from the theatrical letter-carrier in yellow clothes to Alexander the Great that stands on a stool.

Both houses have already commenced hostilities. War, open war, and no quarter received or given! Two singing-women,[2] like heralds, have begun the contest; the whole town

---

[1] Drury Lane, of which Garrick was the manager and lessee, and Covent Garden, of which Rich, represented by Beard, the singer, was the manager and lessee.

[2] Miss Brent and Mrs. Vincent. Mrs. Vincent made her first appearance (on any stage) at Drury Lane, 23d Sept., 1760, as Polly, in the "Beggar's Opera." Miss Brent (a scholar of Dr. Arne's) made her first appearance at Covent Garden, as Polly, in the same play, on the 10th Oct., 1759; and was so successful that she carried all before her.—See Essay V. of Unacknowledged Essays, in Vol. III.

> "Lo! *Vincent* comes—with simple grace arrayed,
> She laughs at paltry arts, and scorns parade.
> Nature through her is by reflection shown,
> Whilst Gay once more knows Polly for his own.
> Talk not to me of diffidence and fear—
> I see it all, but must forgive it here.
> Defects like these, which modest terrors cause,
> From impudence itself extort applause,

is divided on this solemn occasion; one has the finest pipe, the other the finest manner; one courtesies to the ground, the other salutes the audience with a smile; one comes on with modesty which asks, the other with boldness which extorts, applause; one wears powder, the other has none; one has the longest waist, but the other appears most easy. All, all is important and serious. The town as yet perseveres in its neutrality; a cause of such moment demands the most mature deliberation; they continue to exhibit, and it is very possible this contest may continue to please to the end of the season.

But the generals of either army have, as I am told, several re-enforcements to lend occasional assistance. If they produce a pair of diamond buckles at one house, we have a pair of eyebrows that can match them at the other. If we outdo them in our attitude, they can overcome us by a shrug; if we can bring more children on the stage, they can bring more guards in red clothes, who strut and shoulder their swords to the astonishment of every spectator.

They tell me here that people frequent the theatre in order to be instructed as well as amused. I smile to hear the assertion. If I ever go to one of their play-houses, what with trumpets, hallooing behind the stage, and bawling upon it, I

Candor and reason still take virtue's part;
We love e'en foibles in so good a heart.
Let Tommy Arne, with usual pomp of style,
Whose chief, whose only merit's to compile,

*   *   *   *   *

Publish proposals, laws for taste prescribe,
And chant the praise of an Italian tribe;
Let him reverse kind Nature's first decrees,
And teach e'en Brent a method not to please;
But never shall a truly British stage
Bear a vile race of eunuchs on the stage.
The boasted work's called national in vain,
If one Italian voice pollutes the strain.
Where tyrants rule, and slaves with joy obey,
Let slavish minstrels pour th' enervate lay;
To Britons far more noble pleasures spring,
In native notes whilst Beard and Vincent sing."
                              CHURCHILL, *The Rosciad.*

am quite dizzy before the performance is over. If I enter the house with any sentiments in my head, I am sure to have none going away; the whole mind being filled with a dead-march, a funeral procession, a cat-call, a jig, or a tempest.

There is, perhaps, nothing more easy than to write properly for the English theatre. I am amazed that none are apprenticed to the trade. The author, when well acquainted with the value of thunder and lightning; when versed in all the mystery of scene-shifting and trap-doors; when skilled in the proper periods to introduce a wire-walker or a water-fall; when instructed in every actor's peculiar talent, and capable of adapting his speeches to the supposed excellence; when thus instructed, he knows all that can give a modern audience pleasure. One player shines in an exclamation, another in a groan, a third in a horror, a fourth in a start, a fifth in a smile, a sixth faints, and a seventh fidgets round the stage with peculiar vivacity; that piece, therefore, will succeed best where each has a proper opportunity of shining: the actor's business is not so much to adapt himself to the poet as the poet's to adapt himself to the actor.

The great secret, therefore, of tragedy-writing at present is a perfect acquaintance with theatrical ah's and oh's; a certain number of these, interspersed with gods! tortures! rack! and damnation! shall distort every actor almost into convulsions, and draw tears from every spectator; a proper use of these will infallibly fill the whole house with applause. But, above all, a whining scene must strike most forcibly. I would advise, from my present knowledge of the audience, the two favorite players of the town to introduce a scene of this sort in every play. Toward the middle of the last act I would have them enter with wild looks and outspread arms: there is no necessity for speaking, they are only to groan at each other; they must vary the tones of exclamation and despair through the whole theatrical gamut, wring their figures into every shape of distress; and, when their calamities have drawn a proper quantity of tears from the sympathetic spectators, they may go off in dumb solemnity at different doors, clasping their hands or slapping their pocket-holes: this, which may be called a tragic pantomime, will answer every purpose of moving the passions as well as words could have done, and it must save those expenses which go to reward an author.

All modern plays that would keep the audience alive must be conceived in this manner; and, indeed, many a modern play is made up on no other plan. This is the merit that lifts up the heart, like opium, into a rapture of insensibility, and can dismiss the mind from all the fatigue of thinking: this is the eloquence that shines in many a long-forgotten scene, which has been reckoned excessively fine upon acting; this the lightning that flashes no less in the hyperbolical tyrant, "who breakfasts on the wind," than in little Norval, "as harmless as the babe unborn." Adieu.

LETTER LXXX.

THE EVIL TENDENCY OF INCREASING PENAL LAWS, OR ENFORCING EVEN THOSE ALREADY IN BEING WITH RIGOR.

From the Same.

I HAVE always regarded the spirit of mercy which appears in the Chinese laws with admiration.[1] An order for the exe-

---

[1] "The most remarkable thing in the Chinese code is its great reasonableness, clearness, and consistency; the business-like brevity and directness of the various provisions, and the plainness and moderation of the language in which they are expressed. There is nothing here of the monstrous verbiage of most other Asiatic productions; none of the superstitious deliration, the miserable incoherence, the tremendous *non sequiturs* and eternal repetitions of those oracular performances; but a clear, concise, and distinct series of enactments, savoring throughout of practical judgment and European good-sense; and if not always conformable to our improved notions of expediency in this country, in general approaching to them more nearly than the codes of most other nations."—*Edinburgh Review*, vol. xvi. p. 481: critique on Sir George Staunton's "Leu Lee, or Penal Code of the Chinese."

"The edition of the penal code of China, circulated in a cheap form for the benefit of the public, is so concisely framed as to be comprehended in little more space than is occupied by one of our statutes. Indeed, the whole code does not contain two thousand different characters or words; so studious have the legislators of China been to simplify and adapt it to common capacities."—*Quarterly Review*, No. CXII. p. 504 (1836).

cution of a criminal is carried from court by slow journeys
of six miles a day, but a pardon is sent down with the most
rapid despatch. If five sons of the same father be guilty of
the same offence, one of them is forgiven, in order to continue
the family and comfort his aged parents in their decline.

Similar to this, there is a spirit of mercy breathes through
the laws of England, which some erroneously endeavor to
suppress; the laws, however, seem unwilling to punish the
offender, or to furnish the officers of justice with every means
of acting with severity. Those who arrest debtors are denied the use of arms; the nightly watch is permitted to repress the disorders of the drunken citizens only with clubs;
Justice, in such a case, seems to hide her terrors, and permits
some offenders to escape rather than load any with a punishment disproportioned to the crime.

Thus it is the glory of an Englishman that he is not only
governed by laws, but that these are also tempered by mercy.
A country restrained by severe laws, and those, too, executed
with severity (as in Japan),[1] is under the most terrible species
of tyranny. A royal tyrant is generally dreadful to the great,
but numerous penal laws grind every rank of people, and
chiefly those least able to resist oppression, the poor.

It is very possible thus for a people to become slaves to
laws of their own enacting, as the Athenians were to those of
Draco. "It might first happen," says the historian, "that
men with peculiar talents for villany attempted to evade the
ordinances already established; their practices, therefore, soon
brought on a new law levelled against them; but the same
degree of cunning which had taught the knave to evade the
former statutes, taught him to evade the latter also; he flew
to new shifts, while Justice pursued with new ordinances;

---

[1] "I have often wondered at the laconic style of those tablets which are hung
up on the roads to notify the emperor's pleasure. There is no reason given how it
came about that such a law was made; no mention of the law-giver's view and intention; nor any graduated penalty put upon the violation thereof. The bare
transgression of the law is capital, without any regard to the degree or heinousness
of the crime, or the favorable circumstances the offender's case may be accompanied with."—KÆMPFER, *History of Japan*, 2 vols. folio, 1727.

still, however, he kept his proper distance, and whenever one crime was judged penal by the state he left committing it in order to practise some unforbidden species of villany. Thus the criminal against whom the threatenings were denounced always escaped free, while the simple rogue alone felt the rigor of justice. In the mean time penal laws became numerous; almost every person in the state, unknowingly, at different times offended, and was every moment subject to a malicious prosecution." In fact, penal laws, instead of preventing crimes, are generally enacted after the commission; instead of repressing the growth of ingenious villany, only multiply deceit, by putting it upon new shifts and expedients of practising it with impunity.

Such laws, therefore, resemble the guards which are sometimes imposed upon tributary princes, apparently, indeed, to secure them from danger, but in reality to confirm their captivity.

Penal laws, it must be allowed, secure property in a state, but they also diminish personal security in the same proportion; there is no positive law, how equitable soever, that may not be sometimes capable of injustice. When a law, enacted to make theft punishable with death, happens to be equitably executed, it can at best only guard our possessions; but when, by favor or ignorance, justice pronounces a wrong verdict, it then attacks our lives, since in such a case the whole community suffers with the innocent victim; if, therefore, in order to secure the effects of one man I should make a law which may take away the life of another, in such a case, to attain smaller good, I am guilty of a greater evil; to secure society in the possession of a bauble I render a real and valuable possession precarious. And, indeed, the experience of every age may serve to vindicate the assertion: no law could be more just than that called *lesæ majestatis*, when Rome was governed by emperors. It was but reasonable that every conspiracy against the administration should be detected and punished; yet what terrible slaughters succeeded in consequence of its enacting! proscriptions, stranglings, poisonings, in almost every family of distinction; yet all done in a legal way—

every criminal had his trial, and lost his life by a majority of witnesses.

And such will ever be the case where punishments are numerous, and where a weak, vicious, but above all, where a mercenary magistrate is concerned in their execution. Such a man desires to see penal laws increased, since he too frequently has it in his power to turn them into instruments of extortion; in such hands the more laws the wider means, not of satisfying justice, but of satiating avarice.

A mercenary magistrate, who is rewarded in proportion, not to his integrity, but to the number he convicts, must be a person of the most unblemished character, or he will lean on the side of cruelty; and when once the work of injustice is begun, it is impossible to tell how far it will proceed. It is said of the hyena that naturally it is no way ravenous, but when once it has tasted human flesh it becomes the most voracious animal of the forest, and continues to persecute mankind ever after. A corrupt magistrate may be considered as a human hyena; he begins, perhaps, by a private snap, he goes on to a morsel among friends, he proceeds to a meal in public, from a meal he advances to a surfeit, and at last sucks blood like a vampire.

Not into such hands should the administration of justice be intrusted, but to those who know how to reward as well as to punish. It was a fine saying of Nangfu, the emperor, who, being told that his enemies had raised an insurrection in one of the distant provinces, "Come, then, my friend," said he, "follow me, and I promise you that we shall quickly destroy them." He marched forward, and the rebels submitted upon his approach. All now thought that he would take the most signal revenge, but were surprised to see the captives treated with mildness and humanity. "How!" cries his first minister, "is this the manner in which you fulfil your promise? Your royal word was given that your enemies should be destroyed, and behold you have pardoned all, and even caressed some!" "I promised," replied the emperor, with a generous air, "to *destroy* my enemies; I have fulfilled my word, for see, they are enemies no longer — I have made *friends* of them."

This, could it always succeed, were the true method of destroying the enemies of a state. Well it were if rewards and mercy alone could regulate the commonwealth; but since punishments are sometimes necessary, let them at least be rendered terrible by being executed but seldom, and let Justice lift her sword rather to terrify than revenge. Adieu.

LETTER LXXXI.

THE LADIES' TRAINS RIDICULED.

From the Same.

I HAVE as yet given you but a short and imperfect description of the ladies of England. Woman, my friend, is a subject not easily understood, even in China; what, therefore, can be expected from my knowledge of the sex, in a country where they are universally allowed to be riddles, and I but a stranger?

To confess a truth, I was afraid to begin the description, lest the sex should undergo some new revolution before it was finished, and my picture should thus become old before it could well be said to have ever been new. To-day they are lifted upon stilts, to-morrow they lower their heels and raise their heads; their clothes at one time are bloated out with whalebone; at present they have laid their hoops aside, and are become as slim as mermaids.[1] All, all is in a state of continual fluctuation, from the mandarin's wife, who rattles through the streets in her chariot, to the humble sempstress, who clatters over the pavement in iron-shod pattens.

What chiefly distinguishes the sex at present is the train.

---

[1] " The Chinese, perhaps, may be said to possess an advantage in the absence of those perpetual and frequently absurd mutations of fashion in Europe, which at one period blow out the same individual like a balloon, whom at another they contract into a mummy. They are not at the mercy and disposal, in matters of taste, of those who make their clothes, and their modes generally last as long as their garments. The only setter of fashions is the board of rites and ceremonies at Pekin, and to depart materially from their ordinances would be considered as something worse than mere *mauvais ton*."—DAVIS's *Chinese*, vol. i. p. 352.

As a lady's quality or fashion was once determined here by the circumference of her hoop, both are now measured by the length of her tail. Women of moderate fortunes are contented with tails moderately long; but ladies of true taste and distinction set no bounds to their ambition in this particular. I am told the Lady Mayoress, on days of ceremony, carries one longer than a bell-wether of Bantam, whose tail, you know, is trundled along in a wheelbarrow.

Sun of China, what contradictions do we find in this strange world! Not only the people of different countries think in opposition to each other, but the inhabitants of a single island are often found inconsistent with themselves. Would you believe it? this very people, my Fum, who are so fond of seeing their women with long tails, at the same time dock their horses to the very rump!

But you may easily guess that I am no ways displeased with a fashion which tends to increase a demand for the commodities of the East, and is so very beneficial to the country in which I was born. Nothing can be better calculated to increase the price of silk than the present manner of dressing. A lady's train is not bought but at some expense, and after it has swept the public walks for a very few evenings is fit to be worn no longer: more silk must be bought in order to repair the breach, and some ladies of peculiar economy are thus found to patch up their tails eight or ten times in a season. This unnecessary consumption may introduce poverty here, but then we shall be the richer for it in China.

The man in black, who is a professed enemy to this manner of ornamenting the tail, assures me there are numberless inconveniences attending it, and that a lady dressed up to the fashion is as much a cripple as any in Nankin. But his chief indignation is levelled at those who dress in this manner without a proper fortune to support it. He assures me that he has known some who would have a tail though they wanted a petticoat, and others who, without any other pretensions, fancied they became ladies merely from the addition of three superfluous yards of ragged silk. "I know a thrifty, good woman," continues he, "who thinking herself obliged to carry a train like her betters, never walks from home without the uneasy apprehensions of wearing it out too soon; every excursion she makes gives her new anxiety; and her train is every bit as importunate, and wounds her peace as much, as the bladder we sometimes see tied to the tail of a cat."

Nay, he ventures to affirm that a train may often bring a lady into the most critical circumstances: " For should a rude fellow," says he, " offer to come up to ravish a kiss, and the lady attempt to avoid it, in retiring she must necessarily tread upon her train and thus fall fairly upon her back, by which means every one knows—her clothes may be spoiled."

The ladies here make no scruple to laugh at the smallness of a Chinese slipper, but I fancy our wives at China would have a more real cause of laughter could they but see the immoderate length of a European train. Head of Confucius! to view a human being crippling herself with a great unwieldy tail for our diversion; backward she cannot go, forward she must move but slowly, and if ever she attempts to turn round, it must be in a circle not smaller than that described by the wheeling crocodile when it would face an assailant. And yet, to think that all this confers importance and majesty! to think that a lady acquires additional respect from fifteen yards of trailing taffety! I can't contain: ha! ha! ha! This is certainly a remnant of European barbarity: the female Tartar, dressed in sheepskins, is in far more convenient drapery. Their own writers have sometimes inveighed against the absurdity of this fashion, but perhaps it has never been ridiculed so well as upon the Italian theatre, where Pasquariello being engaged to attend on Countess of Fernambroco, having one of his hands employed in carrying her muff, and the other her lapdog, he bears her train majestically along by sticking it in the waistband of his breeches. Adieu.

LETTER LXXXII.

THE SCIENCES USEFUL IN A POPULOUS STATE PREJUDICIAL IN A BARBAROUS ONE.

From the Same.

A DISPUTE has for some time divided the philosophers of Europe: it is debated whether arts and sciences are more serviceable or prejudicial to mankind. They who maintain the cause of literature endeavor to prove their usefulness from the impossibility of a large number of men subsisting in a small tract of country without them; from the pleasure which attends the acquisition; and from the influence of knowledge in promoting practical morality.

They who maintain the opposite opinion display the happiness and innocence of those uncultivated nations who live without learning; urge the numerous vices which are to be found only in polished society; enlarge upon the oppression, the cruelty, and the blood which must necessarily be shed in order to cement civil society; and insist upon the happy equality of conditions in a barbarous state, preferable to the unnatural subordination of a more refined constitution.

This dispute, which has already given so much employment to speculative indolence, has been managed with much ardor, and (not to suppress our sentiments) with but little sagacity. They who insist that the sciences are useful in refined society are certainly right, and they who maintain that barbarous nations are more happy without them are right also; but when one side, for this reason, attempts to prove them as universally useful to the solitary barbarian as to the native of a crowded commonwealth, or when the other endeavors to banish them as prejudicial to all society, even from populous states as well as from the inhabitants of the wilderness, they are both wrong; since that knowledge which makes the happiness of a refined European would be a torment to the precarious tenant of an Asiatic wild.

Let me, to prove this, transport the imagination for a moment to the midst of a forest in Siberia. There we behold the inhabitant, poor indeed, but equally fond of happiness with the most refined philosopher of China. The earth lies uncultivated and uninhabited for miles around him; his little family and he the sole and undisputed possessors. In such circumstances, nature and reason will induce him to prefer a hunter's life to that of cultivating the earth. He will certainly adhere to that manner of living which is carried on at the smallest expense of labor, and that food which is most agreeable to the appetite; he will prefer indolent though precarious luxury to a laborious though permanent competence; and a knowledge of his own happiness will determine him to persevere in native barbarity.

In like manner his happiness will incline him to bind himself by no law. Laws are made in order to secure present property; but he is possessed of no property which he is afraid to lose, and desires no more than will be sufficient to sustain him; to enter into compacts with others would be undergoing a voluntary obligation without the expectance of any reward. He and his countrymen are tenants, not rivals, in the same inexhaustible forest; the increased possessions of one by no means diminishes the expectations arising from equal assiduity in another; there is no need of laws, therefore, to repress ambition, where there can be no mischief attending its most boundless gratifications.

Our solitary Siberian will, in like manner, find the sciences not only entirely useless in directing his practice, but disgusting even in speculation. In every contemplation our curiosity must be first excited by the appearances of things, before our reason undergoes the fatigue of investigating the causes. Some of those appearances are produced by experiment, others by minute inquiry; some arise from a knowledge of foreign climates, and others from an intimate study of our own. But there are few objects in comparison which present themselves to the inhabitant of a barbarous country; the game he

II.—25

hunts, or the transient cottage he builds, make up the chief objects of his concern; his curiosity, therefore, must be proportionably less; and if that is diminished the reasoning faculty will be diminished in proportion.

Besides, sensual enjoyment adds wings to curiosity. We consider few objects with ardent attention but those which have some connection with our wishes, our pleasures, or our necessities. A desire of enjoyment first interests our passions in the pursuit, points out the object of investigation, and reason then comments where sense has led the way. An increase in the number of our enjoyments, therefore, necessarily produces an increase of scientific research; but, in countries where almost every enjoyment is wanting, reason there seems destitute of its great inspirer, and speculation is the business of fools when it becomes its own reward.

The barbarous Siberian is too wise, therefore, to exhaust his time in quest of knowledge which neither curiosity prompts nor pleasure impels him to pursue. When told of the exact admeasurement of a degree upon the equator at Quito, he feels no pleasure in the account; when informed that such a discovery tends to promote navigation and commerce, he finds himself no way interested in either. A discovery which some have pursued at the hazard of their lives affects him with neither astonishment nor pleasure. He is satisfied with thoroughly understanding the few objects which contribute to his own felicity; he knows the properest places where to lay the snare for the sable, and discerns the value of furs with more than European sagacity. More extended knowledge would only serve to render him unhappy; it might lend a ray to show him the misery of his situation, but could not guide him in his efforts to avoid it. Ignorance is the happiness of the poor.

The misery of a being endowed with sentiments above its capacity of fruition is most admirably described in one of the fables of Lokman,[1] the Indian moralist. "An elephant that

---

[1] An Abyssinian philosopher of high repute among the Eastern nations. Mohammed has given his name to a chapter of the Koran, in which he introduces

had been peculiarly serviceable in fighting the battles of Wistnow was ordered by the god to wish for whatever he thought proper, and the desire should be attended with immediate gratification. The elephant thanked his benefactor on bended knees, and desired to be endowed with the reason and the faculties of a man. Wistnow was sorry to hear the foolish request, and endeavored to dissuade him from his misplaced ambition; but, finding it to no purpose, gave him at last such a portion of wisdom as could correct even the Zend-Avesta of Zoroaster. The reasoning elephant went away rejoicing in his new acquisition; and though his body still retained its ancient form, he found his appetites and passions entirely altered. He first considered that it would not only be more comfortable but also more becoming to wear clothes; but, unhappily, he had no method of making them himself, nor had he the use of speech to demand them from others; and this was the first time he felt real anxiety. He soon perceived how much more elegantly men were fed than he, therefore he began to loathe his usual food, and longed for those delicacies which adorn the tables of princes; but here again he found it impossible to be satisfied, for though he could easily obtain flesh, yet he found it impossible to dress it in any degree of perfection. In short, every pleasure that contributed to the felicity of mankind served only to render him more miserable, as he found himself utterly deprived of the power of enjoyment. In this manner he led a repining, discontented life, detesting himself, and displeased with his ill-judged ambition; till at last his benefactor, Wistnow, taking compassion on his forlorn situation, restored him to the ignorance and the happiness which he was originally formed to enjoy."

No, my friend, to attempt to introduce the sciences into a nation of wandering barbarians is only to render them more

---

God as saying, "I have bestowed wisdom on Lokman." Many of his apophthegms are scattered in the writings of the Orientals, an entertaining selection from which will be found in D'Herbelot. The reliques of his fables were published (1636) at Leyden, in Arabic and Latin, and translated (1714) into French by Galland, at Paris, and more recently (1799) by Marcel.

miserable than even Nature designed they should be.   A life of simplicity is best fitted to a state of solitude.

The great lawgiver of Russia attempted to improve the desolate inhabitants of Siberia by sending among them some of the politest men of Europe.   The consequence has shown that the country was as yet unfit to receive them; they languished for a time with a sort of exotic malady; every day degenerated from themselves; and at last, instead of rendering the country more polite, they conformed to the soil, and put on barbarity.

No, my friend, in order to make the sciences useful in any country it must first become populous: the inhabitant must go through the different stages of hunter, shepherd, and husbandman; then, when property becomes valuable, and consequently gives cause for injustice; then, when laws are appointed to repress injury and secure possession; when men, by the sanction of those laws, become possessed of superfluity; when luxury is thus introduced, and demands its continual supply, then it is that the sciences become necessary and useful; the state then cannot subsist without them; they must then be introduced, at once to teach men to draw the greatest possible quantity of pleasure from circumscribed possession, and to restrain them within the bounds of moderate enjoyment.

The sciences are not the cause of luxury, but its consequence; and this destroyer thus brings with it an antidote which resists the virulence of its own poison.   By asserting that luxury introduces the sciences, we assert a truth; but if, with those who reject the utility of learning, we assert that the sciences also introduce luxury, we shall be at once false, absurd, and ridiculous.   Adieu.

LETTER LXXXIII.

SOME CAUTIONS ON LIFE, TAKEN FROM A MODERN PHILOSOPHER
OF CHINA.

From Lien Chi Altangi to Hingpo, by the Way of Moscow.

You are now arrived at an age, my son, when pleasure dissuades from application: but rob not, by present gratification, all the succeeding period of life of its happiness. Sacrifice a little pleasure at first to the expectance of greater. The study of a few years will make the rest of life completely easy.

But instead of continuing the subject myself, take the following instructions borrowed from a modern philosopher of China:[1] "He who has begun his fortune by study will certainly confirm it by perseverance. The love of books damps the passion for pleasure; and when this passion is once extinguished life is then cheaply supported: thus a man, being possessed of more than he wants, can never be subject to great disappointments, and avoids all those meannesses which indigence sometimes unavoidably produces.

"There is unspeakable pleasure attending the life of a voluntary student. The first time I read an excellent book, it is to me just as if I had gained a new friend. When I read over a book I have perused before, it resembles the meeting with an old one. We ought to lay hold of every incident in life for improvement, the trifling as well as the important. It is not one diamond alone which gives lustre to another; a common coarse stone is also employed for that purpose. Thus I ought to draw advantage from the insults and contempt I meet with from a worthless fellow. His brutality ought to induce me to self-examination, and correct every blemish that may have given rise to his calumny.

---

[1] A translation of this passage may also be seen in Du Halde, vol. ii. fol. ed. pp. 47 and 58. This extract will at least serve to show that fondness for humor which appears in the writings of the Chinese.—GOLDSMITH.

"Yet with all the pleasures and profits which are generally produced by learning, parents often find it difficult to induce their children to study. They often seem dragged to what wears the appearance of application. Thus, being dilatory in the beginning, all future hopes of eminence are entirely cut off. If they find themselves obliged to write two lines more polite than ordinary, their pencil then seems as heavy as a millstone, and they spend ten years in turning two or three periods with propriety.

"These persons are most at a loss when a banquet is almost over; the plate and the dice go round, that the number of little verses, which each is obliged to repeat, may be determined by chance. The booby, when it comes to his turn, appears quite stupid and insensible. The company divert themselves with his confusion; and sneers, winks, and whispers are circulated at his expense. As for him, he opens a pair of large, heavy eyes, stares at all about him, and even offers to join in the laugh, without ever considering himself as the burden of all their good-humor.

"But it is of no importance to read much, except you be regular in your reading. If it be interrupted for any considerable time, it can never be attended with proper improvement. There are some who study for one day with intense application, and repose themselves for ten days after. But wisdom is a coquette, and must be courted with unabating assiduity.

"It was a saying of the ancients, that a man never opens a book without reaping some advantage by it. I say with them, that every book can serve to make us more expert, except romances,[1] and these are no better than the instruments of debauchery. They are dangerous fictions, where love is the ruling passion.

---

[1] "Above all things let him [his brother's son] never touch a romance or novel; these paint beauty in colors more charming than nature, and describe happiness that man never tastes. How delusive, how destructive, are those pictures of consummate bliss! They teach the youthful mind to sigh after beauty and happiness which never existed; to despise the little good which Fortune has mixed in our cup, by expecting more than she ever gave."—GOLDSMITH to his Brother, circâ Feb., 1759.

"The most indecent strokes there pass for turns of wit; intrigue and criminal liberties for gallantry and politeness. Assignations, and even villany, are put in such strong lights, as may inspire even grown men with the strongest passion; how much more, therefore, ought the youth of either sex to dread them, whose reason is so weak, and whose hearts are so susceptible of passion!

"To slip in by a back-door, or leap a wall, are accomplishments that, when handsomely set off, enchant a young heart. It is true, the plot is commonly wound up by a marriage, concluded with the consent of parents, and adjusted by every ceremony prescribed by law. But as in the body of the work there are many passages that offend good morals, overthrow laudable customs, violate the laws, and destroy the duties most essential to society, virtue is thereby exposed to the most dangerous attacks.

"But, say some, the authors of these romances have nothing in view but to represent vice punished and virtue rewarded. Granted. But will the greater number of readers take notice of these punishments and rewards? Are not their minds carried to something else? Can it be imagined that the heart with which the author inspires the love of virtue can overcome that crowd of thoughts which sway them to licentiousness? To be able to inculcate virtue by so leaky a vehicle, the author must be a philosopher of the first rank. But in our age we can find but few first-rate philosophers.

"Avoid such performances where vice assumes the face of virtue: seek wisdom and knowledge without ever thinking you have found them. A man is wise while he continues in the pursuit of wisdom; but when he once fancies that he has found the object of his inquiry, he then becomes a fool. Learn to pursue virtue from the man that is blind, who never makes a step without first examining the ground with his staff.

"The world is like a vast sea; mankind, like a vessel sailing on its tempestuous bosom. Our prudence is its sails, the sciences serve us for oars, good or bad fortune are the favorable or contrary winds, and judgment is the rudder; without this last, the vessel is tossed by every billow, and will find shipwreck in every breeze. In a word, obscurity and indigence are the parents of vigilance and economy; vigilance and economy, of riches and honor; riches and honor, of pride and luxury; pride and luxury, of impurity and idleness; and impurity and idleness again produce indigence and obscurity. Such are the revolutions of life." Adieu.

LETTER LXXXIV.

THE ANECDOTES OF SEVERAL POETS WHO LIVED AND DIED IN CIRCUMSTANCES OF WRETCHEDNESS.

From Lien Chi Altangi to Fum Hoam, first President of the Ceremonial Academy, at Pekin, in China.

I FANCY the character of a poet is in every country the same: fond of enjoying the present, careless of the future; his conversation that of a man of sense, his actions those of a fool; of fortitude able to stand unmoved at the bursting of an earthquake, yet of sensibility to be affected by the breaking of a teacup—such is his character, which, considered in every light, is the very opposite of that which leads to riches.[1]

The poets of the West are as remarkable for their indigence as their genius, and yet, among the numerous hospitals designed to relieve the poor, I have heard of but one erected for the benefit of decayed authors. This was founded by Pope Urban the Eighth, and called the retreat of the incurables; intimating that it was equally impossible to reclaim the patients who sued for reception from poverty or from poetry. To be sincere, were I to send you an account of the lives of the Western poets, either ancient or modern, I fancy you would think me employed in collecting materials for a history of human wretchedness.

Homer is the first poet and beggar of note among the an-

------

[1] A sketch drawn, no doubt, from Goldsmith's own character, and certainly with strong points of resemblance.

cients: he was blind, and sung his ballads about the streets;
but it is observed that his mouth was more frequently filled
with verses than with bread.   Plautus, the comic poet, was
better off; he had two trades—he was a poet for his diversion, and helped to turn a mill in order to gain a livelihood.
Terence was a slave, and Boethius died in jail.[1]

Among the Italians, Paulo Borghese, almost as good a poet
as Tasso, knew fourteen different trades, and yet died because
he could get employment in none.   Tasso himself, who had
the most amiable character of all poets, has often been obliged
to borrow a crown from some friend in order to pay for a
month's subsistence.   He has left us a pretty sonnet, addressed
to his cat, in which he begs the light of her eyes to write by,
being too poor to afford himself a candle.   But Bentivoglio,
poor Bentivoglio! chiefly demands our pity.   His comedies
will last with the Italian language.   He dissipated a noble
fortune in acts of charity and benevolence; but, falling into
misery in his old age, was refused to be admitted into a hospital which he himself had erected.

In Spain, it is said, the great Cervantes died of hunger;
and it is certain that the famous Camoens ended his days in
a hospital.[2]

If we turn to France we shall there find even stronger instances of the ingratitude of the public.   Vaugelas,[3] one of
the politest writers, and one of the honestest men of his time,
was surnamed the Owl, from his being obliged to keep within all day, and venture out only by night, through fear of his
creditors.   His last will is very remarkable.   After having
bequeathed all his worldly substance to the discharging his
debts, he goes on thus: "But as there still may remain some
creditors unpaid, even after all that I have shall have been

---

[1] Boethius was beheaded in prison at Pavia, in 526, by order of Theodore, King
of the Goths.   His work, "De Consolatione Philosophiæ," written during his imprisonment, was translated into Anglo-Saxon by Alfred the Great, and into English
by Queen Elizabeth.   Dr. Johnson advised Miss Carter to undertake a version of it.

[2] Camoens died in an alms-house in 1579.

[3] Vaugelas was born at Chambéry in 1585, and died at Paris in 1650, aged sixty-
five years, thirty of which he devoted to a translation of Quintus Curtius.

disposed of, in such a case, it is my last will that my body should be sold to the surgeons to the best advantage, and that the purchase should go to the discharging those debts which I owe to society; so that if I could not, while living, at least when dead, I may be useful."

Cassandre [1] was one of the greatest geniuses of his time; yet all his merit could not procure him a bare subsistence. Being by degrees driven into a hatred of all mankind, from the little pity he found among them, he even ventured at last ungratefully to impute his calamities to Providence. In his last agonies, when the priest entreated him to rely on the justice of Heaven, and ask mercy from him that made him, "If God," replies he, "has shown me no justice here, what reason have I to expect any from him hereafter?" But being answered that a suspension of justice was no argument that should induce us to doubt of its reality—"Let me entreat you," continued his confessor, "by all that is dear, to be reconciled to God, your Father, your Maker, and Friend." "No," replied the exasperated wretch, "you know the manner in which he left me to live; and," pointing to the straw on which he was stretched, "you see the manner in which he leaves me to die!"

But the sufferings of the poet in other countries is nothing when compared to his distresses here; the names of Spenser and Otway, Butler and Dryden, are every day mentioned as a national reproach: some of them lived in a state of precarious indigence, and others literally died of hunger.

At present the few poets of England no longer depend on the great for subsistence; they have now no other patrons but the public, and the public, collectively considered, is a good and a generous master. It is, indeed, too frequently mistaken as to the merits of every candidate for favor; but, to make amends, it is never mistaken long. A performance, indeed, may be forced for a time into reputation, but, destitute

---

[1] François Cassandre, who translated Aristotle's "Rhetoric" into French, and died in 1695, was a man of very violent temper and of imprudent conduct. He is thus described by Boileau:

"Je suis rustique et fier, et j'ai l'âme grossière."

of real merit, it soon sinks; time, the touchstone of what is truly valuable, will soon discover the fraud, and an author should never arrogate to himself any share of success till his works have been read at least ten years with satisfaction.

A man of letters at present, whose works are valuable, is perfectly sensible of their value. Every polite member of the community, by buying what he writes, contributes to reward him. The ridicule, therefore, of living in a garret might have been wit in the last age, but continues such no longer, because no longer true. A writer of real merit now may easily be rich, if his heart be set only on fortune; and for those who have no merit it is but fit that such should remain in merited obscurity. He may now refuse an invitation to dinner without fearing to incur his patron's displeasure, or to starve by remaining at home. He may now venture to appear in company with just such clothes as other men generally wear, and talk even to princes with all the conscious superiority of wisdom. Though he cannot boast of fortune here, yet he can bravely assert the dignity of independence. Adieu.

LETTER LXXXV.

THE TRIFLING SQUABBLES OF STAGE-PLAYERS RIDICULED.

From the Same.

I have interested myself so long in all the concerns of this people that I am almost become an Englishman. I now begin to read with pleasure of their taking towns or gaining battles, and secretly wish disappointment to all the enemies of Britain. Yet still my regard to mankind fills me with concern for their contentions. I could wish to see the disturbances of Europe once more amicably adjusted; I am an enemy to nothing in this good world but war; I hate fighting between rival states; I hate it between man and man; I hate fighting even between women!

I already informed you that while Europe was at variance

we were also threatened from the stage with an irreconcilable
opposition, and that our singing women were resolved to sing
at each other to the end of the season. O my friend, those
fears were just! They are not only determined to sing at
each other to the end of the season, but, what is worse, to
sing the same song; and what is still more insupportable, to
make us pay for hearing.

If they be for war, for my part I should advise them to
have a public congress, and there fairly squall at each other.
What signifies sounding the trumpet of defiance at a distance,
and calling in the town to fight their battles? I would have
them come boldly into one of the most open and frequented
streets, face to face, and there try their skill in quavering.

However this may be, resolved I am that they shall not
touch one single piece of silver more of mine. Though I
have ears for music, thanks be to Heaven, they are not alto-
gether ass's ears. What! Polly and the Pick-pocket to-night,[1]
Polly and the Pick-pocket to-morrow night, and Polly and
the Pick-pocket again! I want patience. I'll hear no more.
My soul is out of tune; all jarring, discord, and confusion.
Rest, rest, ye dear three clinking shillings, in my pocket's bottom: the music you make is more harmonious to my spirit
than catgut, rosin, or all the nightingales that ever chirruped
in petticoats.

But what raises my indignation to the greatest degree is,
that this piping does not only pester me on the stage, but is
my punishment in private conversation. What is it to me
whether the "fine pipe" of one, or the "great manner" of
the other be preferable? What care I if one has a better top
or the other a nobler bottom? How am I concerned if one
sings from the stomach or the other sings with a snap? Yet,
paltry as these matters are, they make a subject of debate
wherever I go; and this musical dispute, especially among the
fair sex, almost always ends in a very unmusical altercation.

Sure the spirit of contention is mixed into the very constitution of the people! Divisions among the inhabitants of

---

[1] "The Beggar's Opera."

other countries arise only from their higher concerns, but subjects the most contemptible are made an affair of party here; the spirit is carried even into their amusements. The very ladies, whose duty should seem to allay the impetuosity of the opposite sex, become themselves party champions, engage in the thickest of the fight, scold at each other, and show their courage, even at the expense of their lovers and their beauty.

There are even a numerous set of poets who help to keep up the contention and write for the stage. Mistake me not; I do not mean pieces to be acted upon it, but panegyrical verses on the performers; for that is the most universal method of writing for the stage at present. It is the business of the stage poet, therefore, to watch the appearance of every new player at his own house, and so come out next day with a flaunting copy of newspaper verses. In these Nature and the actor may be set to run races, the player always coming off victorious; or Nature may mistake him for herself; or old Shakspeare may put on his winding-sheet and pay him a visit; or the tuneful Nine may strike up their harps in his praise; or, should it happen to be an actress, Venus, the beauteous Queen of Love, and the naked Graces, are ever in waiting; the lady must be herself a goddess bred and born; she must— But you shall have a specimen of one of these poems, which may convey a more precise idea:

"ON SEEING MRS. —— PERFORM IN THE CHARACTER OF ———.

"To you, bright fair, the Nine address their lays,
And tune my feeble voice to sing thy praise.
The heart-felt power of every charm divine,
Who can withstand their all-commanding shine?
See how she moves along with every grace,
While soul-brought tears steal down each shining face!
She speaks, 'tis rapture all and nameless bliss—
Ye gods! what transport e'er compar'd to this?
As when in Paphian groves the Queen of Love,
With fond complaint address'd the listening Jove,
'Twas joy and endless blisses all around,
And rocks forgot their hardness at the sound.
Then first, at last e'en Jove was taken in,
And felt her charms, without disguise, within."

And yet think not, my friend, that I have any particular animosity against the champions who are at the head of the present commotion. On the contrary, I could find pleasure in their music, if served up at proper intervals; if I heard it only on proper occasions, and not about it wherever I go. In fact, I could patronize them both; and as an instance of my condescension in this particular they may come and give me a song at my lodgings on any evening when I am at leisure, provided they keep a becoming distance, and stand, while they continue to entertain me, with decent humility at the door.

You perceive I have not read the seventeen books of Chinese ceremonies to no purpose. I know the proper share of respect due to every rank in society. Stage-players, fire-eaters, singing-women, dancing-dogs, wild beasts, and wire-walkers, as their efforts are exerted for our amusement, ought not entirely to be despised. The laws of every country should allow them to play their tricks at least with impunity. They should not be branded with the ignominious appellation of vagabonds; at least they deserve a rank in society equal to the mystery of barbers or undertakers; and, could my influence extend so far, they should be allowed to earn even forty or fifty pounds a year, if eminent in their profession.

I am sensible, however, that you will censure me for profusion in this respect, bred up as you are in the narrow prejudices of Eastern frugality. You will undoubtedly assert that such a stipend is too great for so useless an employment. Yet how will your surprise increase when told that, though the law holds them as vagabonds,[1] many of them earn more than a thousand a year! You are amazed. There is cause for amazement. A vagabond with a thousand a year is indeed a curiosity in nature; a wonder far surpassing the flying-fish, petrified crab, or travelling lobster. However, from my great love to the profession, I would willingly have them divested of part of their contempt and part of their finery;

---

[1] In China stage-players are considered infamous, and inadmissible as candidates for the office of a mandarin. By an enactment of the Emperor Kien-lung it requires three generations to wipe off the stain.

the law should kindly take them under the wing of protection, fix them into a corporation like that of the barbers,
and abridge their ignominy and their pensions.   As to their
abilities in other respects, I would leave that entirely to the
public, who are certainly in this case the properest judges—
whether they despise them or no.

Yes, my Fum, I would abridge their pensions.   A theatrical warrior, who conducts the battles of the stage, should be
cooped up with the same caution as a bantam cock that is
kept for fighting.   When one of those animals is taken from
its native dunghill, we retrench it both in the quantity of its
food and the number of its seraglio: players should in the
same manner be fed, not fattened; they should be permitted
to get their bread, but not to eat the people's bread into the
bargain; and, instead of being permitted to keep four mis-
tresses, in conscience they should be contented only with two.

Were stage-players thus brought into bounds, perhaps we
should find their admirers less sanguine, and consequently
less ridiculous, in patronizing them.   We should no longer
be struck with the absurdity of seeing the same people whose
valor makes such a figure abroad, apostrophizing in the praise
of a bouncing blockhead, and wrangling in the defence of a
copper-tailed actress at home.

I shall conclude my letter with the sensible admonition of
Mê, the philosopher.   "You love harmony," says he, "and
are charmed with music.   I do not blame you for hearing a
fine voice, when you are in your closet, with a lovely parterre
under your eye, or in the night-time, while perhaps the moon
diffuses her silver rays.   But is a man to carry this passion
so far as to let a company of comedians, musicians, and singers grow rich upon his exhausted fortune?   If so, he resembles one of those dead bodies whose brains the embalmer has
picked out through its ears."   Adieu.

LETTER LXXXVI.

From the Same.

OF all the places of amusement where gentlemen and ladies are entertained, I have not been yet to visit Newmarket.
This, I am told, is a large field; where, upon certain occasions, three or four horses are brought together, then set
a-running, and that horse which runs fastest wins the wager.

This is reckoned a very polite and fashionable amusement
here, much more followed by the nobility than partridge-
fighting at Java or paper kites in Madagascar. Several of the
great here, I am told, understand as much of farriery as their
grooms; and a horse with any share of merit can never want
a patron among the nobility.

We have a description of this entertainment almost every
day in some of the gazettes, as, for instance: "On such a day
the Give-and-Take Plate was run for between his grace's Crab,
his lordship's Periwinkle, and Squire Smackem's Slamerkin.
All rode their own horses. There was the greatest concourse
of nobility that has been known here for several seasons.
The odds were in favor of Crab in the beginning; but Slamerkin, after the first heat, seemed to have the match hollow:
however, it was soon seen that Periwinkle improved in wind,
which at last turned out accordingly; Crab was run to a
stand-still, Slamerkin was knocked up, and Periwinkle was
brought in with universal applause." Thus, you see, Periwinkle received universal applause; and, no doubt, his lordship came in for some share of that praise which was so liberally bestowed upon Periwinkle. Sun of China! how glorious must the senator appear in his cap and leather breeches,
his whip crossed in his mouth, and thus coming to the goal,

among the shouts of grooms, jockeys, pimps, stable-bred dukes, and degraded generals!

From the description of this princely amusement, now transcribed, and from the great veneration I have for the characters of its principal promoters, I make no doubt but I shall look upon a horse-race with becoming reverence, predisposed as I am by a similar amusement, of which I have lately been a spectator; for just now I happened to have an opportunity of being present at a cart-race.

Whether this contention between three carts of different parishes was promoted by a subscription among the nobility, or whether the grand jury, in council assembled, had gloriously combined to encourage plaustral [1] merit, I cannot take upon me to determine; but certain it is, the whole was conducted with the utmost regularity and decorum, and the company, which made a brilliant appearance, were universally of opinion that the sport was high, the running fine, and the riders influenced by no bribe.

It was run on the road from London to a village called Brentford, between a turnip-cart, a dust-cart, and a dung-cart; each of the owners condescending to mount and be his own driver. The odds at starting were Dust against Dung five to four; but, after half a mile's going, the knowing ones found themselves all on the wrong side, and it was Turnip against the field, brass to silver.

Soon, however, the contest became more doubtful; Turnip, indeed, kept the way, but it was perceived that Dung had better bottom. The road re-echoed with the shouts of the spectators. "Dung against Turnip! Turnip against Dung!" was now the universal cry; neck and neck; one rode lighter but the other had more judgment. I could not but particularly observe the ardor with which the fair sex espoused the cause of the different riders on this occasion; one was charmed with the unwashed beauties of Dung; another was captivated with the patibulary aspect of Turnip; while, in

---

[1] This, and another word in the same letter, *patibulary*, are among the very few words which Goldsmith has ventured to coin.

the mean time, unfortunate, gloomy Dust, who came whipping behind, was cheered by the encouragements of some and pity of all.

The contention now continued for some time without a possibility of determining to whom victory designed the prize. The winning-post appeared in view, and he who drove the turnip-cart assured himself of success; and successful he might have been had his horse been as ambitious as he; but, on approaching a turn from the road which led homewards, the horse fairly stood still, and refused to move a foot farther. The dung-cart had scarce time to enjoy this temporary triumph when it was pitched headlong into a ditch by the wayside and the rider left to wallow in congenial mud. Dust, in the mean time, soon came up, and not being far from the post, came in, amid the shouts and acclamations of all the spectators, and greatly caressed by all the quality of Brentford. Fortune was kind only to one, who ought to have been favorable to all; each had peculiar merit, each labored hard to earn the prize, and each richly deserved the cart he drove.

I do not know whether this description may not have anticipated that which I intended giving of Newmarket.[1] I am told there is little else to be seen even there. There may be some minute differences in the dress of the spectators, but

---

[1] "Since the year 1753 the race-ground at Newmarket has been the property of the Jockey Club. Betting-posts are placed on various parts of the heath, at some one of which the sportsmen assemble immediately after each race, to make their bets on the one that is to follow. As not more than half an hour elapses during the events, the scene is one of the most animated description, and a stranger would imagine that all the tongues of Babel were let loose again. No country under the heavens produces such a scene as this. 'What do you bet on this race, my lord?' says a vulgar-looking man on a shabby hack, with a shocking bad hat. 'I want to back the field,' says my lord. '*So do I*,' says the *leg*. 'I'll bet 500 to 200 you don't name the winner,' exclaims my lord. 'I'll take *six*,' exclaims the leg. 'I'll bet it you,' roars my lord. '*I'll double it*,' bellows the leg. 'Done,' shouts the peer. '*Treble it?*' 'No.' The bet is entered, and so much for *wanting to back the field*. Scores of such scenes take place in these momentous half-hours. All bets are paid the following morning, and £50,000 or more have been known to exchange hands in one day. Yet Newmarket is but a speck on the ocean when compared with the sum-total of our provincial meetings, of which there are annually about one hundred and twenty in England, Scotland, and Wales."—*The Turf in* 1833. (See *Quarterly Rev.*, vol. lix. p. 389.)

none at all in their understandings. The quality of Brentford are as remarkable for politeness and delicacy as the breeders of Newmarket. The quality of Brentford drive their own carts, and the honorable fraternity of Newmarket ride their own horses. In short, the matches in one place are as rational as those in the other; and it is more than probable that turnips, dust, and dung are all that can be found to furnish out description in either.

Forgive me, my friend, but a person like me, bred up in a philosophic seclusion, is apt to regard, perhaps, with too much asperity those occurrences which sink man below his station in nature, and diminish the intrinsic value of humanity. ·

LETTER LXXXVII.

THE FOLLY OF THE WESTERN PARTS OF EUROPE IN EMPLOYING THE RUSSIANS TO FIGHT THEIR BATTLES.

From Fum Hoam to Lien Chi Altangi.

You tell me the people of Europe are wise; but where lies their wisdom? You say they are valiant, too; yet I have some reason to doubt of their valor. They are engaged in war among each other, yet apply to the Russians, their neighbors and ours, for assistance. Cultivating such an alliance argues at once imprudence and timidity. All subsidies paid for such an aid is strengthening the Russians, already too powerful, and weakening the employers, already exhausted by intestine commotions.

I cannot avoid beholding the Russian empire as the natural enemy of the more western parts of Europe; as an enemy already possessed of great strength, and from the nature of the government every day threatening to become more powerful. This extensive empire, which both in Europe and Asia occupies almost a third of the Old World, was about two centuries ago divided into separate kingdoms and dukedoms, and, from such a division, consequently feeble. Since the times, however, of Johan Basilides it has increased in

strength and extent; and those untrodden forests, those innumerable savage animals which formerly covered the face
of the country, are now removed, and colonies of mankind
planted in their room.   A kingdom thus enjoying peace internally, possessed of an unbounded extent of dominion, and
learning the military art at the expense of others abroad,
must every day grow more powerful; and it is probable we
shall hear Russia in future times, as formerly, called the
officina gentium.

It was long the wish of Peter, their great monarch, to have
a fort in some of the western parts of Europe; many of his
schemes and treaties were directed to this end, but, happily
for Europe, he failed in them all.   A fort in the power of
this people would be like the possession of a flood-gate; and
whenever ambition, interest, or necessity prompted, they might
then be able to deluge the whole Western world with a barbarous inundation.

Believe me, my friend, I cannot sufficiently contemn the
politicians of Europe who thus make this powerful people
arbitrators in their quarrel.   The Russians are now at that
period between refinement and barbarity which seems most
adapted to military achievement; and if once they happen to
get footing in the western parts of Europe, it is not the feeble
efforts of the sons of effeminacy and dissension that can serve
to remove them.   The fertile valley and soft climate will
ever be sufficient inducements to draw whole myriads from
their native deserts, the trackless wild, or snowy mountain.

History, experience, reason, nature, expand the book of
wisdom before the eyes of mankind, but they will not read.
We have seen with terror a winged phalanx of famished
locusts, each singly contemptible, but from multitude become
hideous, cover like clouds the face of day, and threaten the
whole world with ruin.   We have seen them settling on the
fertile plains of India and Egypt, destroying in an instant
the labors and the hopes of nations; sparing neither the
fruit of the earth nor the verdure of the fields, and changing
into a frightful desert landscapes of once luxuriant beauty.
We have seen myriads of ants issuing together from the

Southern desert, like a torrent whose source was inexhaustible, succeeding each other without end, and renewing their
destroyed forces with unwearied perseverance, bringing desolation wherever they came, banishing men and animals, and,
when destitute of all subsistence, in heaps infecting the wilderness which they had made. Like these have been the
migrations of men. When as yet savage, and almost resembling their brute partners in the forest, subject like them only
to the instincts of nature, and directed by hunger alone in the
choice of an abode, how have we seen whole armies starting
wild at once from their forests and their dens! Goths, Huns,
Vandals, Saracens, Turks, Tartars, myriads of men, animals in
human form, without country, without name, without laws,
outpowering by numbers all opposition, ravaging cities, over-
turning empires; and, after having destroyed whole nations,
and spread extensive desolation, how have we seen them sink
oppressed by some new enemy, more barbarous and even
more unknown than they! Adieu.

LETTER LXXXVIII.

THE LADIES ADVISED TO GET HUSBANDS. A STORY TO THIS PURPOSE.

From Lien Chi Altangi to Fum Hoam, first President of the Ceremonial Academy at Pekin, in China.

As the instruction of the fair sex in this country is entirely
committed to the care of foreigners—as their language-mas-
ters, music-masters, hair-frizzers, and governesses are all from
abroad—I had some intentions of opening a female academy
myself, and made no doubt, as I was quite a foreigner, of
meeting a favorable reception.

In this I intended to instruct the ladies in all the conjugal
mysteries: wives should be taught the art of managing husbands, and maids the skill of properly choosing them; I would
teach a wife how far she might venture to be sick without
giving disgust; she should be acquainted with the great ben-

efits of the colic in the stomach, and all the thorough-bred insolence of fashion; maids should learn the secret of nicely distinguishing every competitor; they should be able to know the difference between a pedant and a scholar, a citizen and a prig, a squire and his horse, a beau and his monkey; but chiefly they should be taught the art of managing their smiles, from the contemptuous simper to the long, laborious laugh.

But I have discontinued the project; for what would signify teaching ladies the manner of governing or choosing husbands, when marriage is at present so much out of fashion that a lady is very well off who can get any husband at all? Celibacy now prevails in every rank of life; the streets are crowded with old bachelors, and the houses with ladies who have refused good offers, and are never likely to receive any for the future.

The only advice, therefore, I could give the fair sex, as things stand at present, is to get husbands as fast as they can. There is certainly nothing in the whole creation, not even Babylon in ruins, more truly deplorable than a lady in the virgin bloom of sixty-three, or a battered unmarried beau, who squibs about from place to place, showing his pigtail wig and his ears. The one appears to my imagination in the form of a double nightcap or a roll of pomatum; the other in the shape of an electuary or a box of pills.

I would once more, therefore, advise the ladies to get husbands. I would desire them not to discard an old lover without very sufficient reasons, nor treat the new with ill-nature till they know him false; let not prudes allege the falseness of the sex, coquettes the pleasures of long courtship, or parents the necessary preliminaries of penny for penny. I have reasons that would silence even a casuist in this particular. In the first place, therefore, I divide the subject into fifteen heads, and then *sic argumentor*— But, not to give you and myself the spleen, be contented at present with an Indian tale:

In a winding of the river Amidar, just before it falls into the Caspian Sea, there lies an island unfrequented by the inhabitants of the Continent. In this seclusion, blessed with all that wild, uncultivated nature could bestow, lived a princess and her two daughters. She had been wrecked upon the coast while her children as yet were infants, who, of consequence, though grown up, were entirely unacquainted with man. Yet, inexperienced as the young ladies were in the opposite sex, both early discovered symptoms, the one of prudery, the other of being a coquette. The eldest was ever learning maxims of wisdom and discretion from her mamma, while the youngest employed all her hours in gazing at her own face in a neighboring fountain.

Their usual amusement in this solitude was fishing: their mother had taught them all the secrets of the art; she showed them which were the most likely places to throw out the line, what baits were most proper for the various seasons, and the best manner to draw up the finny prey, when they had hooked it. In this manner they spent their time, easy and innocent, till one day the princess, being indisposed, desired them to go and catch her a sturgeon or a shark for supper, which she fancied might sit easy on her stomach. The daughters obeyed, and clapping on a gold-fish, the usual bait on those occasions, went and sat upon one of the rocks, letting the gilded hook glide down with the stream.

On the opposite shore, farther down at the mouth of the river, lived a diver for pearls, a youth who by long habit in his trade was almost grown amphibious, so that he could remain whole hours at the bottom of the water without ever fetching breath. He happened to be at that very instant diving when the ladies were fishing with the gilded hook. Seeing, therefore, the bait, which to him had the appearance of real gold, he was resolved to seize the prize; but both his hands being already filled with pearl oysters, he found himself obliged to snap at it with his mouth: the consequence is easily imagined; the hook, before unperceived, was instantly fastened in his jaw, nor could he, with all his efforts or his floundering, get free.

"Sister!" cries the youngest princess, "I have certainly caught a monstrous fish; I never perceived anything struggle so at the end of my line before; come and help me to draw it in." They both now, therefore, assisted in fishing up the diver on shore; but nothing could equal their surprise upon seeing him. "Bless my eyes!" cries the prude, "what have we got here? This is a very odd fish, to be sure! I never saw anything in my life look so queer: what eyes, what terrible claws, what a monstrous snout! I have read of this monster somewhere before; it certainly must be a tanlang, that eats women; let us throw it back into the sea where we found it."

The diver, in the mean time, stood upon the beach at the end of the line, with the hook in his mouth, using every art that he thought could best excite pity, and particularly looking extremely tender, which is usual in such circumstances. The coquette, therefore, in some measure influenced by the innocence of his looks, ventured to contradict her companion. "Upon my word, sister," says she, "I see nothing in the animal so very terrible as you are pleased to apprehend; I think it may serve well enough for a change. Always sharks, and sturgeons, and lobsters, and crawfish make me quite sick. I fancy a slice of this, nicely grilladed, and dressed up with shrimp sauce, would be very pretty eating. I fancy mamma would like a bit with pickles above all things in the world; and if it should not sit easy on her stomach, it will be time enough to discontinue it when found disagreeable, you know." "Horrid!" cries the prude; "would the girl be poisoned? I tell you it is a tanlang; I have read of it in twenty places. It is everywhere described as the most pernicious animal that ever infested the ocean. I am certain it is the most insidious, ravenous creature in the world, and is certain destruction if taken internally." The youngest sister was now, therefore, obliged to submit: both assisted in drawing the hook with some violence from the diver's jaw; and he, finding himself at liberty, bent his breast against the broad wave and disappeared in an instant.

Just at this juncture the mother came down to the beach to know the cause of her daughters' delay; they told her every circumstance, describing the monster they had caught. The old lady was one of the most discreet women in the world; she was called the black-eyed princess, from two black eyes she had received in her youth, being a little addicted to boxing in her liquor. "Alas, my children," cries she, "what have you done! the fish you caught was a man-fish, one of the most tame domestic animals in the world. We could have let him run and play about the garden, and he would have been twenty times more entertaining than our squirrel or monkey." "If that be all," says the young coquette, "we will fish for him again. If that be all, I'll hold three toothpicks to one pound of snuff I catch him whenever I please." Accordingly, they threw in their line once more, but, with all their gilding and paddling and assiduity, they could never after catch the diver. In this state of solitude and disappointment they continued for many years, still fishing, but without success; till at last the genius of the place, in pity to their distresses, changed the prude into a shrimp and the coquette into an oyster. Adieu.

LETTER LXXXIX.

THE FOLLY OF REMOTE OR USELESS DISQUISITIONS AMONG THE LEARNED.

From the Same.

I AM amused, my dear Fum, with the labors of some of the learned here. One shall write you a whole folio on the dissection of a caterpillar. Another shall swell his works with a description of the plumage on the wing of a butterfly; a third shall see a little world on a peach-leaf, and publish a book to describe what his readers might see more clearly in two minutes, only by being furnished with eyes and a microscope.

I have frequently compared the understandings of such men to their own glasses. Their field of vision is too contracted to take in the whole of any but minute objects; they view all nature bit by bit: now the proboscis, now the antennæ, now the pinnæ of—a flea. Now the polypus comes to breakfast upon a worm; now it is kept up to see how long it will live without eating; now it is turned inside outward; and now it sickens and dies. Thus they proceed, laborious in trifles, constant in experiment, without one single abstraction, by which alone knowledge may be properly said to increase; till at last their ideas, ever employed upon minute things, contract to the size of the diminutive object, and a single mite shall fill the whole mind's capacity.

Yet, believe me, my friend, ridiculous as these men are to the world, they are set up as objects of esteem for each other. They have particular places appointed for their meetings; in which one shows his cockle-shell, and is praised by all the society; another produces his powder, makes some experiments that result in nothing, and comes off with admiration and applause; a third comes out with the important discovery of some new process in the skeleton of a mole, and is set down as the accurate and sensible; while one still more fortunate than the rest, by pickling, potting, and preserving monsters, rises into unbounded reputation.

The labors of such men, instead of being calculated to amuse the public, are laid out only in diverting each other. The world becomes very little the better or the wiser for knowing what is the peculiar food of an insect that is itself the food of another, which in its turn is eaten by a third; but there are men who have studied themselves into a habit of investigating and admiring such minutiæ. To these such subjects are pleasing, as there are some who contentedly spend whole days in endeavoring to solve enigmas, or disentangle the puzzling-sticks of children.

But of all the learned those who pretend to investigate remote antiquity have least to plead in their own defence, when they carry this passion to a faulty excess. They are generally found to supply by conjecture the want of record, and then by perseverance are wrought up into a confidence of the truth of opinions which even to themselves at first appeared founded only in imagination.

The Europeans have heard much of the kingdom of China; its politeness, arts, commerce, laws, and morals are, however, but very imperfectly known among them. They have even now in their Indian warehouses numberless utensils, plants, minerals, and machines, of the use of which they are entirely ignorant; nor can any among them even make a probable guess for what they might have been designed. Yet, though this people be so ignorant of the present real state of China, the philosophers I am describing have entered into long, learned, laborious disputes about what China was two thousand years ago. China and European happiness are but little connected even at this day; but European happiness and China two thousand years ago have certainly no connection at all. However, the learned have written on and pursued the subject through all the labyrinths of antiquity; though the early dews and the tainted gale be passed away, though no footsteps remain to direct the doubtful chase, yet still they run forward, open upon the uncertain scent, and, though in fact they follow nothing, are earnest in the pursuit. In this chase, however, they all take different ways. One, for example, confidently assures us that China was peopled by a colony from Egypt. Sesostris, he observes, led his army as far as the Ganges; therefore, if he went so far, he might still have gone as far as China, which is but about a thousand miles from thence; therefore he did go to China; therefore China was not peopled before he went there; therefore it was peopled by him. Besides, the Egyptians have pyramids: the Chinese have in like manner their porcelain tower; the Egyptians used to light up candles upon every rejoicing: the Chinese have lanthorns upon the same occasion; the Egyptians had their great river: so had the Chinese. But what serves to put the matter past a doubt is that the ancient kings of China and those of Egypt were called by the same names. The Emperor Ki is certainly the same with King Atoes; for if we only change *K* into *A*, and *i* into *toes*, we shall have the name Atoes; and with equal ease Menes may be proved to be the same with the Emperor Yu; therefore the Chinese are a colony from Egypt.

But another of the learned is entirely different from the last; and he will have the Chinese to be a colony planted by Noah just after the deluge. First, from the vast similitude there is between the name of Fohi, the founder of the Chinese monarchy, and that of Noah, the preserver of the human race; Noah, Fohi—very like each other, truly: they have each but four letters, and only two of the four happen to differ. But, to strengthen the argument, Fohi, as the Chinese chronicle asserts, had no father. Noah, it is true, had a father, as the European Bible tells us; but then, as this father was probably drowned in the flood, it is just the same as if he had no father at all: therefore Noah and Fohi are the same. Just after the flood the earth was covered with mud; if it was covered with mud it must have been incrustated mud; if it was incrustated it was clothed with verdure; this was a fine, unembarrassed road for Noah to fly from his wicked children: he therefore did fly from them, and took a journey of two thousand miles for his own amusement; therefore Noah and Fohi are the same.

Another sect of literati—for they all pass among the vulgar for very great scholars—assert that the Chinese came neither from the colony of Sesostris nor from Noah, but are descended from Magog, Meshec, and Tubal, and therefore neither Sesostris, nor Noah, nor Fohi are the same.

It is thus, my friend, that indolence assumes the airs of wisdom, and, while it tosses the cup-and-ball with infantine folly, desires the world to look on, and calls the stupid pastime philosophy and learning.[1]   Adieu.

---

[1] " That shrewd critic and commentator on the writings of the Jesuits on China, M. Pauw, exposed the absurdity of this supposition that the Chinese are an Egyptian colony; and we entirely agree that such an assumption is not supported by any testimony, either direct or circumstantial.   In truth, there exists not the slightest shadow of resemblance between the Chinese written characters or symbols and the hieroglyphics of Egypt; and, we may add, neither do the physical characteristics of color, form, and features in the two races in the least accord—whether we take the present Copts, the figures on the temples, or the mummies in the tombs to be the true representatives of the ancient Egyptians."—*Quart. Rev.*, vol. lvi. p. 493.

LETTER XC.

THE ENGLISH SUBJECT TO THE SPLEEN.

From the Same.

When the men of this country are once turned of thirty they regularly retire every year, at proper intervals, to lie-in of the spleen. The vulgar, unfurnished with the luxurious comforts of the soft cushion, down bed, and easy-chair, are obliged, when the fit is on them, to nurse it up by drinking, idleness, and ill-humor. In such dispositions unhappy is the foreigner who happens to cross them; his long chin, tarnished coat, or pinched hat are sure to receive no quarter. If they meet no foreigner, however, to fight with, they are in such cases generally content with beating each other.

The rich, as they have more sensibility, are operated upon with greater violence by this disorder. Different from the poor, instead of becoming more insolent, they grow totally unfit for opposition. A general here, who would have faced a culverin when well, if the fit be on him shall hardly find courage to snuff a candle. An admiral, who could have opposed a broadside without shrinking, shall sit whole days in his chamber, mobbed up in double nightcaps, shuddering at the intrusive breeze, and distinguishable from his wife only by his black beard and heavy eyebrows.

In the country, this disorder mostly attacks the fair sex; in town, it is most unfavorable to the men. A lady who has pined whole years amid cooing doves and complaining nightingales, in rural retirement, shall resume all her vivacity in one night at a city gaming-table; her husband, who roared, hunted, and got drunk at home, shall grow splenetic in town, in proportion to his wife's good-humor. Upon their arrival in London they exchange their disorders. In consequence of her parties and excursions, he puts on the furred cap and scarlet stomacher, and perfectly resembles an Indian husband, who, when his wife is safely delivered, permits her to transact business abroad, while he undergoes all the formality of keeping his bed, and receiving all the condolence in her place.

But those who reside constantly in town owe this disorder mostly to the influence of the *weather*.[1] It is impossible to describe what a variety of transmutations an east wind will produce; it has been known to change a lady of fashion into a parlor couch, an alderman into a plate of custards, and a dispenser of justice into a rat-trap. Even philosophers themselves are not exempt from its influence; it has often converted a poet into a coral and bells, and a patriot senator into a dumb-waiter.

Some days ago I went to visit the man in black, and entered his house with that cheerfulness which the certainty of a favorable reception always inspires. Upon opening the door of his apartment, I found him, with the most rueful face imaginable, in a morning-gown and a flannel nightcap, earnestly employed in learning to blow the German flute. Struck with the absurdity of a man in the decline of life thus blowing away all his constitution and spirits, even without the consolation of being musical, I ventured to ask what could induce him to attempt learning so difficult an instrument so late in life. To this he made no reply, but, groaning, and still holding the flute to his lips, continued to gaze at me for some moments very angrily, and then proceeded to practise his gamut as before. After having produced a variety of the

---

[1] " I must needs add one thing more in favor of our climate, which I heard the king (Charles II.) say, and I thought new and right, and truly like a king of England that loved and esteemed his own country; it was in reply to some of the company that were reviling our climate, and extolling those of Italy and Spain, or at least of France : he said he thought that was the best climate where he could be abroad in the air with pleasure, or at least without trouble or inconvenience, the most days in the year and the most hours of the day; and this he thought he could be in England more than in any country he knew of in Europe. And I believe it is true, not only of the hot and the cold, but even among our neighbors in France, and the Low Countries themselves, where the heats and the colds, and changes of seasons are less treatable than they are with us."—Sir William Temple's *Works*, ed. 1770, vol. iii. p. 219.

most hideous tones in nature, at last, turning to me, he demanded whether I did not think he had made a surprising progress in two days? "You see," continues he, "I have got the *ambusheer* already, and as for fingering, my master tells me I shall have that in a few lessons more." I was so much astonished with this instance of inverted ambition that I knew not what to reply, but soon discerned the cause of all his absurdities: my friend was under a metamorphosis by the power of spleen, and flute-blowing was unluckily become his adventitious passion.

In order, therefore, to banish his anxiety imperceptibly by seeming to indulge it, I began to descant on those gloomy topics by which philosophers often get rid of their own spleen, by communicating it: the wretchedness of a man in this life; the happiness of some, wrought out of the miseries of others; the necessity that wretches should expire under punishment, that rogues might enjoy affluence in tranquillity: I led him on from the inhumanity of the rich to the ingratitude of the beggar; from the insincerity of refinement to the fierceness of rusticity; and at last had the good-fortune to restore him to his usual serenity of temper, by permitting him to expatiate upon all the modes of human misery.

"Some nights ago," says my friend, "sitting alone by my fire, I happened to look into an account of the detection of a set of men called the thief-takers. I read over the many hideous cruelties of those haters of mankind; of their pretended friendship to wretches they meant to betray; of their sending men out to rob, and then hanging them. I could not avoid sometimes interrupting the narrative by crying out, 'Yet these are men!' As I went on I was informed that they had lived by this practice several years, and had been enriched by the price of blood. 'And yet,' cried I, 'I have been sent into the world, and am desired to call these men my brothers!' I read that the very man who led the condemned wretch to the gallows was he who falsely swore his life away. 'And yet,' continued I, 'that perjurer had just such a nose, such lips, such hands, and such eyes as Newton.' I at last came to the account of the wretch that was searched after

GOLDSMITH'S COMPLETE WORKS.

robbing one of the thief-takers of half a crown. Those of the confederacy knew that he had got but that single half-crown in the world; after a long search, therefore, which they knew would be fruitless, and taking from him the half-crown, which they knew was all he had, one of the gang compassionately cried out, 'Alas! poor creature, let him keep all the rest he has got; it will do him service in Newgate, where we are sending him.' This was an instance of such complicated guilt and hypocrisy that I threw down the book in an agony of rage, and began to think with malice of all the human kind. I sat silent for some minutes; and soon perceiving the ticking of my watch beginning to grow noisy and troublesome, I quickly placed it out of hearing and strove to resume my serenity. But the watchman soon gave me a second alarm. I had scarcely recovered from this when my peace was assaulted by the wind at my window; and when that ceased to blow I listened for death-watches in the wainscot. I now found my whole system discomposed. I strove to find a resource in philosophy and reason; but what could I oppose, or where direct my blow, when I could see no enemy to combat? I saw no misery approaching, nor knew any I had to fear, yet still I was miserable. Morning came: I sought for tranquillity in dissipation, sauntered from one place of public resort to another, but found myself disagreeable to my acquaintance and ridiculous to others. I tried at different times dancing, fencing, and riding; I solved geometrical problems, shaped tobacco-stoppers, wrote verses, and cut paper. At last I placed my affections on music, and find that earnest employment, if it cannot cure, at least will palliate every anxiety." Adieu.

LETTER XCI.

THE INFLUENCE OF CLIMATE AND SOIL UPON THE TEMPER AND DISPOSITIONS OF THE ENGLISH.

From the Same.

IT is no unpleasing contemplation to consider the influence which soil and climate have upon the disposition of the inhabitants, the animals, and vegetables of different countries. That among the brute creation is much more visible than in man, and that in vegetables more than either. In some places those plants which are entirely poisonous at home lose their deleterious quality by being carried abroad. There are serpents in Macedonia so harmless as to be used as playthings for children; and we are told that in some parts of Fez there are lions so very timorous as to be scared away, though coming in herds, by the cries of women.

I know of no country where the influence of climate and soil is more visible than in England; the same hidden cause which gives courage to their dogs and cocks gives also fierceness to their men. But chiefly this ferocity appears among the vulgar. The polite of every country pretty nearly resemble each other. But, as in simpling it is among the uncultivated productions of nature we are to examine the characteristic differences of climate and soil, so in an estimate of the genius of a people we must look among the sons of unpolished rusticity. The vulgar English, therefore, may be easily distinguished from all the rest of the world by superior pride, impatience, and a peculiar hardiness of soul.

Perhaps no qualities in the world are more susceptible of a fine polish than these; artificial complaisance and easy deference being superinduced over these generally form a great character; something at once elegant and majestic, affable yet sincere. Such in general are the better sort; but

II.—27

they who are left in primitive rudeness are the least disposed for society with others, or comfort internally, of any people under the sun.

The poor, indeed, of every country are but little prone to treat each other with tenderness; their own miseries are too apt to engross all their pity; and perhaps, too, they give but little commiseration, as they find but little from others. But in England the poor treat each other, upon every occasion, with more than savage animosity, and as if they were in a state of open war by nature. In China if two porters should meet in a narrow street, they would lay down their burdens, make a thousand excuses to each other for the accidental interruption, and beg pardon on their knees; if two men of the same occupation should meet here, they would first begin to scold, and at last to beat each other. One would think they had miseries enough resulting from penury and labor not to increase them by ill-nature among themselves, and subjection to new penalties; but such considerations never weigh with them.

But, to recompense this strange absurdity, they are in the main generous, brave, and enterprising. They feel the slightest injuries with a degree of ungoverned impatience, but resist the greatest calamities with surprising fortitude.[1] Those miseries under which any other people in the world would sink they have often shown they were capable of enduring; if accidentally cast upon some desolate coast, their perseverance is beyond what any other nation is capable of sustaining; if imprisoned for crimes, their efforts to escape are greater than among others. The peculiar strength of their prisons, when compared to those elsewhere, argues their hardiness; even the strongest prisons I have ever seen in other countries would be very insufficient to confine the untamable spirit of an Englishman. In short, what man dares do in circumstances of danger an Englishman will. His virtues

---

[1] "Stern o'er each bosom Reason holds her state
With daring aims irregularly great," etc.
See *The Traveller*, i. 17.

seem to sleep in the calm, and are called out only to combat the kindred storm.

But the greatest eulogy of this people is the generosity of their miscreants—the tenderness, in general, of their robbers and highwaymen. Perhaps no people can produce instances of the same kind, where the desperate mix pity with injustice; still show that they understand a distinction in crimes, and even in acts of violence have still some tincture of remaining virtue. In every other country robbery and murder go almost always together; here it seldom happens, except upon ill-judged resistance or pursuit. The banditti of other countries are unmerciful to a supreme degree; the highwayman and robber here are generous, at least to the public, and pretend to virtues in their intercourse among each other. Taking, therefore, my opinion of the English from the virtues and vices practised among the vulgar, they at once present to a stranger all their faults, and keep their virtues up only for the inquiring eye of a philosopher.

Foreigners are generally shocked at their insolence upon first coming among them: they find themselves ridiculed and insulted in every street; they meet with none of those trifling civilities so frequent elsewhere, which are instances of mutual good-will, without previous acquaintance: they travel through the country, either too ignorant or too obstinate to cultivate a closer acquaintance, meet every moment something to excite their disgust, and return home to characterize this as the region of spleen, insolence, and ill-nature. In short, England would be the last place in the world I would travel to by way of amusement, but the first for instruction. I would choose to have others for my acquaintance, but Englishmen for my friends.

LETTER XCII.

THE MANNER IN WHICH SOME PHILOSOPHERS MAKE ARTIFICIAL MISERY.

To the Same.

THE mind is ever ingenious in making its own distress. The wandering beggar, who has none to protect, or feed, or to shelter him, fancies complete happiness in labor and a full meal; take him from rags and want, feed, clothe, and employ him, his wishes now rise one step above his station; he could be happy were he possessed of raiment, food, and ease. Suppose his wishes gratified even in these, his prospects widen as he ascends; he finds himself in affluence and tranquillity, indeed, but indolence soon breeds anxiety, and he desires not only to be freed from pain, but to be possessed of pleasure: pleasure is granted him, and this but opens his soul to ambition; and ambition will be sure to taint his future happiness either with jealousy, disappointment, or fatigue.

But of all the arts of distress found out by man for his own torment, perhaps that of philosophic misery is most truly ridiculous; a passion nowhere carried to so extravagant an excess as in the country where I now reside. It is not enough to engage all the compassion of a philosopher here that his own globe is harassed with wars, pestilence, or barbarity; he shall grieve for the inhabitants of the moon, if the situation of her imaginary mountains happens to alter; and dread the extinction of the sun, if the spots on his surface happen to increase. One should imagine that philosophy was introduced to make men happy, but here it serves to make hundreds miserable.

My landlady, some days ago, brought me the diary of a philosopher of this desponding sort, who had lodged in the apartment before me. It contains the history of a life which seems to be one continued tissue of sorrow, apprehension, and distress. A single week will serve as a specimen of the whole:

"*Monday.*—In what a transient, decaying situation are we placed; and what various reasons does philosophy furnish to make mankind unhappy! A single grain of mustard shall continue to produce its similitude through numberless successions; yet what has been granted to this little seed has been denied to our planetary system: the mustard-seed is still unaltered, but the system is growing old, and must quickly fall to decay. How terrible will it be when the motions of all the planets have at last become so irregular as to need repairing; when the moon shall fall into frightful paroxysms of alteration; when the earth, deviating from its ancient track, and, with every other planet, forgetting its circular revolutions, shall become so eccentric that, unconfined by the laws of system, it shall fly off into boundless space, to knock against some distant world, or fall in upon the sun, either extinguishing his light or burnt up by his flames in a moment! Perhaps, while I write, this dreadful change is begun. Shield me from universal ruin! Yet idiot man laughs, sings, and rejoices, in the very face of the sun, and seems no way touched with his situation.

"*Tuesday.*—Went to bed in great distress; awaked, and was comforted by considering that this change was to happen at some indefinite time; and therefore, like death, the thoughts of it might easily be borne. But there is a revolution, a fixed, determined revolution, which must certainly come to pass; yet which, by good-fortune, I shall never feel, except in my posterity. The obliquity of the equator with the ecliptic is now twenty minutes less than when it was observed two thousand years ago by Piteas. If this be the case, in six thousand the obliquity will be still less by a whole degree. This being supposed, it is evident that our earth, as Louville has clearly proved, has a motion by which the climates must necessarily change place, and in the space of about one million of years England shall actually travel to the Antarctic pole. I shudder at the change! How shall our unhappy grandchildren endure the hideous climate? A million of years will soon be accomplished—they are but a moment when compared to eternity: then shall our charming country, as I may say, in a moment of time resemble the hideous wilderness of Nova Zembla.

"*Wednesday.*—To-night, by my calculation, the long-predicted comet is to make its first appearance. Heavens! what terrors are impending over our little dim speck of earth! Dreadful visitation! Are we to be scorched in its fires, or only smothered in the vapor of its tail? That is the question. Thoughtless mortals! go build houses, plant orchards, purchase estates, for to-morrow you die. But what if the comet should not come? That would be equally fatal. Comets are servants which periodically return to supply the sun with fuel. If our sun, therefore, should be disappointed of the expected supply, and all his fuel be in the mean time burnt out, he must expire like an exhausted taper. What a miserable situation must our earth be in without his enlivening ray! Have we not seen several neighboring suns entirely disappear? Has not a fixed star, near the tail of the Ram, lately been quite extinguished?

"*Thursday.*—The comet has not yet appeared. I am sorry for it: first, sorry because my calculation is false; secondly, sorry lest the sun should want fuel; thirdly, sorry lest the wits should laugh at our erroneous predictions; and fourthly, sorry because, if it appears to-night, it must necessarily come within the sphere of the earth's attraction; and Heaven help the unhappy country on which it happens to fall!

"*Friday.*—Our whole society have been out, all eager in search of the comet. We have seen not less than sixteen comets in different parts of the heavens. However, we are unanimously resolved to fix upon one only to be the comet expected. That near Virgo wants nothing but a tail to fit it out completely for terrestrial admiration.

"*Saturday.*—The moon is, I find, at her old pranks. Her appulses, librations, and other irregularities indeed amaze me. My daughter, too, is this morning gone off with a grenadier. No way surprising; I was never able to give her a relish for wisdom. She ever promised to be a mere expletive in the creation. But the moon, the moon gives me real uneasiness; I fondly fancied I had fixed her. I had thought her constant, and constant only to me; but every night discovers her infidelity, and proves me a desolate and abandoned lover." Adieu.

LETTER XCIII.

THE FONDNESS OF SOME TO ADMIRE THE WRITINGS OF LORDS, ETC.

To the Same.

It is surprising what an influence titles shall have upon the mind, even though these titles be of our own making. Like children, we dress up the puppets in finery, and then stand in astonishment at the plastic wonder. I have been told of a rat-catcher here who strolled for a long time about the villages near town without finding any employment: at last, however, he thought proper to take the title of his Majesty's Rat-catcher in Ordinary, and thus succeeded beyond his expectations: when it was known that he caught rats at court, all were ready to give him countenance and employment.

But of all the people, they who make books seem most perfectly sensible of the advantage of titular dignity. All seem convinced that a book written by vulgar hands can neither instruct nor improve; none but kings, chams, and mandarins can write with any probability of success.[1] If the titles inform me right, not only kings and courtiers, but emperors themselves, in this country periodically supply the Press.

A man here who should write, and honestly confess that he wrote for bread, might as well send his manuscript to fire the baker's oven; not one creature will read him: all must be court-bred poets, or pretend at least to be court-bred, who can

---

[1] Goldsmith, in his necessities, compiled a "History of England" in a series of Letters from a Nobleman to his Son, and the immediate and large sale of the work was owing more to the title than the execution. The letters were said to be Lord Chesterfield's, or at least Lord Lyttelton's. As Oliver Goldsmith's they would then (1764) have had but a slender sale, if, indeed, they would have found a publisher.

expect to please. Should the caitiff fairly avow a design of emptying our pockets and filling his own, every reader would instantly forsake him; even those who write for bread themselves would combine to worry him, perfectly sensible that his attempts only served to take the bread out of their mouths.

And yet this silly prepossession the more amazes me, when I consider that almost all the excellent productions in wit that have appeared here were purely the offspring of necessity; their Drydens, Butlers, Otways, and Farquhars were all writers for bread.[1] Believe me, my friend, hunger has a most amazing faculty of sharpening the genius; and he who with a full belly can think like a hero, after a course of fasting shall rise to the sublimity of a demigod.

But what will most amaze is, that this very set of men, who are now so much depreciated by fools, are, however, the very best writers they have among them at present. For my own part, were I to buy a hat, I would not have it from a stocking-maker, but a hatter; were I to buy shoes, I should not go to the tailor's for that purpose. It is just so with regard to wit: did I, for my life, desire to be well served, I would apply only to those who made it their trade and lived by it. You smile at the oddity of my opinion; but be assured, my friend, that wit is in some measure mechanical, and that a man long habituated to catch at even its resemblance will at last be happy enough to possess the substance. By a long habit of writing he acquires a justness of thinking, and a mastery of manner, which holiday-writers, even with ten times his genius, may vainly attempt to equal.

How, then, are they deceived who expect from title, dignity, and exterior circumstance an excellence which is in some measure acquired by habit and sharpened by necessity! You have seen, like me, many literary reputations promoted by

---

[1] "I have many a fatigue to encounter before that happy time comes when your poor old, simple friend may again give a loose to the luxuriance of his nature, sitting by the fireside at Kilmore; recount the various adventures of a hard-fought life; laugh over the follies of the day; join his flute to your harpsichord; and forget that he ever starved in those streets where Butler and Otway starved before him."—GOLDSMITH *to Mrs. Lawder*, August, 1758.

the influence of fashion, which have scarce survived the possessor; you have seen the poor hardly earn the little reputation they acquired, and their merit only acknowledged when they were incapable of enjoying the pleasures of popularity: such, however, is the reputation worth possessing; that which is hardly earned is hardly lost.   Adieu.

LETTER XCIV.

THE PHILOSOPHER'S SON IS AGAIN SEPARATED FROM HIS BEAUTIFUL COMPANION.

From Hingpo, in Moscow, to Lien Chi Altangi, in London.

WHERE will my disappointments end? Must I still be doomed to accuse the severity of my fortune, and show my constancy in distress, rather than moderation in prosperity? I had at least hopes of conveying my charming companion safe from the reach of every enemy, and of again restoring her to her native soil. But those hopes are now no more.

Upon leaving Terki we took the nearest road to the dominions of Russia. We passed the Ural mountains, covered with eternal snow, and traversed the forests of Ufa, where the prowling bear and shrieking hyena keep an undisputed possession. We next embarked upon the rapid river Bulija, and made the best of our way to the banks of the Wolga, where it waters the fruitful valleys of Casan.

There were two vessels in company, properly equipped and armed, in order to oppose the Wolga pirates, who, we were informed, infested this river. Of all mankind these pirates are the most terrible. They are composed of the criminals and outlawed peasants of Russia, who fly to the forests that lie along the banks of the Wolga for protection. Here they join in parties, lead a savage life, and have no other subsistence but plunder. Being deprived of houses, friends, or a fixed habitation, they become more terrible even than the tiger, and as insensible to all the feelings of humanity. They neither give quarter to those they conquer nor receive it when over-powered themselves. The severity of the laws against them serves to increase their barbarity, and seems to make them a neutral species of beings, between the wildness of the lion and the subtlety of the man. When taken alive their punishment is hideous. A floating gibbet is erected, which is let run down with the stream; here, upon an iron hook stuck under their ribs, and upon which the whole weight of their body depends, they are left to expire in the most terrible agonies; some being thus found to linger several days successively.

We were but three days' voyage from the confluence of this river into the Wolga, when we perceived at a distance behind us an armed bark coming up, with the assistance of sails and oars, in order to attack us. The dreadful signal of death was hung upon the mast, and our captain with his glass could easily discern them to be pirates. It is impossible to express our consternation on this occasion; the whole crew instantly came together to consult the properest means of safety. It was, therefore, soon determined to send off our women and valuable commodities in one of our vessels, and that the men should stay in the other and boldly oppose the enemy. This resolution was soon put into execution, and I now reluctantly parted from the beautiful Zelis, for the first time since our retreat from Persia. The vessel in which she was disappeared to my longing eyes in proportion as that of the pirates approached us. They soon came up; but, upon examining our strength, and perhaps sensible of the manner in which we had sent off our most valuable effects, they seemed more eager to pursue the vessel we had sent away than attack us. In this manner they continued to harass us for three days, still endeavoring to pass us without fighting. But on the fourth day, finding it entirely impossible, and despairing to seize the expected booty, they desisted from their endeavors, and left us to pursue our voyage without interruption.

Our joy on this occasion was great; but soon a disappointment more terrible, because unexpected, succeeded. The bark in which our women and treasure were sent off was wrecked upon the banks of the Wolga for want of a proper number of hands to manage her, and the whole crew carried by the peasants up the country. Of this, however, we were not sensible till our arrival at Moscow, where, expecting to meet our separated bark, we were informed of its misfortune and our loss.

Need I paint the situation of my mind on this occasion? Need I describe all I feel when I despair of beholding the beautiful Zelis more? Fancy had dressed the future prospect of my life in the gayest coloring; but one unexpected stroke of fortune has robbed it of every charm. Her dear idea mixes with every scene of pleasure, and without her presence to enliven it the whole becomes tedious, insipid, insupportable. I will confess—now that she is lost, I will confess I loved her; nor is it in the power of time or of reason to erase her image from my heart. Adieu.

LETTER XCV.[1]

THE FATHER CONSOLES HIM UPON THIS OCCASION.

From Lien Chi Altangi to Hingpo, at Moscow.

YOUR misfortunes are mine; but, as every period of life is marked with its own, you must learn to endure them. Disappointed love makes the misery of youth; disappointed ambition that of manhood; and successless avarice that of age. These three attack us through life, and it is our duty to stand upon our guard. To love we ought to oppose dissipation, and endeavor to change the object of the affections; to ambition, the happiness of indolence and obscurity; and to avarice, the fear of soon dying. These are the shields with which we should arm ourselves; and thus make every scene of life, if not pleasing, at least supportable.

---

[1] This letter is a rhapsody from the maxims of the philosopher. *Vide* "Lett. Curieuses et Édifiantes;" *vide etiam* "Du Halde," vol. ii. p. 98.—GOLDSMITH.

Men complain of not finding a place of repose. They are in the wrong; they have it for seeking. What they should indeed complain of is that the heart is an enemy to that very repose they seek. To themselves alone should they impute their discontent. They seek within the short span of life to satisfy a thousand desires, each of which alone is unsatiable. One month passes and another comes on; the year ends and then begins; but man is still unchanging in folly,[1] still blindly continuing in prejudice. To the wise man every climate and every soil is pleasing; to him a parterre of flowers is the famous valley of gold; to him a little brook *the fountain of the young peach-trees;*[2] to such a man the melody of birds is more ravishing than the harmony of a full concert, and the tincture of the cloud preferable to the touch of the finest pencil.

The life of man is a journey—a journey that must be travelled, however bad the roads or the accommodation. If in the beginning it is found dangerous, narrow, and difficult, it must either grow better in the end, or we shall by custom learn to bear its inequality.

But, though I see you incapable of penetrating into grand principles, attend at least to a simile adapted to every apprehension. I am mounted upon a wretched ass. I see another man before me upon a sprightly horse, at which I find some uneasiness. I look behind me, and see numbers on foot, stooping under heavy burdens; let me learn to pity their estate, and thank Heaven for my own.

Shingfu, when under misfortunes, would in the beginning weep like a child; but he soon recovered his former tranquillity. After indulging grief for a few days he would become, as usual, the most merry old man in all the province of Shansi. About the time that his wife died his possessions

---

[1] "The lapse of ages changes all things — time—language — the earth — the bounds of the sea—the stars of the sky, and everything about, around, and underneath man, except man himself; who has always been and always will be an unlucky rascal. The infinite variety of lives conduct but to death, and the infinity of wishes lead but to disappointment."—BYRON, *Works*, vol. v. p. 66, ed. 1832.

[2] This passage the editor does not understand.—GOLDSMITH.

were all consumed by fire, and his only son sold into captivity; Shingfu grieved for one day, and the next went to dance at a mandarin's door for his dinner. The company were surprised to see the old man so merry when suffering such great losses; and the mandarin himself, coming out, asked him how he, who had grieved so much and given way to the calamity the day before, could now be so cheerful? "You ask me one question," cries the old man; "let me answer by asking another: which is the most durable, a hard thing or a soft thing; that which resists, or that which makes no resistance?" "A hard thing, to be sure," replied the mandarin. "There you are wrong," returned Shingfu. "I am now fourscore years old; and if you look in my mouth you will find that I have lost all my teeth, but not a bit of my tongue." Adieu.

LETTER XCVI.

THE CONDOLENCE AND CONGRATULATION UPON THE DEATH OF THE LATE KING RIDICULED.—ENGLISH MOURNING DESCRIBED.

From Lien Chi Altangi to Fum Hoam, first President of the Ceremonial Academy at Pekin, in China.

THE manner of grieving for our departed friends in China is very different from that of Europe. The mourning color of Europe is black, that of China white. When a parent or relation dies here, for they seldom mourn for friends, it is only clapping on a suit of sables, grimacing in it for a few days, and all, soon forgotten, goes on as before; not a single creature missing the deceased, except, perhaps, a favorite house-keeper or a favorite cat.

On the contrary, with us in China it is a very serious affair. The piety with which I have seen you behave on one of these occasions should never be forgotten. I remember it was upon the death of thy grandmother's maiden sister. The coffin was exposed in the principal hall in public view; before it were placed the figures of eunuchs, horses, tortoises, and other

animals, in attitudes of grief and respect. The more distant
relations of the old lady, and I among the number, came to
pay our compliments of condolence, and to salute the deceased
after the manner of our country. We had scarce presented
our wax-candles and perfumes, and given the howl of departure,[1] when, crawling on his belly from under a curtain, out
came the reverend Fum Hoam himself, in all the dismal
solemnity of distress. Your looks were set for sorrow; your
clothing consisted of a hempen bag tied round the neck with
a string. For two long months did this mourning continue.
By night you lay stretched on a single mat, and sat on the
stool of discontent by day. Pious man! who could thus set
an example of sorrow and decorum to our country. Pious
country! where, if we do not grieve at the departure of our
friends for their sakes, at least we are taught to regret them
for our own.

All is very different here; amazement all! What sort of
a people am I got among? Fum, thou son of Fo, what sort
of people am I got among? No crawling round the coffin,
no dressing up in hempen bags, no lying on mats, or sitting
on stools! Gentlemen here shall put on first mourning with
as sprightly an air as if preparing for a birth-night; and widows shall actually dress for another husband in their weeds
for the former. The best jest of all is, that our merry mourners clap bits of muslin on their sleeves, and these are called
weepers. Weeping muslin! alas, alas, very sorrowful truly!
These weepers, then, it seems, are to bear the whole burden
of the distress.

But I have had the strongest instance of this contrast, this
tragi-comical behavior in distress, upon a recent occasion.
Their king,[2] whose departure though sudden was not unexpected, died after a reign of many years. His age and un-

---

[1] "When a parent or elder relation among the Chinese dies, the lineal descendants, clothed in white cloth, with bandages of the same color round their heads, sit
weeping round the corpse on the ground, the women keeping up a dismal howl,
after the manner of the Irish."—DAVIS's *Chinese*, vol. i. p. 295.

[2] George the Second, who died October 25, 1760, in the seventy-seventh year of
his age, and the thirty-fourth of his reign.

certain state of health served, in some measure, to diminish the sorrow of his subjects; and their expectations from his successor seemed to balance their minds between uneasiness and satisfaction. But how ought they to have behaved on such an occasion? Surely, they ought rather to have endeavored to testify their gratitude to their deceased friend than to proclaim their hopes of the future! Sure, even the successor must suppose their love to wear the face of adulation, which so quickly changed the object! However, the very same day on which the old king died they made rejoicing for the new.

For my part, I have no conception of this new manner of mourning and rejoicing in a breath, of being merry and sad, of mixing a funeral procession with a jig and a bonfire. At least it would have been just that they who flattered the king while living for virtues which he had not, should lament him dead for those he really had.

In this universal cause for national distress, as I had no interest myself, so it is but natural to suppose I felt no real affliction. "In all the losses of our friends," says a European philosopher, " we first consider how much our own welfare is affected by their departure, and moderate our real grief just in the same proportion."[1] Now, as I had neither received nor expected to receive favors from kings or their flatterers—as I had no acquaintance in particular with the late monarch—as I know that the place of a king is soon supplied—and, as the Chinese proverb has it, that though the world may sometimes want cobblers to mend their shoes, there is no danger of its wanting emperors to rule their kingdoms—from such considerations I could bear the loss of a king with the most philosophic resignation. However, I thought it my duty at least

[1] "Dans l'adversité de nos meilleurs amis, nous trouvons toujours quelque chose qui ne nous déplait pas."—*Rochefoucault.*

> " In all distresses of our friends,
>   We first consult our private ends;
>   While Nature, kindly bent to ease us,
>   Points out some circumstance to please us."
>   Swift, *On his own Death.*

to appear sorrowful, to put on a melancholy aspect, or to set my face by that of the people.

The first company I came among after the news became general was a set of jolly companions, who were drinking prosperity to the ensuing reign. I entered the room with looks of despair, and even expected applause for the super-lative misery of my countenance. Instead of that, I was universally condemned by the company for a grimacing son of a whore, and desired to take away my penitential phiz to some other quarter. I now corrected my former mistake, and with the most sprightly air imaginable entered a company where they were talking over the ceremonies of the approach-ing funeral. Here I sat for some time with an air of pert vivacity, when one of the chief mourners, immediately ob-serving my good-humor, desired me, if I pleased, to go and grin somewhere else; they wanted no disaffected scoundrels there. Leaving this company, therefore, I was resolved to assume a look perfectly neutral, and have ever since been studying the fashionable air — something between jest and earnest; a complete virginity of face, uncontaminated with the smallest symptom of meaning.

But though grief be a very slight affair here, the mourning, my friend, is a very important concern. When an emperor dies in China, the whole expense of the solemnities is defray-ed from the royal coffers. When the great die here, mandarins are ready enough to order mourning, but I do not see that they are so ready to pay for it. If they send me down from court the gray undress-frock, or the black coat without pocket-holes, I am willing enough to comply with their commands, and wear both; but, by the head of Confucius! to be obliged to wear black, and buy it into the bargain, is more than my tranquillity of temper can bear. What! order me to wear mourning before they know whether I can buy it or no! Fum, thou son of Fo, what sort of a people am I got among? where being out of black is a certain symptom of poverty; where those who have miserable faces cannot have mourning, and those who have mourning will not wear a miserable face!

LETTER XCVII.

ALMOST EVERY SUBJECT OF LITERATURE HAS BEEN ALREADY
EXHAUSTED.

From the Same.

It is usual for the booksellers here, when a book has given
universal pleasure upon one subject, to bring out several more
upon the same plan; which are sure to have purchasers and
readers, from that desire which all men have to view a pleasing object on every side. The first performance serves rather to awaken than satisfy attention; and when that is once
moved the slightest effort serves to continue its progression:
the merit of the first diffuses a light sufficient to illuminate
the succeeding efforts; and no other subject can be relished
till that is exhausted. A stupid work, coming thus immediately in the train of an applauded performance, weans the
mind from the object of its pleasure; and resembles the
sponge thrust into the mouth of a discharged culverin, in
order to adapt it for a new explosion.

This manner, however, of drawing off a subject, or a peculiar mode of writing, to the dregs, effectually precludes a revival of that subject or manner for some time for the future:
the sated reader turns from it with a kind of literary nausea,
and though the titles of books are the part of them most
read, yet he has scarce perseverance enough to wade through
the title-page.

Of this number I own myself one. I am now grown cal-
lous to several subjects and different kinds of composition.
Whether such originally pleased I will not take upon me to
determine; but at present I spurn a new book merely upon
seeing its name in an advertisement; nor have the smallest
curiosity to look beyond the first leaf, even though in the

II.—28

second the author promises his own face "neatly engraved on copper."

I am become a perfect epicure in reading; plain beef or solid mutton will never do. I am for a Chinese dish of bears' claws and birds' nests. I am for sauce strong with assafœtida or fuming with garlic. For this reason, there are a hundred very wise, learned, virtuous, well-intended productions that have no charms for me. Thus, for the soul of me, I could never find courage nor grace enough to wade above two pages deep into "Thoughts upon God and Nature," or "Thoughts upon Providence," or "Thoughts upon Free Grace," or indeed into "Thoughts" upon anything at all. I can no longer meditate with "Meditations for Every Day in the Year." "Essays upon Divers Subjects" cannot allure me, though never so interesting; and as for Funeral Sermons, or even Thanksgiving Sermons, I can neither weep with the one nor rejoice with the other.

But it is chiefly in gentle poetry where I seldom look farther than the title. The truth is, I take up books to be told something new; but here, as it is now managed, the reader is told nothing. He opens the book, and there finds very good words truly, and much exactness of rhyme, but no information. A parcel of gaudy images pass on before his imagination like the figures in a dream; but curiosity, induction, reason, and the whole train of affections are fast asleep. The *jucunda et idonea vitæ*, those sallies which mend the heart while they amuse the fancy, are quite forgotten; so that a reader who would take up some modern applauded performances of this kind must, in order to be pleased, first leave his good-sense behind him, take for his recompense and guide bloated and compound epithet, and dwell on paintings, just, indeed, because labored with minute exactness.

If we examine, however, our internal sensations, we shall find ourselves but little pleased with such labored vanities; we shall find that our applause rather proceeds from a kind of contagion caught up from others, and which we contribute to diffuse, than from what we privately feel. There are some subjects of which almost all the world perceive the futility, yet all combine in imposing them upon each other as worthy of praise. But chiefly this imposition obtains in literature, where men publicly contemn what they relish with rapture in private, and approve abroad what has given them disgust at home. The truth is, we deliver those criticisms in public which are supposed to be best calculated, not to do justice to the author, but to impress others with an opinion of our superior discernment.

But let works of this kind, which have already come off with such applause, enjoy it all. It is neither my wish to diminish, as I was never considerable enough to add to, their fame. But, for the future, I fear there are many poems of which I shall find spirits to read but the title. In the first place, all odes upon winter, or summer, or autumn; in short, all odes, epodes, and monodies whatsoever, shall hereafter be deemed too polite, classical, obscure, and refined to be read, and entirely above human comprehension. Pastorals are pretty enough—for those that like them; but to me Thyrsis is one of the most insipid fellows I ever conversed with; and, as for Corydon, I do not choose his company. Elegies and epistles are very fine to those to whom they are addressed; and as for epic poems, I am generally able to discover the whole plan in reading the two first pages.

Tragedies, however, as they are now made, are good, instructive, moral sermons enough; and it would be a fault not to be pleased with good things. There I learn several great truths; as, that it is impossible to see into the ways of futurity; that punishment always attends the villain; that love is the fond soother of the human breast; that we should not resist Heaven's will, for in resisting Heaven's will Heaven's will is resisted; with several other sentiments equally new, delicate, and striking. Every new tragedy, therefore, I shall go to see; for reflections of this nature make a tolerable harmony, when mixed up with a proper quantity of drum, trumpet, thunder, lightning, or the scene-shifter's whistle. Adieu.

LETTER XCVIII.

A DESCRIPTION OF THE COURTS OF JUSTICE IN WESTMINSTER HALL.

From Lien Chi Altangi to Fum Hoam, first President of the Ceremonial Academy at Pekin, in China.

I HAD some intentions lately of going to visit Bedlam, the place where those who go mad are confined. I went to wait upon the man in black to be my conductor; but I found him preparing to go to Westminster Hall, where the English hold their courts of justice. It gave me some surprise to find my friend engaged in a lawsuit, but more so when he informed me that it had been depending for several years. "How is it possible," cried I, "for a man who knows the world to go to law? I am well acquainted with the courts of justice in China; they resemble rat-traps every one of them—nothing more easy than to get in, but to get out again is attended with some difficulty, and more cunning than rats are generally found to possess."

"Faith," replied my friend, "I should not have gone to law but that I was assured of success before I began; things were presented to me in so alluring a light that I thought by barely declaring myself a candidate for the prize I had nothing more to do than to enjoy the fruits of the victory. Thus have I been upon the eve of an imaginary triumph every term these ten years—have travelled forward with victory ever in my view, but ever out of reach; however, at present, I fancy we have hampered our antagonist in such a manner that, without some unforeseen demur, we shall this day lay him fairly on his back."

"If things be so situated," said I, "I do not care if I attend you to the courts, and partake in the pleasure of your success. But prithee," continued I, as we set forward, "what reasons have you to think an affair at last concluded which has given you so many former disappointments?" "My lawyer tells me," returned he, "that I have Salkeld and Ventris strong in my favor, and that there are no less than fifteen cases in point." "I understand," said I: "those are two of your judges who have already declared their opinions." "Pardon me," replied my friend, "Salkeld and Ventris are lawyers who, some hundred years ago, gave their opinions on cases similar to mine; these opinions which make for me my lawyer is to cite, and those opinions which look another way are cited by the lawyer employed by my antagonist; as I observed, I have Salkeld and Ventris for me, he has Coke and Hale for him; and he that has most opinions is most likely to carry his cause." "But where is the necessity," cried I, "of prolonging a suit by citing the opinions and reports of others, since the same good-sense which determined lawyers in former ages may serve to guide your judges at this day? They at that time gave their opinions only from the light of reason; your judges have the same light at present to direct them; let me even add, a greater, as in former ages there were many prejudices from which the present is happily free. If arguing from authorities be exploded from every other branch of learning, why should it be particularly adhered to in this? I plainly foresee how such a method of investigation must embarrass every suit, and even perplex the student; ceremonies will be multiplied, formalities must increase, and more time will thus be spent in learning the arts of litigation than in the discovery of right."

"I see," cries my friend, "that you are for a speedy administration of justice; but all the world will grant that the more time that is taken up in considering any subject the better it will be understood. Besides, it is the boast of an Englishman that his property is secure, and all the world will grant that a deliberate administration of justice is the best way to secure his property. Why have we so many lawyers but to secure our property? why so many formalities but to secure our property? Not less than one hundred thousand families live in opulence, elegance, and ease merely by securing our property."

"To embarrass justice," returned I, "by a multiplicity of laws, or to hazard it by a confidence in our judges, are, I grant, the opposite rocks on which legislative wisdom has ever split: in one case the client resembles that emperor who is said to have been suffocated with the bedclothes which were only designed to keep him warm; in the other to that town which let the enemy take possession of its walls, in order to show the world how little they depended upon aught but courage for safety. But, bless me! what numbers do I see here, all in black—how is it possible that half this multitude find employment?" "Nothing so easily conceived," returned my companion; "they live. by watching each other. For instance, the catchpole watches the man in debt, the attorney watches the catchpole, the. counsellor watches the attorney, the solicitor the counsellor, and all find sufficient employment." "I conceive you," interrupted I; "they watch each other, but it is the client that pays them all for watching. It puts me in mind of a Chinese fable, which is entitled 'Five Animals at a Meal.'

"A grasshopper filled with dew was merrily singing under a shade; a whangam, that eats grasshoppers, had marked it for its prey, and was just stretching forth to devour it; a serpent, that had for a long time fed only on whangams, was coiled up to fasten on the whangam; a yellow bird was just upon the wing to dart upon the serpent; a hawk had just stooped from above to seize the yellow bird; all were intent on their prey, and unmindful of their danger; so the whangam ate the grasshopper, the serpent ate the whangam, the yellow bird the serpent, and the hawk the yellow bird; when, sousing from on high, a vulture gobbled up the hawk, grasshopper, whangam, and all in a moment."

I had scarce finished my fable when the lawyer came to inform my friend that his cause was put off till another term; that money was wanted to retain, and that all the world was of opinion that the very next hearing would bring him off victorious. "If so, then," cries my friend, "I believe it will be my wisest way to continue the cause for another term; and, in the mean time, my friend here and I will go and see Bedlam." Adieu.

LETTER XCIX.

A VISIT FROM THE LITTLE BEAU.—THE INDULGENCE WITH WHICH THE FAIR SEX ARE TREATED IN SEVERAL PARTS OF ASIA.

From the Same.

I LATELY received a visit from the little beau, who I found had assumed a new flow of spirits with a new suit of clothes. Our discourse happened to turn upon the different treatment of the fair sex here and in Asia, with the influence of beauty in refining our manners and improving our conversation.

I soon perceived he was strongly prejudiced in favor of the Asiatic method of treating the sex, and that it was impossible to persuade him but that a man was happier who had four wives at his command than he who had only one. "It is true," cries he, "your men of fashion in the East are slaves, and under some terror of having their throats squeezed by a bowstring; but what then? they can find ample consolation in a seraglio; they make, indeed, an indifferent figure in conversation abroad, but then they have a seraglio to console them at home. I am told they have no balls, drums, nor operas, but then they have got a seraglio; they may be deprived of wine and French cookery, but they have a seraglio. A seraglio, a seraglio, my dear creature, wipes off every inconvenience in the world.

"Besides, I am told, your Asiatic beauties are the most convenient women alive, for they have no souls: positively there is nothing in nature I should like so much as ladies without souls; soul here is the utter ruin of half the sex. A girl of eighteen shall have soul enough to spend a hundred pounds in the turning of a trump. Her mother shall have soul enough to ride a sweepstake match at a horse-race; her maiden aunt shall have soul enough to purchase the furniture of a whole toy-shop; and others shall have soul enough to behave as if they had no souls at all."

" With respect to the soul," interrupted I, " the Asiatics are much kinder to the fair sex than you imagine; instead of one soul, Fohi, the idol of China, gives every woman three; the Bramins give them fifteen; and even Mohammed himself nowhere excludes the sex from paradise. Abulfeda[1] reports that an old woman one day importuning him to know what she ought to do in order to gain paradise: ' My good lady,' answered the prophet, ' old women never get there.' ' What! never get to paradise!' returned the matron, in a fury. ' Never,' says he, ' for they always grow young by the way.'

" No, sir," continued I, " the men of Asia behave with more deference to the sex than you seem to imagine. As you of Europe say grace upon sitting down to dinner, so it is the custom in China to say grace when a man goes to bed to his wife." "And may I die," returned my companion, " but it is a very pretty ceremony; for, seriously, sir, I see no reason why a man should not be as grateful in one situation as in the other. Upon honor, I always find myself much more disposed to gratitude on the couch of a fine woman than upon sitting down to a sirloin of beef."

"Another ceremony," said I, resuming the conversation, " in favor of the sex among us is, the bride's being allowed after marriage her three days of freedom. During this interval a thousand extravagances are practised by either sex. The lady is placed upon the nuptial bed, and numberless monkey tricks are played round to divert her. One gentleman smells her perfumed handkerchief, another attempts to untie her garters, a third pulls off her shoe to play hunt the slipper, another pretends to be an idiot, and endeavors to raise a laugh by grimacing; in the mean time the glass goes briskly about, till ladies, gentlemen, wife, husband, and all are mixed together in one inundation of arrack punch."

" Strike me dumb, deaf, and blind," cried my companion,

---

[1] Ismael Abulfeda, a learned geographer and historian, born at Damascus in 1273; died 1331. His " Life of Mohammed " was printed at Oxford in 1723.

"but that's very pretty! There's some sense in your Chinese ladies' condescensions; but among us you shall scarcely find one of the whole sex that shall hold her good-humor for three days together. No later than yesterday I happened to say some civil things to a citizen's wife of my acquaintance, not because I loved, but because I had charity; and, what do you think was the tender creature's reply? Only that she detested my pig-tail wig, high-heeled shoes, and sallow complexion! That is all—nothing more! Yes, by the heavens, though she was more ugly than an unpainted actress, I found her more insolent than a thorough-bred woman of quality!"

He was proceeding in this wild manner, when his invective was interrupted by the man in black, who entered the apartment, introducing his niece, a young lady of exquisite beauty. Her very appearance was sufficient to silence the severest satirist of the sex; easy without pride and free without impudence, she seemed capable of supplying every sense with pleasure; her looks, her conversation were natural and unconstrained; she had neither been taught to languish nor ogle, to laugh without a jest or sigh without sorrow. I found that she had just returned from abroad, and had been conversant in the manners of the world. Curiosity prompted me to ask several questions, but she declined them all. I own I never found myself so strongly prejudiced in favor of apparent merit before; and could willingly have prolonged our conversation, but the company after some time withdrew. Just, however, before the little beau took his leave he called me aside, and requested I would change him a twenty-pound bill; which, as I was incapable of doing, he was contented with borrowing half a crown. Adieu.

LETTER C.

A LIFE OF INDEPENDENCE PRAISED.

From Lien Chi Altangi to Hingpo, by the way of Moscow.

FEW virtues have been more praised by moralists than generosity: every practical treatise of ethics tends to increase our sensibility of the distresses of others, and to relax the grasp of frugality. Philosophers that are poor praise it because they are gainers by its effects; and the opulent Seneca himself has written a treatise on benefits, though he was known to give nothing away.[1]

But, among the many who have enforced the duty of giving, I am surprised there are none to inculcate the ignominy of receiving; to show that by every favor we accept we in some measure forfeit our native freedom, and that a state of continual dependence on the generosity of others is a life of gradual debasement.

Were men taught to despise the receiving obligations with the same force of reasoning and declamation that they are instructed to confer them, we might then see every person in society filling up the requisite duties of his station with cheerful industry, neither relaxed by hope nor sullen from disappointment.

Every favor a man receives in some measure sinks him below his dignity; and in proportion to the value of the benefit

---

[1] "A better moralist than Seneca hath said, 'He who maketh haste to be rich shall not be innocent.' This was notoriously our philosopher's case. Juvenal gives him the epithet of *prædives*. Dio attributes the insurrection of the Britons in a great measure to his avarice and rapacity; and P. Suilius appears, from Tacitus, to have attacked him on this head with a violence which no common arts of enriching himself could have provoked: 'By what system of ethics has this professor, in less than four years, amassed three hundred million sesterces? His snares are spread through all the city; last wills and testaments are his quarry, and the rich who have no children are his prey. Italy is overwhelmed, the provinces are exhausted; and he is still unsatisfied.'"—GIFFORD, *Juvenal*, vol. i. p. 355.

or the frequency of its acceptance he gives up so much of his natural independence. He, therefore, who thrives upon the unmerited bounty of another, if he has any sensibility, suffers the worst of servitude; the shackled slave may murmur without reproach, but the humble dependent is taxed with ingratitude upon every symptom of discontent; the one may rave round the walls of his cell, but the other lingers in all the silence of mental confinement. To increase his distress, every new obligation but adds to the former load which kept the vigorous mind from rising; till at last, elastic no longer, it shapes itself to constraint, and puts on habitual servility.

It is thus with the feeling mind; but there are some who, born without any share of sensibility, receive favor after favor, and still cringe for more; who accept the offer of generosity with as little reluctance as the wages of merit, and even make thanks for past benefits an indirect petition for new; such, I grant, can suffer no debasement from dependence, since they were originally as vile as was possible to be; dependence degrades only the ingenuous, but leaves the sordid mind in pristine meanness. In this manner, therefore, long-continued generosity is misplaced, or it is injurious; it either finds a man worthless or it makes him so; and true it is, that the person who is contented to be often obliged ought not to have been obliged at all.

Yet, while I describe the meanness of a life of continued dependence, I would not be thought to include those natural or political subordinations which subsist in every society; for in such, though dependence is exacted from the inferior, yet the obligation on either side is mutual. The son must rely upon his parent for support, but the parent lies under the same obligations to give that the other has to expect; the subordinate officer must receive the commands of his superior, but for this obedience the former has a right to demand an intercourse of favor. Such is not the dependence I would depreciate, but that where every expected favor must be the result of mere benevolence in the giver: where the benefit can be kept without remorse, or transferred without injustice. The character of a legacy-hunter, for instance, is detestable in some countries, and despicable in all; this universal contempt of a man who infringes upon none of the laws of society some moralists have arraigned as a popular and unjust prejudice, never considering the necessary degradations a wretch must undergo who previously expects to grow rich by benefits, without having either natural or social claims to enforce his petitions.

But this intercourse of benefaction and acknowledgment is often injurious, even to the giver as well as the receiver. A man can gain but little knowledge of himself or of the world amid a circle of those whom hope or gratitude has gathered round him; their unceasing humiliations must necessarily increase his comparative magnitude, for all men measure their own abilities by those of their company; thus, being taught to overrate his merit, he in reality lessens it; increasing in confidence, but not in power, his professions end in empty boast, his undertakings in shameful disappointment.

It is perhaps one of the severest misfortunes of the great that they are, in general, obliged to live among men whose real virtue is lessened by dependence, and whose minds are enslaved by obligation. The humble companion may have at first accepted patronage with generous views; but soon he feels the mortifying influence of conscious inferiority, by degrees sinks into a flatterer, and from flattery at last degenerates into stupid veneration. To remedy this, the great often dismiss their old dependents and take new. Such changes are falsely imputed to levity, falsehood, or caprice in the patron, since they may be more justly ascribed to the client's gradual deterioration.

No, my son, a life of independence is generally a life of virtue. It is that which fits the soul for every generous flight of humanity, freedom, and friendship. To give should be our pleasure, but to receive, our shame; serenity, health, and affluence attend the desire of rising by labor; misery, repentance, and disrespect that of succeeding by extorted benevolence. The man who can thank himself alone for the happiness he enjoys is truly blest; and lovely, far more lovely, the sturdy gloom of laborious indigence than the fawning simper of thriving adulation. Adieu.

LETTER CI.

THE PEOPLE MUST BE CONTENTED TO BE GUIDED BY THOSE
WHOM THEY HAVE APPOINTED TO GOVERN.—A STORY TO THIS
EFFECT.

*From Lien Chi Altangi to Fum Hoam, first President of the Ceremonial Academy
at Pekin, in China.*

IN every society some men are born to teach and others to
receive instruction; some to work, and others to enjoy in
idleness the fruits of their industry; some to govern, and
others to obey.   Every people, how free so ever, must be
contented to give up part of their liberty and judgment to
those who govern, in exchange for their hopes of security;
and the motives which first influenced their choice in the
election of their governors should ever be weighed against
the succeeding apparent inconsistencies of their conduct.   All
cannot be rulers, and men are generally best governed by a
few.   In making way through the intricacies of business the
smallest obstacles are apt to retard the execution of what is
to be planned by a multiplicity of counsels; the judgment of
one alone being always fittest for winding through the labyrinths of intrigue and the obstructions of disappointment.
A serpent which as the fable observes, is furnished with one
head and many tails, is much more capable of subsistence and
expedition than another which is furnished with but one tail
and many heads.

Obvious as these truths are, the people of this country
seem insensible of their force.   Not satisfied with the advantages of internal peace and opulence, they still murmur at
their governors and interfere in the execution of their designs, as if they wanted to be something more than happy.
But as the Europeans instruct by argument, and the Asiatics
mostly by narration, were I to address them, I should convey
my sentiments in the following story:

"Takupi had long been Prime-minister of Tipartala, a fertile country that stretches along the western confines of China. During his administration whatever advantages could be derived from arts, learning, and commerce were seen to bless the people; nor were the necessary precautions of providing for the security of the state forgotten. It often happens, however, that when men are possessed of all they want, they then begin to find torment from imaginary afflictions, and lessen their present enjoyments by foreboding that those enjoyments are to have an end. The people now, therefore, endeavored to find out grievances; and, after some search, actually began to think themselves aggrieved. A petition against the enormities of Takupi was carried to the throne in due form; and the queen who governed the country, willing to satisfy her subjects, appointed a day in which his accusers should be heard and the minister should stand upon his defence.

"The day being arrived, and the minister brought before the tribunal, a carrier, who supplied the city with fish, appeared among the number of his accusers. He exclaimed that it was the custom, time immemorial, for carriers to bring their fish upon a horse in a hamper; which, being placed on one side, and balanced by a stone on the other, was thus conveyed with ease and safety; but that the prisoner, moved either by a spirit of innovation, or perhaps bribed by the hampermakers, had obliged all carriers to use the stone no longer, but balance one hamper with another—an order entirely repugnant to the customs of all antiquity, and those of the kingdom of Tipartala in particular.

"The carrier finished, and the whole court shook their heads at the innovating minister, when a second witness appeared. He was inspector of the city buildings, and accused the disgraced favorite of having given orders for the demolition of an ancient ruin, which obstructed the passage through one of the principal streets. He observed that such buildings were noble monuments of barbarous antiquity—contributed finely to show how little their ancestors understood of architecture; and for that reason such monuments should be held sacred, and suffered gradually to decay.

"The last witness now appeared. This was a widow, who had laudably attempted to burn herself upon her husband's funeral pile. But the innovating minister had prevented the execution of her design, and was insensible to her tears, protestations, and entreaties.

"The queen could have pardoned the two former offences; but this last was considered as so gross an injury to the sex, and so directly contrary to all the customs of antiquity, that it called for immediate justice. 'What!' cried the queen, 'not suffer a woman to burn herself when she thinks proper? The sex are to be very prettily tutored, no doubt, if they must be restrained from entertaining their female friends now and then with a fried wife or roasted acquaintance. I sentence the criminal to be banished my presence forever, for his injurious treatment of the sex.'

"Takupi had been hitherto silent, and spoke only to show the sincerity of his resignation. 'Great queen,' cried he, 'I acknowledge my crime, and since I am to be banished, I beg it may be to some ruined town or desolate village in the country I have governed. I shall find some pleasure in improving the soil, and bringing back a spirit of industry among the inhabitants.' His request appearing reasonable, it was immediately complied with, and a courtier had orders to fix upon a place of banishment answering the minister's description. After some months' search, however, the inquiry proved fruitless; neither a desolate village nor a ruined town was found in the whole kingdom. 'Alas,' said Takupi then to the queen, 'how can that country be ill-governed which has neither a desolate village nor a ruined town in it?' The queen perceived the justice of his expostulation, and the minister was received into more than former favor."

LETTER CII.

From the Same.

THE ladies here are by no means such ardent gamesters as the women of Asia. In this respect I must do the English justice; for I love to praise where applause is justly merited. Nothing is more common in China than to see two women of fashion continue gaming till one has won all the other's clothes and stripped her quite naked; the winner thus marching off in a double suit of finery, and the loser shrinking behind in the primitive simplicity of nature.

No doubt you remember when Shang, our maiden aunt, played with a sharper. First her money went; then her trinkets were produced; her clothes followed, piece by piece, soon after; when she had thus played herself quite naked, being a woman of spirit, and willing to pursue her own, she staked her teeth. Fortune was against her even here, and her teeth followed her clothes; at last she played for her left eye, and, oh hard fate! this, too, she lost; however, she had the consolation of biting the sharper, for he never perceived that it was made of glass till it became his own.

How happy, my friend, are the English ladies, who never rise to such an inordinance of passion! Though the sex here are naturally fond of games of chance, and are taught to manage games of skill from their infancy, yet they never pursue ill-fortune with such amazing intrepidity. Indeed, I may entirely acquit them of ever playing—I mean, playing for their eyes or their teeth.

It is true, they often stake their fortune, their beauty, health, and reputation at a gaming-table. It even sometimes happens that they play their husbands into a jail; yet still they preserve a decorum unknown to our wives and daughters of China. I have been present at a rout in this country, where a woman of fashion, after losing her money, has sat writhing in all the agonies of bad-luck; and yet, after all, never once attempted to strip a single petticoat, or cover the board, as her last stake, with her head-clothes.

However, though I praise their moderation at play, I must not conceal their assiduity. In China our women, except upon some great days, are never permitted to finger a dice-box; but here every day seems to be a festival; and night itself, which gives others rest, only serves to increase the female gamester's industry. I have been told of an old lady in the country who, being given over by the physicians, played with the curate of her parish to pass the time away; having won all his money, she next proposed playing for her funeral charges; the proposal was accepted, but, unfortunately, the lady expired just as she had taken in her game.

There are some passions which, though differently pursued, are attended with equal consequences in every country. Here they game with more perseverance, there with greater fury; here they strip their families, there they strip themselves naked. A lady in China who indulges a passion for gaming often becomes a drunkard; and by flourishing a dice-box in one hand she generally comes to brandish a dram-cup in the other. Far be it from me to say there are any who drink drams in England; but it is natural to suppose that when a lady has lost everything else but her honor, she will be apt to toss that into the bargain; and, grown insensible to nicer feelings, behave like the Spaniard who, when all his money was gone, endeavored to borrow more by offering to pawn his whiskers. Adieu.

II.—29

LETTER CIII.

THE CHINESE PHILOSOPHER BEGINS TO THINK OF QUITTING
ENGLAND.

From Lien Chi Altangi to ——, *Merchant in Amsterdam.*

I HAVE just received a letter from my son, in which he informs me of the fruitlessness of his endeavors to recover the lady with whom he fled from Persia. He strives to cover, under the appearance of fortitude, a heart torn with anxiety and disappointment. I have offered little consolation, since that but too frequently feeds the sorrow which it pretends to deplore, and strengthens the impression which nothing but the external rubs of time and accident can thoroughly efface.

He informs me of his intention of quitting Moscow the first opportunity, and travelling by land to Amsterdam. I must, therefore, upon his arrival, entreat the continuance of your friendship, and beg of you to provide him with proper directions for finding me in London. You can scarcely be sensible of the joy I expect upon seeing him once more: the ties between the father and the son among us of China are much more closely drawn than with you of Europe.

The remittances sent me from Argun to Moscow came in safety. I cannot sufficiently admire that spirit of honesty which prevails through the whole country of Siberia: perhaps the savages of that desolate region are the only untutored people of the globe that cultivate the moral virtues, even without knowing that their actions merit praise. I have been told surprising things of their goodness, benevolence, and generosity; and the uninterrupted commerce between China and Russia serves as a collateral confirmation.

"Let us," says the Chinese law-giver, "admire the rude virtues of the ignorant, but rather imitate the delicate morals of the polite." In the country where I reside, though honesty and benevolence be not so congenial, yet art supplies the place of nature. Though here every vice is carried to excess, yet every virtue is practised also with unexampled superiority. A city like this is the soil for great virtues and great vices; the villain can soon improve here in the deepest mysteries of deceiving; and the practical philosopher can every day meet new incitements to mend his honest intentions. There are no pleasures, sensual or sentimental, which this city does not produce; yet, I know not how, I could not be content to reside here for life. There is something so seducing in that spot in which we first had existence, that nothing but it can please. Whatever vicissitudes we experience in life, however we toil, or wheresoever we wander, our fatigued wishes still recur to home for tranquillity: we long to die in that spot which gave us birth, and in that pleasing expectation opiate every calamity.

You now, therefore, perceive that I have some intentions of leaving this country; and yet my designed departure fills me with reluctance and regret. Though the friendships of travellers are generally more transient than vernal snows, still I feel an uneasiness at breaking the connections I have formed since my arrival; particularly, I shall have no small pain in leaving my usual companion, guide, and instructor.

I shall wait for the arrival of my son before I set out. He shall be my companion in every intended journey for the future. In his company I can support the fatigues of the way with redoubled ardor, pleased at once with conveying instruction and exacting obedience. Adieu.

LETTER CIV.

THE ARTS SOME MAKE USE OF TO APPEAR LEARNED.

From Lien Chi Altangi to Fum Hoam, first President of the Ceremonial Academy
at Pekin.

OUR scholars of China have a most profound veneration for forms. A first-rate beauty never studied the decorums of dress with more assiduity; they may properly enough be said to be clothed with wisdom from head to foot; they have their philosophical caps and philosophical whiskers, their philosophical slippers and philosophical fans: there is even a philosophical standard for measuring the nails; and yet, with all this seeming wisdom, they are often found to be mere empty pretenders.

A philosophical beau is not so frequent in Europe; yet I am told that such characters are found here. I mean such as punctually support all the decorums of learning, without being really very profound, or naturally possessed of a fine understanding: who labor hard to obtain the titular honors attending literary merit, who flatter others, in order to be flattered in turn, and only study to be thought students.

A character of this kind generally receives company in his study, in all the pensive formality of slippers, night-gown, and easy-chair. The table is covered with a large book, which is always kept open, and never read; his solitary hours being dedicated to dozing, mending pens, feeling his pulse, peeping through the microscope, and sometimes reading amusing books, which he condemns in company. His library is preserved with the most religious neatness, and is generally a repository of scarce books, which bear a high price, because too dull or useless to become common by the ordinary methods of publication.

Such men are generally candidates for admittance into

literary clubs, academies, and institutions, where they regularly meet to give and receive a little instruction, and a great deal of praise. In conversation they never betray ignorance, because they never seem to receive information. Offer a new observation, they have heard it before; pinch them in an argument, and they reply with a sneer.

Yet, how trifling soever these little arts may appear, they answer one valuable purpose, of gaining the practisers the esteem they wish for. The bounds of a man's knowledge are easily concealed, if he has but prudence; but all can readily see and admire a gilt library, a set of long nails, a silver standish, or a well-combed whisker, who are incapable of distinguishing a dunce.

When Father Matthew,[1] the first European missioner, entered China, the court was informed that he possessed great skill in astronomy; he was therefore sent for, and examined. The established astronomers of state undertook this task, and made their report to the emperor that his skill was but very superficial, and no way comparable to their own. The missioner, however, appealed from their judgment to experience, and challenged them to calculate an eclipse of the moon that was to happen a few nights following. "What!" said some, "shall a barbarian without nails pretend to vie with men in astronomy who have made it the study of their lives; with men who know half the knowable characters of words, who wear scientifical caps and slippers, and who have gone through every literary degree with applause?" They accepted the challenge, confident of success. The eclipse began: the Chinese produced a most splendid apparatus, and were fifteen minutes wrong; the missioner, with a single instrument, was exact to a second. This was convincing; but the court

---

[1] Father Matthew Ricci, who may justly be considered as the first founder of the Catholic mission to China, was born at Macerata in 1552. By his intimate knowledge of the mathematical and experimental sciences he had the means of making friends and converts. He was much esteemed by the emperor, and was permitted to build a church at Pekin, where he died in 1610, leaving behind him some valuable memoirs respecting China which have been made use of by Père Frigault in his history of that empire.—See MORERI, and DAVIS's *Chinese*, vol. i. p. 30.

astronomers were not to be convinced: instead of acknowledging their error, they assured the emperor that their calculations were certainly exact, but that the stranger without nails had actually bewitched the moon. "Well, then," cries the good emperor, smiling at their ignorance, "you shall still continue to be servants of the moon, but I constitute this man her controller."

China is thus replete with men whose only pretensions to knowledge arise from external circumstances; and in Europe every country abounds with them in proportion to its ignorance. Spain and Flanders, who are behind the rest of Europe in learning at least three centuries, have twenty literary titles and marks of distinction unknown in France or England: they have their *Clarissimi* and *Præclarissimi*, their *Accuratissimi* and *Minutissimi;* a round cap entitles one student to argue, and a square cap permits another to teach; while a cap with a tassel almost sanctifies the head it happens to cover. But, where true knowledge is cultivated, these formalities begin to disappear; the ermined cowl, the solemn beard, and the sweeping train are laid aside; philosophers dress, and talk, and think like other men; and lamb-skin dressers, and cap-makers, and tail-carriers now deplore a literary age.

For my own part, my friend, I have seen enough of presuming ignorance never to venerate wisdom but where it actually appears. I have received literary titles and distinctions myself; and by the quantity of my own wisdom know how very little wisdom they can confer. Adieu.

LETTER CV.

THE INTENDED CORONATION DESCRIBED.

From Lien Chi Altangi to Fum Hoam, first President of the Ceremonial Academy at Pekin.

THE time for the young king's coronation[1] approaches; the great and the little world look forward with impatience. A knight from the country, who has brought up his family to see and be seen on this occasion, has taken all the lower part of the house where I lodge. His wife is laying in a large quantity of silks, which the mercer tells her are to be fashionable next season; and miss, her daughter, has actually had her ears bored previously to the ceremony. In all this bustle of preparation I am considered as mere lumber, and have been shoved up two stories higher, to make room for others my landlady seems perfectly convinced are my betters; but whom, before me, she is contented with only calling very good company.

The little beau, who has now forced himself into my intimacy, was yesterday giving me a minute detail of the intended procession. All men are eloquent upon their favorite topic; and this seemed peculiarly adapted to the size and turn of his understanding. His whole mind was blazoned over with a variety of glittering images: coronets, escutcheons, lace, fringe, tassels, stones, bugles, and spun glass. "Here," cried he, "Garter is to walk; and there Rouge Dragon marches with the escutcheons on his back. Here Clarencieux moves forward, and there Blue Mantle disdains to be left behind. Here the Aldermen march two and two, and there the

---

[1] That of George III., on the 22d September, 1761. This paper originally appeared in *The Public Ledger*. Goldsmith wrote three more papers on this subject. See Essays XXV. and XXVI. of Collected Essays, and essay among Unacknowledged Essays—all in Vol. III. of this edition.

undaunted Champion of England, no way terrified at the very numerous appearance of gentlemen and ladies, rides forward in complete armor, and, with an intrepid air, throws down his glove. Ah!" continued he, "should any be so hardy as to take up that fatal glove, and so accept the challenge, we should see fine sport: the Champion would show him no mercy; he would soon teach him all his passes, with a witness! However, I am afraid we shall have none willing to try it with him upon the approaching occasion, for two reasons; first, because his antagonist would stand a chance of being killed in the single combat; and secondly, because if he escapes the Champion's arm he would certainly be hanged for treason. No, no; I fancy none will be so hardy as to dispute it with a Champion like him, inured to arms; and we shall probably see him prancing unmolested away, holding his bridle thus in one hand, and brandishing his dram-cup in the other."

Some men have a manner of describing which only wraps the subject in more than former obscurity; thus was I unable, with all my companion's volubility, to form a distinct idea of the intended procession. I was certain that the inauguration of a king should be conducted with solemnity and religious awe; and I could not be persuaded that there was much solemnity in this description. "If this be true," cried I to myself, "the people of Europe surely have a strange manner of mixing solemn and fantastic images together — pictures at once replete with burlesque and the sublime. At a time when the king enters into the most solemn compact with his people, nothing surely should be admitted to diminish from the real majesty of the ceremony. A ludicrous image brought in at such a time throws an air of ridicule upon the whole. It some way resembles a picture I have seen, designed by Albert Durer, where, amid all the solemnity of that awful scene, a Deity judging, and a trembling world awaiting the decree, he has introduced a merry mortal trundling his scolding wife to hell in a wheelbarrow.

My companion, who mistook my silence during this interval of reflection for the rapture of astonishment, proceeded to describe those frivolous parts of the show that most struck his imagination, and to assure me that if I stayed in this country some months longer I should see fine things. "For my own part," continued he, "I know already of fifteen suits of clothes that would stand on one end with gold lace, all designed to be first shown there; and as for diamonds, rubies, emeralds, and pearls, we shall see them as thick as brass nails in a sedan-chair. And then we are all to walk so majestically, thus: this foot always behind the foot before. The ladies are to fling nosegays, the court poets to scatter verses, the spectators are to be all in full dress, Mrs. Tibbs in a new sack, ruffles, and Frenched hair—look where you will, one thing finer than another! Mrs. Tibbs courtesies to the duchess; her grace returns the compliment with a bow. 'Largess!' cries the herald. 'Make room!' cries the gentleman usher. 'Knock him down!' cries the guard. Ah!" continued he, amazed at his own description, "what an astonishing scene of grandeur can art produce from the smallest circumstance, when it thus actually turns to wonder one man putting on another man's hat!"

I now found his mind was entirely set upon the fopperies of the pageant, and quite regardless of the real meaning of such costly preparations. "Pageants," says Bacon, "are pretty things, but we should rather study to make them elegant than expensive." Processions, cavalcades, and all that fund of gay frippery furnished out by tailors, barbers, and tire-women mechanically influence the mind into veneration; an emperor in his nightcap would not meet with half the respect of an emperor with a glittering crown. Politics resemble religion: attempting to divest either of ceremony is the most certain method of bringing either into contempt. The weak must have their inducements to admiration as well as the wise; and it is the business of a sensible government to impress all ranks with a sense of subordination, whether this be effected by a diamond buckle or a virtuous edict, a sumptuary law or a glass necklace.

This interval of reflection only gave my companion spirits to begin his description afresh; and, as a greater inducement to raise my curiosity, he informed me of the vast sums that were given by the spectators for places. "That the ceremony must be fine," cries he, "is very evident from the fine price that is paid for seeing it. Several ladies have assured me they would willingly part with one eye rather than be prevented from looking on with the other. Come, come," continues he, "I have a friend who, for my sake, will supply us with places at the most reasonable rates; I'll take care you shall not be imposed upon; and he will inform you of the use, finery, rapture, splendor, and enchantment of the whole ceremony better than I."

Follies often repeated lose their absurdity and assume the appearance of reason. His arguments were so often and so strongly enforced, that I had actually some thoughts of becoming a spectator. We accordingly went together to bespeak a place, but guess my surprise when the man demanded a purse of gold for a single seat! I could hardly believe him serious upon making the demand. "Prithee, friend," cried I, "after I have paid twenty pounds for sitting here an hour or two, can I bring a part of the coronation back?" "No, sir." "How long can I live upon it after I have come?" "Not long, sir." "Can a coronation clothe, feed, or fatten me?" "Sir," replied the man, "you seem to be under a mistake; all that you can bring away is the pleasure of having it to say that you saw the coronation." "Blast me!" cries Tibbs, "if that be all, there is no need of paying for that, since I am resolved to have that pleasure, whether I am there or no!"

I am conscious, my friend, that this is but a very confused description of the intended ceremony. You may object that I neither settle rank, precedency, nor place; that I seem ignorant whether Gules walks before or behind Garter; that I have neither mentioned the dimensions of a lord's cap, nor measured the length of a lady's tail. I know your delight is in minute description, and this I am unhappily disqualified from furnishing; yet, upon the whole, I fancy it will be no way comparable to the magnificence of our late Emperor Whangti's procession when he was married to the moon, at which Fum Hoam himself presided in person. Adieu.

LETTER CVI.

FUNERAL ELEGIES WRITTEN UPON THE GREAT RIDICULED.—A
SPECIMEN OF ONE.

To the Same.

IT was formerly the custom here, when men of distinction
died, for their surviving acquaintance to throw each a slight
present into the grave. Several things of little value were
made use of for that purpose—perfumes, relics, spices, bitter herbs, camomile, wormwood, and verses. This custom,
however, is almost discontinued, and nothing but verses alone
are now lavished on such occasions—an oblation which they
suppose may be interred with the dead, without any injury
to the living.

Upon the death of the great, therefore, the poets and undertakers are sure of employment. While one provides the
long cloak, black staff, and mourning-coach, the other produces the pastoral or elegy, the monody or apotheosis. The
nobility need be under no apprehensions, but die as fast as
they think proper—the poet and undertaker are ready to supply them; these can find metaphorical tears and family escutcheons at half an hour's warning; and when the one has
soberly laid the body in the grave, the other is ready to fix it
figuratively among the stars.

There are several ways of being poetically sorrowful on
such occasions. The bard is now some pensive youth of
science, who sits deploring among the tombs; again, he is
Thyrsis complaining in a circle of harmless sheep. Now Bri-
tannia sits upon her own shore, and gives a loose to maternal
tenderness; at another time, Parnassus, even the mountain
Parnassus, gives way to sorrow, and is bathed in tears of
distress.

But the most usual manner is this: Damon meets Menalcas, who has got a most gloomy countenance. The shepherd asks his friend whence that look of distress? to which the other replies that Pollio is no more. "If that be the case, then," cries Damon, "let us retire to yonder bower at some distance off, where the cypress and the jasmine add fragrance to the breeze; and let us weep alternately for Pollio, the friend of shepherds and the patron of every muse." "Ah!" returns his fellow-shepherd, "what think you, rather, of that grotto by the fountain side? the murmuring stream will help to assist our complaints, and a nightingale on a neighboring tree will join her voice to the concert." When the place is thus settled, they begin: the brook stands still to hear their lamentations, the cows forget to graze, and the very tigers start from the forest with sympathetic concern. By the tombs of our ancestors, my dear Fum, I am quite unaffected in all this distress: the whole is liquid laudanum to my spirits; and a tiger of common sensibility has twenty times more tenderness than I.[1]

But though I could never weep with the complaining shepherd, yet I am sometimes induced to pity the poet, whose trade is thus to make demigods and heroes for a dinner. There is not in nature a more dismal figure than a man who sits down to premeditated flattery: every stanza he writes tacitly reproaches the meanness of his occupation, till at last his stupidity becomes more stupid, and his dulness more diminutive.

I am amazed, therefore, that none have yet found out the

---

[1] "In his amorous effusions he [Prior] is less happy; for they are not dictated by nature or by passion, and have neither gallantry nor tenderness. They have the coldness of Cowley, without his wit, the dull exercises of a skilful versifier, resolved at all adventures to write something about Chloe, and trying to be amorous by dint of study. His fictions, therefore, are mythological. Venus, after the example of the Greek epigram, asks when she was seen *naked and bathing*. Then *Cupid* is *mistaken;* then *Cupid* is *disarmed;* then he loses his darts to *Ganymede;* then *Jupiter* sends him a summons by *Mercury*. Then *Chloe* goes a-hunting, with an *ivory quiver graceful at her side;* Diana mistakes her for one of her nymphs, and Cupid laughs at the blunder. All this is surely despicable; and even when he tries to act the lover, without the help of gods or goddesses, his thoughts are unaffecting or remote. He talks not 'like a man of this world.'"—JOHNSON's *Life of Prior.*

secret of flattering the worthless, and yet of preserving a safe conscience. I have often wished for some method by which a man might do himself and his deceased patron justice, without being under the hateful reproach of self-conviction. After long lucubration I have hit upon such an expedient, and sent you the specimen of a poem upon the decease of a great man, in which the flattery is perfectly fine, and yet the poet perfectly innocent.

ON THE DEATH OF THE RIGHT HONORABLE ————.[1]

Ye muses, pour the pitying tear
    For Pollio snatch'd away:
Oh, had he liv'd another year!
    ——*He had not died to-day.*

Oh, were ye born to bless mankind
    In virtuous times of yore,
Heroes themselves had fallen behind!
    ——*Whene'er he went before.*

How sad the groves and plains appear,
    And sympathetic sheep:
E'en pitying hills would drop a tear:
    ——*If hills could learn to weep.*

His bounty in exalted strain
    Each bard might well display,
Since none implored relief in vain!
    ——*That went relieved away.*

And hark! I hear the tuneful throng
    His obsequies forbid;
He still shall live, shall live as long
    ——*As ever dead man did.*

---

[1] Written in the same style of humor as his "Elegy on Mrs. Mary Blaize," Vol. I. p. 110.

LETTER CVII.

THE ENGLISH TOO FOND OF BELIEVING EVERY REPORT WITH-
OUT EXAMINATION. — A STORY OF AN INCENDIARY TO THIS
PURPOSE.

To the Same.

IT is the most usual method in every report first to examine
its probability, and then act as the conjuncture may require.
The English, however, exert a different spirit in such circumstances; they first act, and when too late begin to examine.
From a knowledge of this disposition, there are several here
who make it their business to frame new reports at every
convenient interval, all tending to denounce ruin, both on
their contemporaries and their posterity.   This denunciation
is eagerly caught up by the public: away they fling to propagate the distress; sell out at one place, buy in at another,
grumble at their governors, shout in mobs, and when they
have thus for some time behaved like fools, sit down coolly to
argue and talk wisdom, to puzzle each other with syllogism,
and prepare for the next report that prevails, which is always
attended with the same success.

Thus are they ever rising above one report, only to sink
into another.   They resemble a dog in a well, pawing to get
free.   When he has raised his upper parts above water, and
every spectator imagines him disengaged, his lower parts
drag him down again and sink him to the nose; he makes
new efforts to emerge, and every effort increasing his weakness, only tends to sink him the deeper.

There are some here who, I am told, make a tolerable subsistence by the credulity of their countrymen.   As they find
the public fond of blood, wounds, and death, they contrive
political ruins suited to every month in the year.   This month
the people are to be eaten up by the French in flat-bottomed
boats; the next by the soldiers, designed to beat the French

back : now the people are going to jump down the gulf of
luxury ; and now nothing but a herring subscription can fish
them up again.[1] Time passes on ; the report proves false ;
new circumstances produce new changes ; but the people
never change—they are persevering in folly.

In other countries those boding politicians would be left to
fret over their own schemes alone, and grow splenetic without
hopes of infecting others ; but England seems to be the very
region where spleen delights to dwell ; a man not only can
give an unbounded scope to the disorder in himself, but may,
if he pleases, propagate it over the whole kingdom, with a
certainty of success. He has only to cry out that the government, the government is all wrong ; that their schemes are
leading to ruin ; that Britons are no more : every good member of the commonwealth thinks it his duty, in such a case, to
deplore the universal decadence with sympathetic sorrow,
and, by fancying the constitution in a decay, absolutely to
impair its vigor.

This people would laugh at my simplicity should I advise
them to be less sanguine in harboring gloomy predictions,
and examine coolly before they attempted to complain. I
have just heard a story, which, though transacted in a private
family, serves very well to describe the behavior of the whole
nation in cases of threatened calamity. As there are public
so there are private incendiaries here. One of the last, either
for the amusement of his friends, or to divert a fit of the
spleen, lately sent a threatening letter to a worthy family in
my neighborhood, to this effect :

"Sir,—Knowing you to be very rich, and finding myself
to be very poor, I think proper to inform you that I have
learned the secret of poisoning man, woman, and child without danger of detection. Don't be uneasy, sir ; you may take
your choice of being poisoned in a fortnight, or poisoned in a
month, or poisoned in six weeks ; you shall have full time to
settle all your affairs. Though I am poor, I love to do things

---

[1] See Vol. II. p. 476, and Vol. III. p. 463.

like a gentleman. But, sir, you must die; I have determined
it within my own breast that you must die. Blood, sir, blood
is my trade; so I could wish you would this day six weeks
take leave of your friends, wife, and family, for I cannot possibly allow you longer time. To convince you more certainly
of the power of my art, by which you may know I speak
truth, take this letter; when you have read it, tear off the
seal, fold it up, and give it to your favorite Dutch mastiff
that sits by the fire; he will swallow it, sir, like a buttered
toast; in three hours four minutes after he has taken it he
will attempt to bite off his own tongue, and half an hour after
burst asunder in twenty pieces. Blood! blood! blood! So
no more at present from, sir, your most obedient, most devoted, humble servant to command, till death."

You may easily imagine the consternation into which this
letter threw the whole good-natured family. The poor man
to whom it was addressed was the more surprised, as not
knowing how he could merit such inveterate malice. All the
friends of the family were convened; it was universally
agreed that it was a most terrible affair, and that the government should be solicited to offer a reward and a pardon: a
fellow of this kind would go on poisoning family after family, and it was impossible to say where the destruction would
end. In pursuance of these determinations the government
was applied to; strict search was made after the incendiary,
but all in vain. At last, therefore, they recollected that the
experiment was not yet tried upon the dog; the Dutch mastiff was brought up and placed in the midst of the friends
and relations, the seal was torn off, the packet folded up with
care, and soon they found, to the great surprise of all—that
the dog would not eat the letter. Adieu.

LETTER CVIII.

THE UTILITY AND ENTERTAINMENT THAT MIGHT RESULT FROM A JOURNEY INTO THE EAST.[1]

To the Same.

I HAVE frequently been amazed at the ignorance of almost all the European travellers who have penetrated any considerable way eastward into Asia. They have been influenced either by motives of commerce or piety; and their accounts are such as might reasonably be expected from men of very narrow or very prejudiced education, the dictates of superstition, or the result of ignorance. Is it not surprising that, in such a variety of adventurers, not one single philosopher should be found? for as to the travels of Gemelli, the learned are long agreed that the whole is but an imposture.[2]

There is scarce any country, how rude or uncultivated soever, where the inhabitants are not possessed of some peculiar secrets, either in nature or art, which might be transplanted with success. In Siberian Tartary, for instance, the natives extract a strong spirit from milk, which is a secret probably unknown to the chemists of Europe. In the most savage parts of India they are possessed of the secret of dyeing vegetable substances scarlet, and of refining lead into a metal which, for hardness and color, is little inferior to silver; not one of which secrets but would in Europe make a man's

---

[1] Reprinted by Goldsmith in 1765, as Essay XVIII.

[2] "I can affirm it to be no less certain that Gemelli was in Mexico and at Acapulco than that Pallas has been in the Crimea and Mr. Salt in Abyssinia. Gemelli's descriptions have that local tint which is the principal charm of the narratives of travels written by the most unlettered men, and which can be given only by those who have been ocular witnesses of what they describe."—BARON DE HUMBOLDT, *Armenian Researches.*

fortune. The power of the Asiatics in producing winds or bringing down rain the Europeans are apt to treat as fabulous, because they have no instances of the like nature among themselves; but they would have treated the secrets of gunpowder and the mariner's compass in the same manner, had they been told the Chinese used such arts before the invention was common with themselves at home.

Of all the English philosophers, I most reverence Bacon, that great and hardy genius; he it is who allows of secrets yet unknown; who, undaunted by the seeming difficulties that oppose, prompts human curiosity to examine every part of nature, and even exhorts man to try whether he cannot subject the tempest, the thunder, and even earthquakes, to human control. Oh, did a man of his daring spirit, of his genius, penetration, and learning, travel to those countries which have been visited only by the superstitious and mercenary, what might not mankind expect! How would he enlighten the regions to which he travelled! and what a variety of knowledge and useful improvement would he not bring back in exchange!

There is probably no country so barbarous that would not disclose all it knew, if it received from the traveller equivalent information; and I am apt to think that a person who was ready to give more knowledge than he received would be welcome wherever he came. All his care in travelling should only be to suit his intellectual banquet to the people with whom he conversed: he should not attempt to teach the unlettered Tartar astronomy, nor yet instruct the polite Chinese in the ruder arts of subsistence; he should endeavor to improve the barbarian in the secrets of living comfortably, and the inhabitant of a more refined country in the speculative pleasures of science. How much more nobly would a philosopher thus employed spend his time than by sitting at home, earnestly intent upon adding one star more to his catalogue, or one monster more to his collection, or still, if possible, more triflingly sedulous in the incatenation of fleas, or the sculpture of a cherry-stone!

I never consider this subject without being surprised that

none of those societies, so laudably established in England for the promotion of arts and learning, have ever thought of sending one of their members into the most eastern parts of Asia, to make what discoveries he was able. To be convinced of the utility of such an undertaking, let them but read the relations of their own travellers. It will be there found that they are as often deceived themselves as they attempt to deceive others. The merchant tells us, perhaps, the price of different commodities, the methods of baling them up, and the properest manner for a European to preserve his health in the country. The missioner, on the other hand, informs us with what pleasure the country to which he was sent embraced Christianity, and the numbers he converted; what methods he took to keep Lent in a region where there was no fish, or the shifts he made to celebrate the rites of his religion in places where there was neither bread nor wine. Such accounts, with the usual appendage of marriage and funerals, inscriptions, rivers, and mountains, make up the whole of a European traveller's diary; but as to all the secrets of which the inhabitants are possessed, those are universally attributed to magic; and when the traveller can give no other account of the wonders he sees performed, very contentedly ascribes them to the power of the devil.

It was a usual observation of Boyle, the English chemist, that if every artist would but discover what new observations occurred to him in the exercise of his trade, philosophy would thence gain innumerable improvements. It may be observed with still greater justice that if the useful knowledge of every country, howsoever barbarous, was gleaned by a judicious observer, the advantages would be inestimable. Are there not even in Europe many useful inventions known or practised but in one place? The instrument, as an example, for cutting down corn in Germany is much more handy and expeditious, in my opinion, than the sickle used in England. The cheap and expeditious manner of making vinegar without previous fermentation is known only in a part of France. If such discoveries, therefore, remain still to be known at home, what funds of knowledge might not be collected in countries yet unexplored, or only passed through by ignorant travellers in hasty caravans![1]

The caution with which foreigners are received in Asia may be alleged as an objection to such a design. But how readily have several European merchants found admission into regions the most suspecting, under the character of *sanjapins*, or Northern pilgrims; to such not even China itself denies access.

To send out a traveller properly qualified for these purposes might be an object of national concern; it would, in some measure, repair the breaches made by ambition, and might show that there were still some who boasted a greater name than that of patriots, who professed themselves lovers of men. The only difficulty would remain in choosing a proper person for so arduous an enterprise. He should be a man of a philosophical turn, one apt to deduce consequences of general utility from particular occurrences; neither swollen with pride, nor hardened by prejudice; neither wedded to one particular system, nor instructed only in one particular science; neither wholly a botanist, nor quite an antiquarian; his mind should be tinctured with miscellaneous knowledge, and his manners humanized by an intercourse with men. He should be in some measure an enthusiast in the design; fond of travelling, from a rapid imagination and an innate love of change; furnished with a body capable of sustaining every fatigue, and a heart not easily terrified at danger.   Adieu.

---

[1] "I hope that a mind comprehensive like yours will find leisure, amidst the cares of your important station, to inquire into many subjects of which the European world either thinks not at all, or thinks with deficient intelligence and uncertain conjecture.   I shall hope that he who once intended to increase the learning of his country by the introduction of the Persian language will examine nicely the traditions and histories of the East; that he will survey the wonders of its ancient edifices, and trace the vestiges of its ruined cities; and that, at his return, we shall know the arts and opinions of a race of men from whom very little has been hitherto derived.   You, sir, have no need of being told by me how much may be added by your attention to experimental knowledge and natural history.   There are arts of manufacture practised in the countries in which you preside which are yet very imperfectly known here, either by artificers or philosophers.   Of the natural productions, animate and inanimate, we yet have so little intelligence, that our books are filled, I fear, with conjectures about things which an Indian peasant knows by his senses."—JOHNSON *to Warren Hastings*, March 30, 1774.

LETTER CIX.

THE CHINESE PHILOSOPHER ATTEMPTS TO FIND OUT FAMOUS MEN.

From the Same.

ONE of the principal tasks I had proposed to myself on my arrival here was to become acquainted with the names and characters of those now living who, as scholars or wits, had acquired the greatest share of reputation. In order to succeed in this design, I fancied the surest method would be to begin my inquiry among the ignorant, judging that his fame would be greatest which was loud enough to be heard by the vulgar. Thus predisposed, I began the search, but only went in quest of disappointment and perplexity. I found every district had a peculiar famous man of its own. Here the story-telling shoemaker had engrossed the admiration on one side of the street, while the bellman, who excels at a catch, was in quiet possession of the other. At one end of a lane the sexton was regarded as the greatest man alive; but I had not travelled half its length till I found an enthusiast teacher had divided his reputation. My landlady, perceiving my design, was kind enough to offer me her advice in this affair. It was true, she observed, she was no judge, but she knew what pleased herself, and if I would rest upon her judgment, I should set down Tom Collins as the most ingenious man in the world; for Tom was able to take off all mankind, and imitate, besides, a sow and pigs to perfection.

I now perceived that taking my standard of reputation among the vulgar would swell my catalogue of great names above the size of a court calendar; I therefore discontinued this method of pursuit, and resolved to prosecute my inquiry in that usual residence of fame, a bookseller's shop.[1] In con-

---

[1] Jacob Tonson's shop in the Strand was long the rendezvous of the most eminent authors in England; a little later, Garrick made Becket's, in Adam Street,

sequence of this, I entreated the bookseller to let me know who were they who now made the greatest figure, either in morals, wit, or learning. Without giving me a direct answer, he pulled a pamphlet from the shelf, "The Young Attorney's Guide." "There, sir," cries he, "there is a touch for you! Fifteen hundred of these moved off in a day; I take the author of this pamphlet, either for title, preface, plan, body, or index, to be the completest hand in England."[1] I found it was in vain to prosecute my inquiry where my informer appeared so incompetent a judge of merit; so, paying for the "Young Attorney's Guide," which good-manners obliged me to buy, I walked off.

My pursuit after famous men now brought me into a print-shop. "Here," thought I, "the painter only reflects the public voice. As every man who deserved it had formerly his statue placed up in the Roman forum, so here, probably, the pictures of none but such as merit a place in our affections are held up for public sale." But guess my surprise when I came to examine this depository of noted faces! all distinctions were levelled here as in the grave, and I could not but regard it as the catacomb of real merit. The brick-dust man took up as much room as the truncheoned hero, and the judge was elbowed by the thief-taker; quacks, pimps, and buffoons increased the group, and noted stallions only made room for more noted strumpets. I had read the works of some of the moderns, previous to my coming to England, with delight and approbation, but I found their faces had no place here; the walls were covered with the names of authors I had never known, or had endeavored to forget; with the little self-advertising things of a day, who had forced themselves into fashion but not into fame. I could read at the bottom of some pictures the names of ——, and ——, and ——, all equally candidates for the vulgar shout, and foremost to propagate their unblushing faces upon brass. My uneasiness, therefore, at not finding my few favorite names among the number was

---

Adelphi (the East Strand corner), his house of call for news and gossip; and every reader of Byron's "Life" remembers Murray's four-o'clock visitors.

[1] Books were formerly advertised as written or translated by eminent *hands*.

changed into congratulation. I could not avoid reflecting on the fine observation of Tacitus on a similar occasion. In this cavalcade of flattery, cries the historian, neither the pictures of Brutus, Cassius, nor Cato were to be seen — *eo clariores quia imagines eorum non deferabantur* — their absence being the strongest proof of their merit.

"It is in vain," cried I, "to seek for true greatness among these monuments of the unburied dead; let me go among the tombs of those who are confessedly famous, and see if any have been lately deposited there who deserve the attention of posterity, and whose names may be transmitted to my distant friend, as an honor to the present age." Determined in my pursuit, I paid a second visit to Westminster Abbey. There I found several new monuments erected to the memory of several great men; the names of the great men I absolutely forget; but I well remember that Roubiliac was the statuary who carved them. I could not help smiling at two modern epitaphs in particular, one of which praised the deceased for being *ortus ex antiquâ stirpe ;* the other commended the dead because *hanc œdem suis sumptibus reœdi ficavit ;* the greatest merit of one consisted in his being descended from an illustrious house ; the chief distinction of the other that he had propped up an old house that was falling. "Alas, alas!" cried I, "such monuments as these confer honor, not upon the great men, but upon little Roubiliac."

Hitherto disappointed in my inquiry after the great of the present age, I was resolved to mix in company, and try what I could learn among critics in coffee-houses ; and here it was that I heard my favorite names talked of even with inverted fame. A gentleman of exalted merit as a writer was branded in general terms as a bad man ; another, of exquisite delicacy as a poet, was reproached for wanting good-nature ; a third was accused of free-thinking ; and a fourth, of having once been a player.[1] "Strange," cried I, "how unjust are man-

---

[1] That Goldsmith had particular persons in his eye when he wrote this account of coffee-house appreciation of authors I have no doubt. The last allusion is, I think, to Murphy ; of the general truth of the criticism it would be easy to multiply proofs.

kind in the distribution of fame! the ignorant, among whom I sought at first, were willing to grant, but incapable of distinguishing the virtues of those who deserved it; among those I now converse with they know the proper objects of admiration, but mix envy with applause."

Disappointed so often, I was now resolved to examine those characters in person of whom the world talked so freely. By conversing with men of real merit,[1] I began to find out those characters which really deserved, though they strove to avoid, applause. I found the vulgar admiration entirely misplaced, and malevolence without its sting. The truly great, possessed of numerous small faults and shining virtues, preserve a sublime in morals as in writing. They who have attained an excellence in either commit numberless transgressions, observable to the meanest understanding. The ignorant critic and dull remarker can readily spy blemishes in eloquence or morals whose sentiments are not sufficiently elevated to observe a beauty. But such are judges neither of books nor of life; they can diminish no solid reputation by their censure, nor bestow a lasting character by their applause. In short, I found by my search that such only can confer real fame upon others who have merit themselves to deserve it. Adieu.

LETTER CX.

SOME PROJECTS FOR INTRODUCING ASIATIC EMPLOYMENTS INTO THE COURTS OF ENGLAND.

To the Same.

THERE are numberless employments in the courts of the Eastern monarchs utterly unpractised and unknown in Europe. They have no such officers, for instance, as the emperor's ear-tickler or tooth-picker; they have never introduced at the courts the mandarin appointed to bear the royal tobac-

---

[1] He had about this time become acquainted with Johnson, whose after influence on his life was indeed great.

co-box, or the grave director of the imperial exercitations in the seraglio. Yet I am surprised that the English have imitated us in none of these particulars, as they are generally pleased with everything that comes from China, and excessively fond of creating new and useless employments. They have filled their houses with our furniture, their public gardens with our fireworks, and their very ponds with our fish. Our courtiers, my friend, are the fish and the furniture they should have imported; our courtiers would fill up the necessary ceremonies of a court better than those of Europe; would be contented with receiving large salaries for doing little—whereas, some of this country are at present discontented, though they receive large salaries for doing nothing.

I lately, therefore, had thoughts of publishing a proposal here for the admission of some new Eastern offices and titles into their court-register. As I consider myself in the light of a cosmopolite, I find as much satisfaction in scheming for the countries in which I happen to reside as for that in which I was born.

The finest apartments in the palace of Pegu are frequently infested with rats. These the religion of the country strictly forbids the people to kill. In such circumstances, therefore, they are obliged to have recourse to some great man of the court who is willing to free the royal apartments even at the hazard of his salvation. After a weak monarch's reign the quantity of court vermin in every corner of the palace is surprising; but a prudent king and a vigilant officer soon drive them from their sanctuaries behind the mats and tapestry, and effectually free the court. Such an officer in England would, in my opinion, be serviceable at this juncture; for if, as I am told, the palace be old, much vermin must undoubtedly have taken refuge behind the wainscot and hangings. A minister should therefore be invested with the title and dignities of court vermin-killer; he should have full power either to banish, take, poison, or destroy them, with enchantments, traps, ferrets, or ratsbane. He might be permitted to brandish his besom without remorse, and brush down every part of the furniture, without sparing a single cobweb, however sacred by long prescription. I communicated this proposal some days ago in a company of the first distinction, and enjoying the most honorable offices of the state. Among the number were the inspector of Great Britain, Mr. Henriquez,[1] the director of the ministry; Ben. Victor, the treasurer;[2] John Lockman, the secretary, and the conductor of the *Imperial Magazine*.[3] They all acquiesced in the utility of my proposal, but were apprehensive it might meet with some obstruction from court upholsterers and chamber - maids, who would object to it from the demolition of the furniture, and the dangerous use of ferrets and ratsbane.

My next proposal is rather more general than the former, and might probably meet with less opposition. Though no people in the world flatter each other more than the English, I know none who understand the art less, and flatter with such little refinement. Their panegyric, like a Tartar feast, is indeed served up with profusion, but their cookery is insupportable. A client here shall dress up a fricassee for his patron that shall offend an ordinary nose before it enters the room. A town shall send up their address to a great minister which shall prove at once a satire on the minister and themselves. If the favorite of the day sits, or stands, or sleeps, there are poets to put it into verse, and priests to preach it in the pulpit. In order, therefore, to free both those who praise and those who are praised from a duty probably disagreeable to both, I would constitute professed flatterers here, as in several courts in India. These are appointed in the courts of their princes to instruct the people where to exclaim with admiration, and where to lay an emphasis of praise. But an officer of this kind is always in waiting when the emperor converses in a familiar manner among his rajahs

---

[1] Jacob Henriquez, a Jew projector. Compare Vol. III. p. 316.

[2] Benjamin (or, as he was invariably called, Ben) Victor, treasurer of Drury Lane Theatre. He published, 1761–'71, a "History of the Theatres of London and Dublin," 3 vols. 12mo, not devoid of useful information.—See GENEST's *English Stage*, v. 539.

[3] A newspaper poet and secretary to the Free British Fishery, an unsuccessful project for establishing a herring fishery.

and other nobility.   At every sentence, when the monarch pauses and smiles at what he has been saying, the karamat-man, as this officer is called, is to take it for granted that his majesty has said a good thing; upon which he cries out, "Karamat! karamat! a miracle! a miracle!" and throws up his hands and his eyes in ecstasy.   This is echoed by the courtiers around, while the emperor sits all this time in sullen satisfaction, enjoying the triumph of his joke, or studying a new repartee.

I would have such an officer placed at every great man's table in England.   By frequent practice he might soon become a perfect master of the art, and in time would turn out pleasing to his patron, no way troublesome to himself, and might prevent the nauseous attempts of many more ignorant pretenders.   The clergy here, I am convinced, would relish this proposal.   It would provide places for several of them. And, indeed, by some of their late productions, many appeared to have qualified themselves as candidates for this office already.

But my last proposal I take to be of the utmost importance.   Our neighbor the Empress of Russia has, you may remember, instituted an order of female knighthood.   The Empress of Germany has also instituted another; the Chinese have had such an order time immemorial.   I am amazed the English have never come into such an institution.   When I consider what kind of men are made knights here, it appears strange that they have never conferred this honor upon women.   They make cheese-mongers and pastry-cooks knights; then why not their wives?   They have called up tallow-chandlers to maintain the hardy profession of chivalry and arms; then why not their wives?   Haberdashers are sworn, as I suppose all knights must be sworn, "never to fly in time of mellay or battle, to maintain and uphold the noble estate of chivalry, with horse harnishe and other knightlye habiliments."   Haberdashers, I say, are sworn to all this; then why not their wives?   Certain I am, their wives understand fighting and feats of "mellay and battle" better than they; and as for "knightlye horse and harnishe," it is probable both know nothing more than the harness of a one-horse chaise.

No, no, my friend; instead of conferring any order upon the husbands, I would knight their wives. However, the state should not be troubled with a new institution upon this occasion. Some ancient exploded order might be revived which would furnish both a motto and a name; the ladies might be permitted to choose for themselves. There are, for instance, the obsolete orders of the Dragon in Germany, of the Rue in Scotland, and the Porcupine in France, all well-sounding names, and very applicable to my intended female institution. Adieu.

LETTER CXI.

ON THE DIFFERENT SECTS IN ENGLAND, PARTICULARLY METHO-DISTS.

To the Same.

RELIGIOUS sects in England are far more numerous than in China. Every man who has interest enough to hire a conventicle here may set up for himself, and sell off a new religion. The sellers of the newest pattern at present give extreme good bargains, and let their disciples have a great deal of confidence for very little money.

Their shops are much frequented, and their customers every day increasing; for people are naturally fond of going to paradise at as small expense as possible.

Yet you must not conceive this modern sect as differing in opinion from those of the established religion. Difference of opinion, indeed, formerly divided their sectaries, and sometimes drew their armies to the field: white gowns and black mantles, flapped hats and cross pocket-holes were once the obvious causes of quarrel; men then had some reason for fighting, they knew what they fought about; but at present they are arrived at such refinement in religion-making that they have actually formed a new sect without a new opinion;

they quarrel for opinions they both equally defend; they hate each other, and that is all the difference between them.

But though their principles are the same, their practice is somewhat different. Those of the established religion laugh when they are pleased, and their groans are seldom extorted but by pain or danger. The new sect, on the contrary, weep for their amusement, and use little music except a chorus of sighs and groans, or tunes that are made to imitate groaning. Laughter is their aversion; lovers court each other from the Lamentations; the bridegroom approaches the nuptial couch in sorrowful solemnity, and the bride looks more dismal than an undertaker's shop. Dancing round the room is with them running in a direct line to the devil; and as for gaming, though but in jest, they would sooner play with a rattle-snake's tail than finger a dice-box.

By this time you perceive that I am describing a sect of enthusiasts, and you have already compared them with the Fakirs, Bramins, and Talapoins of the East. Among these, you know, are generations that have been never known to smile, and voluntary affliction makes up all the merit they can boast of. Enthusiasms in every country produce the same effects; stick the Fakir with pins, or confine the Bramin to a vermin hospital; spread the Talapoin on the ground, or load the sectary's brow with contrition: those worshippers who discard the light of reason are ever gloomy; their fears increase in proportion to their ignorance, as men are continually under apprehensions who walk in darkness.

Yet there is still a stronger reason for the enthusiast's being an enemy to laughter; namely, his being himself so proper an object of ridicule. It is remarkable that the propagators of false doctrines have ever been averse to mirth, and always begin by recommending gravity when they intended to disseminate imposture. Fohi, the idol of China, is represented as having never laughed; Zoroaster, the leader of the Bramins, is said to have laughed but twice—upon his coming into the world, and upon his leaving it; and Mohammed himself, though a lover of pleasure, was a professed opposer of gayety. Upon a certain occasion, telling his followers that they would all appear naked at the resurrection, his favorite wife represented such an assembly as immodest and unbecoming. "Foolish woman!" cried the grave prophet, "though the whole assembly be naked, on that day they shall have forgotten to laugh." Men like him opposed ridicule, because they knew it to be a most formidable antagonist, and preached up gravity, to conceal their own want of importance.

Ridicule has ever been the most powerful enemy of enthusiasm, and properly the only antagonist that can be opposed to it with success. Persecution only serves to propagate new religions; they acquire fresh vigor beneath the executioner and the axe; and, like some vivacious insects, multiply by dissection. It is also impossible to combat enthusiasm with reason, for though it makes a show of resistance, it soon eludes the pressure; refers you to distinctions not to be understood, and feelings which it cannot explain. A man who would endeavor to fix an enthusiast by argument might as well attempt to spread quicksilver with his fingers. The only way to conquer a visionary is to despise him; the stake, the fagot, and the disputing doctor in some measure ennoble the opinions they are brought to oppose: they are harmless against innovating pride; contempt alone is truly dreadful. Hunters generally know the most vulnerable part of the beasts they pursue, by the care which every animal takes to defend the side which is weakest; on what side the enthusiast is most vulnerable may be known by the care which he takes in the beginning to work his disciples into gravity, and guard them against the power of ridicule.

When Philip the Second was King of Spain there was a contest in Salamanca between two orders of friars for superiority. The legend of one side contained more extraordinary miracles, but the legend of the other was reckoned most authentic. They reviled each other, as is usual in disputes of divinity; the people were divided into factions, and a civil war appeared unavoidable. In order to prevent such an imminent calamity, the combatants were prevailed upon to submit their legends to the fiery trial, and that which came forth untouched by the fire was to have the victory, and to be honored with a double share of reverence. Whenever the people flock to see a miracle, it is a hundred to one but that they see a miracle; incredible, therefore, were the numbers that were gathered round upon this occasion. The friars on each side approached, and confidently threw their respective legends into the flames, when lo! to the utter disappointment of all the assembly, instead of a miracle, both legends were consumed. Nothing but thus turning both parties into contempt could have prevented the effusion of blood. The people now laughed at their former folly, and wondered why they fell out. Adieu.

LETTER CXII.

AN ELECTION DESCRIBED.

To the Same.

The English are at present employed in celebrating a feast which becomes general every seventh year; the Parliament of the nation being then dissolved,[1] and another appointed to be chosen. This solemnity falls infinitely short of our feast of the lanterns in magnificence and splendor; it is also surpassed by others of the East in unanimity and pure devotion; but no festival in the world can compare with it for eating. Their eating, indeed, amazes me; had I five hundred heads, and were each head furnished with brains, yet would they all be insufficient to compute the number of cows, pigs, geese, and turkeys which upon this occasion die for the good of their country.

To say the truth, eating seems to make a grand ingredient in all English parties of zeal, business, or amusement. When a church is to be built or a hospital to be endowed, the directors assemble, and instead of consulting upon it, they eat upon it, by which means the business goes forward with success. When the poor are to be relieved, the officers appoint-

---

[1] On the 20th of March, 1761, consequent on the death of George II.

ed to dole out public charity assemble and eat upon it; nor
has it ever been known that they filled the bellies of the poor
till they had previously satisfied their own. But in the election of magistrates the people seem to exceed all bounds; the
merits of a candidate are often measured by the number of
his treats; his constituents assemble, eat upon him, and lend
their applause, not to his integrity or sense, but to the quantities of his beef and brandy.

And yet I could forgive this people their plentiful meals
on this occasion, as it is extremely natural for every man to
eat a great deal when he gets it for nothing; but what amazes
me is, that all this good living no way contributes to improve
their good-humor. On the contrary, they seem to lose their
temper as they lose their appetites; every morsel they swallow and every glass they pour down serves to increase their
animosity. Many an honest man, before as harmless as a
tame rabbit, when loaded with a single election dinner has
become more dangerous than a charged culverin. Upon one
of these occasions I have actually seen a bloody-minded man-
milliner sally forth at the head of a mob, determined to face
a desperate pastry-cook, who was general of the opposite
party.

But you must not suppose they are without a pretext for
thus beating each other. On the contrary, no man here is so
uncivilized as to beat his neighbor without producing very
sufficient reasons. One candidate, for instance, treats with
gin, a spirit of their own manufacture; another always drinks
brandy imported from abroad. Brandy is a wholesome liquor,
gin a liquor wholly their own. This, then, furnishes an obvious cause of quarrel—whether it be most reasonable to get
drunk with gin or get drunk with brandy? The mob meet
upon the debate, fight themselves sober, and then draw off to
get drunk again, and charge for another encounter. So that
the English may now properly be said to be engaged in war;
since, while they are subduing their enemies abroad, they are
breaking each other's heads at home.

I lately made an excursion to a neighboring village, in
order to be a spectator of the ceremonies practised upon this

occasion. I left town in company with three fiddlers, nine dozen of hams, and a corporation poet, which were designed as re-enforcements to the gin-drinking party. We entered the town with a very good face; the fiddlers, no way intimidated by the enemy, kept handling their arms up the principal street. By this prudent manœuvre they took peaceable possession of their head-quarters, amid the shouts of multitudes, who seemed perfectly rejoiced at hearing their music, but above all at seeing their bacon.

I must own I could not avoid being pleased to see all ranks of people on this occasion levelled into an equality, and the poor, in some measure, enjoying the primitive privileges of nature. If there was any distinction shown, the lowest of the people seemed to receive it from the rich. I could perceive a cobbler with a levee at his door, and a haberdasher giving audience from behind his counter. But my reflections were soon interrupted by a mob, who demanded whether I was for the distillery or the brewery? As these were terms with which I was totally unacquainted, I chose at first to be silent; however, I know not what might have been the consequence of my reserve, had not the attention of the mob been called off to a skirmish between a brandy-drinker's cow and a gin-drinker's mastiff, which turned out, greatly to the satisfaction of the mob, in favor of the mastiff.

The spectacle, which afforded high entertainment, was at last ended by the appearance of one of the candidates, who came to harangue the mob; he made a very pathetic speech upon the late excessive importation of foreign drams, and the downfall of the distillery. I could see some of the audience shed tears. He was accompanied in his procession by Mrs. Deputy and Mrs. Mayoress. Mrs. Deputy was not in the least in liquor; and as for Mrs. Mayoress, one of the spectators assured me, in my ear, that—she was a very fine woman before she had the small-pox.

Mixing with the crowd, I was now conducted to the hall where the magistrates are chosen; but what tongue can describe this scene of confusion! the whole crowd seemed equally inspired with anger, jealousy, politics, patriotism, and

II.—31

punch. I remarked one figure that was carried up by two men upon this occasion. I at first began to pity his infirmities as natural, but soon found the fellow so drunk that he could not stand; another made his appearance to give his vote, but though he could stand, he actually lost the use of his tongue and remained silent; a third, who, though excessively drunk, could both stand and speak, being asked the candidate's name for whom he voted, could be prevailed upon to make no other answer but "Tobacco and brandy."

In short, an election hall seems to be a theatre where every passion is seen without disguise, a school where fools may readily become worse, and where philosophers may gather wisdom. Adieu.

LETTER CXIII.

A LITERARY CONTEST OF GREAT IMPORTANCE; IN WHICH BOTH SIDES FIGHT BY EPIGRAM.

From the Same.

THE disputes among the learned here are now carried on in a much more compendious manner than formerly. There was a time when folio was brought to oppose folio, and a champion was often listed for life under the banners of a single sorites. At present the controversy is decided in a summary way; an epigram or an acrostic finishes the debate, and the combatant, like the incursive Tartar, advances and retires with a single blow.

An important literary debate at the present engrosses the attention of the town. It is carried on with sharpness, and a proper share of this epigrammatical fury. An author,[1] it seems, has taken an aversion to the faces of several players, and has written verses to prove his dislike; the players fall upon the author, and assure the town he must be dull, and

---

[1] Charles Churchill. Churchill's "Rosciad," published in March, 1761, without the author's name, is said (and truly) to have occasioned a greater sensation in the public mind than had ever before been excited by any poetical performance.

their faces must be good, because he wants a dinner; a critic comes to the poet's assistance,[1] asserting that the verses were perfectly original, and so smart that he could never have written them without the assistance of friends; the friends, upon this, arraign the critic, and plainly prove the verses to be all the author's own. So at it they are, all four together, by the ears: the friends at the critic, the critic at the players, the players at the author, and the author at the players again. It is impossible to determine how this many-sided contest will end, or which party to adhere to. The town, without siding with any, views the combat in suspense, like the fabled hero of antiquity, who beheld the earth-born brothers give and receive mutual wounds, and fall by indiscriminate destruction.

This is, in some measure, the state of the present dispute; but the combatants here differ in one respect from the champions of the fable. Every new wound only gives vigor for another blow; though they appear to strike, they are in fact mutually swelling themselves into consideration, and thus advertising each other away into fame. "To-day," says one, "my name shall be in the *Gazette*, the next day my rival's; people will naturally inquire about us; thus we shall at least make a noise in the streets, though we have got nothing to sell." I have read of a dispute of a similar nature which was managed here about twenty years ago. Hildebrand Jacob,[2] as I think he was called, and Charles Johnson,[3] were poets, both at that time possessed of great reputation; for Johnson had written eleven plays, acted with great success; and Jacob,

---

[1] In *The Critical Review*. Out of this criticism grew the famous "Apology addressed to the Critical Reviewers by C. Churchill."

[2] Author of "The Fatal Constancy," a tragedy, of "The Nest of Plays," consisting of three comedies, etc. He was descended from Sir John Jacob, of Bromley, one of the farmers of the Customs, and in 1740 succeeded to the title of baronet. He died November, 1790, in his seventy-sixth year, and was buried in St. Anne's, Soho.

[3] Author of "The Victim" and "Cobbler of Preston." Died 1748. Pope has immortalized him as "fat Johnson," and in his "Fragment of a Satire" has thus spoken of him:

"Jo—n, who now to sense, now nonsense, leaning,
Means not, but blunders round about a meaning."

though he had written but five, had five times thanked the
town for their unmerited applause. They soon became mutually enamored of each other's talents : they wrote, they felt,
they challenged the town for each other. Johnson assured
the public that no poet alive had the easy simplicity of Jacob,
and Jacob exhibited Johnson as a masterpiece in the pathetic.
Their mutual praise was not without effect : the town saw their
plays, were in raptures—read, and, without censuring them,
forgot them. So formidable a union, however, was soon opposed by Tibbald.[1] Tibbald asserted that the tragedies of
the one had faults, and the comedies of the other substituted
wit for vivacity : the combined champions flew at him like
tigers, arraigned the censurer's judgment, and impeached his
sincerity. It was a long time a dispute among the learned
which was in fact the greatest man, Jacob, Johnson, or Tibbald ; they had all written for the stage with great success,
their names were seen in almost every paper, and their works
in every coffee-house. However, in the hottest of the dispute a fourth combatant made his appearance, and swept
away the three combatants, tragedy, comedy, and all, into
undistinguished ruin.

From this time they seemed consigned into the hands of
criticism ; scarce a day passed in which they were not arraigned as detested writers. The critics, those enemies of
Dryden and Pope, were their enemies. So Jacob and Johnson, instead of mending by criticism, called it envy ; and, because Dryden and Pope were censured, they compared themselves to Dryden and Pope.

But to return. The weapon chiefly used in the present controversy is epigram ; and certainly never was a keener made
use of. They have discovered surprising sharpness on both
sides. The first that came out upon this occasion was a kind
of new composition in this way, and might more properly be
called an epigrammatic thesis than an epigram. It consists,
first, of an argument in prose ; next follows a motto from

---

[1] Lewis Theobald, the editor of Shakspeare, and the hero of the first "Dun-
ciad." Died 1744.

Roscommon; then comes the epigram; and lastly, notes serving to explain the epigram. But you shall have it, with all its decorations:

AN EPIGRAM

*Addressed to the Gentlemen reflected on in " The Rosciad," a Poem,
by the Author.*

> Worried with debts and past all hopes of bail,
> His pen he prostitutes, t' avoid a jail.—Roscom.

> " Let not the *hungry* Bavius' angry stroke
> Awake resentment, or your rage provoke;
> But, pitying his distress, let virtue[1] shine,
> And, giving each your bounty,[2] *let him dine;*
> For, thus retain'd, as learned counsel can,
> Each case, however bad, he'll new japan;
> And, by a quick transition, plainly show
> 'Twas no defect of yours, but *pocket low,*
> That caused his *putrid kennel* to o'erflow."

The last lines are certainly executed in a very masterly manner. It is of that species of argumentation called the perplexing. It effectually flings the antagonist into a mist; there is no answering it: the laugh is raised against him, while he is endeavoring to find out the jest. At once he shows that the author has a kennel, and that this kennel is putrid, and that this putrid kennel overflows. But why does it overflow? It overflows because the author happens to have low pockets! There was also another new attempt in this way—a prosaic epigram which came out upon this occasion. This is so full of matter that a critic might split it into fifteen epigrams, each properly fitted with its sting. You shall see it:

To G. C. *and* R. L.[3]

> "'Twas you, or I, or he, or all together;
> 'Twas one, both, three of them, they know not whether;
> This I believe, between us great or small,
> You, I, he, wrote it not—'twas Churchill's all."

There, there's a perplex! I could have wished, to make it

---

[1] Charity.—Goldsmith.

[2] Settled at one shilling, the price of the poem.—Goldsmith.

[3] George Colman and Robert Lloyd.

quite perfect, the author, as in the case before, had added notes. Almost every word admits a scholium, and a long one too. I, YOU, HE! Suppose a stranger should ask, "And who are you?" Here are three obscure persons spoken of, that may in a short time be utterly forgotten. Their names should have consequently been mentioned in notes at the bottom. But when the reader comes to the words "great" and "small" the maze is inextricable. Here the stranger may dive for a mystery, without ever reaching the bottom. Let him know, then, that "small" is a word purely introduced to make good rhyme, and "great" was a very proper word to keep "small" company.

Yet, by being thus a spectator of others' dangers, I must own I begin to tremble in this literary contest for my own. I begin to fear that my challenge to Doctor Rock [1] was unadvised, and has procured me more antagonists than I had at first expected. I have received private letters from several of the literati here that fill my soul with apprehension. I may safely aver that "I never gave any creature in this good city offence," except only my rival Doctor Rock; yet, by the letters I every day receive, and by some I have seen printed, I am arraigned at one time as being a dull fellow, at another as being pert; I am here petulant, there I am heavy. By the head of my ancestors, they treat me with more inhumanity than a flying-fish. If I dive and run my nose to the bottom, there a devouring shark is ready to swallow me up; if I skim the surface, a pack of dolphins are at my tail to snap me; but when I take wing and attempt to escape them by flight, I become a prey to every ravenous bird that winnows the bosom of the deep. Adieu.

---

[1] See Letter LXVIII.

LETTER CXIV.[1]

AGAINST THE MARRIAGE ACT.—A FABLE.

To the Same.

THE formalities, delays, and disappointments that precede a treaty of marriage here are usually as numerous as those previous to a treaty of peace. The laws of this country are finely calculated to promote all commerce but the commerce between the sexes. Their encouragements for propagating hemp, madder, and tobacco are indeed admirable. Marriages are the only commodity that meets with none.

Yet, from the vernal softness of the air, the verdure of the fields, the transparency of the streams, and the beauty of the women, I know few countries more proper to invite to courtship. Here Love might sport among painted lawns and warbling groves, and revel upon gales wafting at once both fragrance and harmony. Yet it seems he has forsaken the island; and when a couple are now to be married mutual love or a union of minds is the last and most trifling consideration. If their goods and chattels can be brought to unite, their sympathetic souls are ever ready to guarantee the treaty. The gentleman's mortgaged lawn becomes enamored of the lady's marriageable grove; the match is struck up, and both parties are piously in love—according to act of parliament.

Thus, they who have fortune are possessed at least of something that is lovely; but I actually pity those that have none. I am told there was a time when ladies with no other merit but youth, virtue, and beauty had a chance for husbands at least among the ministers of the church or the officers of the army. The blush and innocence of sixteen was said to have a powerful influence over these two professions. But of late

---

[1] Reprinted by Goldsmith in 1765, as Essay XXIII.

all the little traffic of blushing, ogling, dimpling, and smiling
has been forbidden by an act, in that case wisely made and
provided. A lady's whole cargo of smiles, sighs, and whispers is declared utterly contraband till she arrives in the
warm latitudes of twenty-two, where commodities of this
nature are too often found to decay. She is then permitted
to dimple and smile, when the dimples and smiles begin to
forsake her; and, when perhaps grown ugly, is charitably
intrusted with an unlimited use of her charms. Her lovers,
however, by this time have forsaken her; the captain has
changed for another mistress; the priest himself leaves her in
solitude to bewail her virginity; and she dies even without
benefit of clergy.

Thus you find the Europeans discouraging love with as
much earnestness as the rudest savage of Sofala. The genius
is surely now no more. In every region I find enemies in
arms to oppress him. Avarice in Europe, jealousy in Persia,
ceremony in China, poverty among the Tartars, and lust in
Circassia, are all prepared to oppose his power. The genius
is certainly banished from earth, though once adored under
such a variety of forms. He is nowhere to be found; and
all that the ladies of each country can produce are but a few
trifling relics, as instances of his former residence and favor.

"The Genius of Love," says the Eastern apologue, "had
long resided in the happy plains of Abra, where every breeze
was health, and every sound produced tranquillity. His temple at first was crowded, but every age lessened the number
of his votaries, or cooled their devotion. Perceiving, therefore, his altars at length quite deserted, he was resolved to remove to some more propitious region, and he apprised the
fair sex of every country where he could hope for a proper
reception to assert their right to his presence among them.
In return to this proclamation embassies were sent from the
ladies of every part of the world to invite him, and to display
the superiority of their claims.

"At first the beauties of China appeared. No country
could compare with them for modesty, either of look, dress,
or behavior; their eyes were never lifted from the ground;

their robes of the most beautiful silk hid their hands, bosom, and neck, while their faces only were left uncovered. They indulged no airs that might express loose desire, and they seemed to study only the graces of inanimate beauty. Their black teeth and plucked eyebrows were, however, alleged by the genius against them, but he set them entirely aside when he came to examine their little feet.[1]

"The beauties of Circassia next made their appearance. They advanced hand-in-hand, singing the most immodest airs, and leading up a dance in the most luxurious attitudes. Their dress was but half a covering; the neck, the left breast, and all the limbs were exposed to view, which, after some time, seemed rather to satiate than inflame desire. The lily and the rose contended in forming their complexions; and a soft sleepiness of eye added irresistible poignance to their charms; but their beauties were obtruded, not offered, to their admirers; they seemed to give rather than receive courtship; and the Genius of Love dismissed them as unworthy his regard, since they exchanged the duties of love, and made themselves not the pursued but the pursuing sex.

"The kingdom of Cashmire next produced its charming deputies. This happy region seemed peculiarly sequestered by nature for his abode. Shady mountains fenced it on one side from the scorching sun, and sea-borne breezes on the other gave peculiar luxuriance to the air. Their complexions were of a bright yellow, that appeared almost transparent, while the crimson tulip seemed to blossom on their checks. Their features and limbs were delicate beyond the statuary's power to express; and their teeth whiter than their own ivory. He was almost persuaded to reside among them,

---

[1] "The dress of the females of China is extremely modest and becoming, and, in the higher classes, as splendid as the most exquisite silks and embroidery can make it. What we often choose to call dress they would regard as absolute nudity. They would frequently be very pretty were it not for the shocking custom of daubing their faces with white and red paint, to which may be added the deformity of cramped feet. The eyebrows of the young women are fashioned until they represent a fine curved line, which is compared to the new-moon when only a day or two old, or to the young leaflet of the willow."—DAVIS's *Chinese*, vol. i. p. 358.

when, unfortunately, one of the ladies talked of appointing his seraglio.

"In this procession the naked inhabitants of Southern America would not be left behind. Their charms were found to surpass whatever the warmest imagination could conceive; and served to show that beauty could be perfect, even with the seeming disadvantage of a brown complexion. But their savage education rendered them utterly unqualified to make the proper use of their power, and they were rejected as being incapable of uniting mental with sensual satisfaction. In this manner the deputies of other kingdoms had their suits rejected; the black beauties of Benin, and the tawny daughters of Borneo; the women of Wida, with well-scarred faces, and the hideous virgins of Caffraria; the squab ladies of Lapland, three feet high, and the giant fair ones of Patagonia.

"The beauties of Europe at last appeared; grace was in their steps, and sensibility sat smiling in every eye. It was the universal opinion, while they were approaching, that they would prevail, and the genius seemed to lend them his most favorable attention. They opened their pretensions with the utmost modesty; but, unfortunately, as their orator proceeded she happened to let fall the words, 'house in town, settlement, and pin-money.' These seemingly harmless terms had instantly a surprising effect; the genius with ungovernable rage burst from amid the circle, and, waving his youthful pinions, left this earth, and flew back to those ethereal mansions from whence he descended.

"The whole assembly was struck with amazement; they now justly apprehended that female power would be no more, since Love had forsaken them. They continued some time thus in a state of torpid despair, when it was proposed by one of the number that, since the real genius had left them, in order to continue their power they should set up an idol in his stead, and that the ladies of every country should furnish him with what each liked best. This proposal was instantly relished and agreed to. An idol was formed by uniting the capricious gifts of all the assembly, though no way resembling the departed genius. The ladies of China

furnished the monster with wings; those of Cashmire supplied him with horns; the dames of Europe clapped a purse
in his hand; and the virgins of Congo furnished him with a
tail. Since that time all the vows addressed to Love are in
reality paid to the idol; but, as in other false religions, the
adoration seems most fervent where the heart is least sincere." Adieu.

LETTER CXV.

ON THE DANGER OF HAVING TOO HIGH AN OPINION OF HUMAN NATURE.

To the Same.

MANKIND have ever been prone to expatiate in the praise
of human nature. The dignity of man is a subject that has
always been the favorite theme of humanity; they have declaimed with that ostentation which usually accompanies such
as are sure of having a partial audience; they have obtained
victories, because there were none to oppose. Yet, from all
I have ever read or seen, men appear more apt to err by having too high than by having too despicable an opinion of
their nature; and, by attempting to exalt their original place
in creation, depress their real value in society.

The most ignorant nations have always been found to think
most highly of themselves. The Deity has ever been thought
peculiarly concerned in their glory and preservation; to have
fought their battles and inspired their teachers; their wizards
are said to be familiar with heaven; and every hero has a
guard of angels as well as men to attend him. When the
Portuguese first came among the wretched inhabitants of
the coast of Africa, these savage nations readily allowed the
strangers more skill in navigation and war; yet still considered them at best but useful servants, brought to their coast
by their guardian serpent, to supply them with luxuries they
could have lived without. Though they could grant the
Portuguese more riches, they could never allow them to have
such a king as their Tottimondelem, who wore a bracelet of

shells round his neck, and whose legs were covered with ivory.

In this manner examine a savage in the history of his country and predecessors; you ever find his warriors able to conquer armies, and his sages acquainted with more than possible knowledge. Human nature is to him an unknown country; he thinks it capable of great things, because he is ignorant of its boundaries; whatever can be conceived to be done he allows to be possible, and whatever is possible he conjectures must have been done. He never measures the actions and powers of others by what himself is able to perform, nor makes a proper estimate of the greatness of his fellows by bringing it to the standard of his own incapacity. He is satisfied to be one of a country where mighty things have been, and imagines the fancied power of others reflects a lustre on himself. Thus, by degrees, he loses the idea of his own insignificance in a confused notion of the extraordinary powers of humanity, and is willing to grant extraordinary gifts to every pretender, because unacquainted with their claims.

This is the reason why demi-gods and heroes have ever been erected in times or countries of ignorance and barbarity; they addressed a people who had high opinions of human nature, because they were ignorant how far it could extend; they addressed a people who were willing to allow that men should be gods, because they were yet imperfectly acquainted with God and with man. These impostors knew that all men are naturally fond of seeing something very great made from the little materials of humanity; that ignorant nations are not more proud of building a tower to reach heaven, or a pyramid to last for ages, than of raising up a demi-god of their own country and creation. The same pride that erects a colossus or a pyramid installs a god or a hero; but though the adoring savage can raise his colossus to the clouds, he can exalt the hero not one inch above the standard of humanity; incapable, therefore, of exalting the idol, he debases himself, and falls prostrate before him.

When man has thus acquired an erroneous idea of the dignity of his species, he and the gods become perfectly intimate; men are but angels, angels are but men, nay, but servants, that stand in waiting to execute human commands. The Persians, for instance, thus address their prophet Haly: "I salute thee, glorious creator, of whom the sun is but the shadow! Masterpiece of the Lord of human creatures! Great star of justice and religion! The sea is not rich and liberal but by the gifts of thy munificent hands. The angel treasurer of heaven reaps his harvest in the fertile gardens of the purity of thy nature. The *primum mobile* would never dart the ball of the sun through the trunk of heaven, were it not to serve the Morning, out of the extreme love she has for thee. The angel Gabriel, messenger of truth, every day kisses the groundsel of thy gate. Were there a place more exalted than the most high throne of God, I would affirm it to be thy place, O master of the faithful! Gabriel, with all his art and knowledge, is but a mere scholar to thee!"[1] Thus, my friend, men think proper to treat angels; but if, indeed, there be such an order of beings, with what a degree of satirical contempt must they listen to the songs of little mortals, thus flattering each other! thus to see creatures, wiser, indeed, than the monkey and more active than the oyster, claiming to themselves a mastery of heaven! minims, the tenants of an atom, thus arrogating a partnership in the creation of universal nature! Sure Heaven is kind, that launches no thunder at those guilty heads! But it is kind, and regards their follies with pity, nor will destroy creatures that it loved into being.

But, whatever success this practice of making demi-gods might have been attended with in barbarous nations, I do not know that any man became a god in a country where the inhabitants were refined. Such countries generally have too close an inspection into human weakness to think it invested with celestial power. They sometimes, indeed, admit the gods of strangers, or of their ancestors, which had their existence in times of obscurity; their weakness being forgotten,

---

[1] Chardin's "Travels," p. 402.—GOLDSMITH.

while nothing but their power and their miracles were remembered. The Chinese, for instance, never had a god of their own country: the idols which the vulgar worship at this day were brought from the barbarous nations around them. The Roman emperors, who pretended to divinity, were generally taught by a poniard that they were mortal; and Alexander, though he passed among barbarous countries for a real god, could never persuade his polite countrymen into a similitude of thinking. The Lacedemonians shrewdly complied with his commands by the following sarcastic edict: Εἴ Ἀλέξανδρος βουλέται εἶναι Θεὺς, Θεὸς ἔστω. Adieu.

LETTER CXVI.

WHETHER LOVE BE A NATURAL OR FICTITIOUS PASSION.

To the Same.

THERE is something irresistibly pleasing in the conversation of a fine woman: even though her tongue be silent, the eloquence of her eyes teaches wisdom. The mind sympathizes with the regularity of the object in view, and, struck with external grace, vibrates into respondent harmony. In this agreeable disposition I lately found myself in company with my friend and his niece. Our conversation turned upon love, which she seemed equally capable of defending and inspiring. We were each of different opinions upon this subject: the lady insisted that it was a natural and universal passion, and produced the happiness of those who cultivated it with proper precaution. My friend denied it to be the work of nature, but allowed it to have a real existence, and affirmed that it was of infinite service in refining society; while I, to keep up the dispute, affirmed it to be merely a name, first used by the cunning part of the fair sex, and admitted by the silly part of ours; therefore no way more natural than taking snuff or chewing opium.

"How is it possible," cried I, "that such a passion can be natural, when our opinions, even of beauty, which inspires it, are entirely the result of fashion and caprice? The ancients, who pretended to be connoisseurs in the art, have praised narrow foreheads, red hair, and eyebrows that joined each other over the nose. Such were the charms that once captivated Catullus, Ovid, and Anacreon. Ladies would at present be out of humor, if their lovers praised them for such graces; and should an antique beauty now revive, her face would certainly be put under the discipline of the tweezer, forehead-cloth, and lead-comb, before it could be seen in public company.

"But the difference between the ancients and moderns is not so great as between the different countries of the present world. A lover of Gongora, for instance, sighs for thick lips; a Chinese lover is poetical in praise of thin. In Circassia a straight nose is thought most consistent with beauty; cross but a mountain which separates it from thé Tartars, and there flat noses, tawny skins, and eyes three inches asunder, are all the fashion. In Persia, and some other countries, a man, when he marries, chooses to have his bride a maid. In the Philippine Islands, if a bridegroom happens to perceive, on the first night, that he is put off with a virgin, the marriage is declared void to all intents and purposes, and the bride sent back with disgrace. In some parts of the East a woman of beauty, properly fed up for sale, often amounts to one hundred crowns; in the kingdom of Loango ladies of the very best fashion are sold for a pig; queens, however, sell better, and sometimes amount to a cow. In short, turn even to England, do not I there see the beautiful part of the sex neglected; and none marrying or making love but old men and old women that have saved money? Do not I see beauty, from fifteen to twenty-one, rendered null and void to all intents and purposes; and those six precious years of womanhood put under a statute of virginity? What! shall I call that rancid passion love which passes between an old bachelor of fifty-six and a widow-lady of forty-nine? Never! never! What advantage is society to reap from an intercourse where the big belly is oftenest on the man's side? Would any persuade me that such a passion was natural, unless the human race were more fit for love as they approached the decline, and, like silk-worms, became breeders just before they expired?"

"Whether love be natural or no," replied my friend, gravely, "it contributes to the happiness of every society into which it is introduced. All our pleasures are short, and can only charm at intervals; love is a method of protracting our greatest pleasure; and surely that gamester who plays the greatest stake to the best advantage will, at the end of life, rise victorious. This was the opinion of Vanini,[1] who affirmed that 'every hour was lost which was not spent in love.' His accusers were unable to comprehend his meaning, and the poor advocate for love was burnt in flames, alas! no way metaphorical. But whatever advantages the individual may reap from this passion, society will certainly be refined and improved by its introduction: all laws calculated to discourage it tend to imbrute the species and weaken the state. Though it cannot plant morals in the human breast, it cultivates them when there: pity, generosity, and honor receive a brighter polish from its assistance; and a single amour is sufficient entirely to brush off the clown."

"But it is an exotic of the most delicate constitution: it requires the greatest art to introduce it into a state, and the smallest discouragement is sufficient to repress it again. Let us only consider with what ease it was formerly extinguished in Rome, and with what difficulty it was lately revived in Europe: it seemed to sleep for ages, and at last fought its way among us through tilts, tournaments, dragons, and all the dreams of chivalry. The rest of the world, China only excepted, are, and have ever been, utter strangers to its delights and advantages. In other countries, as men find themselves stronger than women, they lay a claim to a rigorous superiority: this is natural, and love, which gives up this natural advantage, must certainly be the effect of art—an art calculated to lengthen out our happier moments, and add new graces to society."

---

[1] A priest, born 1585, at Tourosano, in the kingdom of Naples, died 1619. After preaching atheism in England, Germany, and Holland, he was apprehended at Toulouse and condemned to the flames.

"I entirely acquiesce in your sentiments," says the lady, " with regard to the advantages of this passion, but cannot avoid giving it a nobler origin than you have been pleased to assign. I must think that those countries where it is rejected are obliged to have recourse to art, to stifle so natural a production, and those nations where it is cultivated only make nearer advances to nature. The same efforts that are used in some places to suppress pity, and other natural passions, may have been employed to extinguish love. No nation, however unpolished, is remarkable for innocence that is not famous for passion; it has flourished in the coldest as well as the warmest regions. Even in the sultry wilds of Southern America the lover is not satisfied with possessing his mistress's person, without having her mind :

> " 'In all my Enna's beauties blest,
>   Amidst profusion still I pine;
> For though she gives me up her breast,
>   Its panting tenant is not mine.' " [1]

"But the effects of love are too violent to be the result of an artificial passion. Nor is it in the power of fashion to force the constitution in those changes which we every day observe. Several have died of it. Few lovers are unacquainted with the fate of the two Italian lovers, Da Corsin and Julia Bellamano, who, after a long separation, expired with pleasure in each other's arms. Such instances are too strong confirmations of the reality of the passion, and serve to show that suppressing it is but opposing the natural dictates of the heart." Adieu.

---

[1] Translation of a South American ode.—GOLDSMITH.

II.—32

LETTER CXVII.

A CITY NIGHT-PIECE.[1]

To the Same.

THE clock just struck two, the expiring taper rises and sinks in the socket, the watchman forgets the hour in slumber, the laborious and the happy are at rest, and nothing wakes but meditation, guilt, revelry, and despair. The drunkard once more fills the destroying bowl, the robber walks his midnight round, and the suicide lifts his guilty arm against his own sacred person.

Let me no longer waste the night over the page of antiquity or the sallies of contemporary genius, but pursue the solitary walk, where Vanity, ever changing, but a few hours past walked before me, where she kept up the pageant, and now, like a froward child, seems hushed with her own importunities.[2]

What a gloom hangs all around! The dying lamp feebly emits a yellow gleam; no sound is heard but of the chiming clock or the distant watch-dog. All the bustle of human pride is forgotten; an hour like this may well display the emptiness of human vanity.

There will come a time when this temporary solitude may be made continual, and the city itself, like its inhabitants, fade away, and leave a desert in its room.

What cities, as great as this, have once triumphed in existence! had their victories as great, joy as just and as unbounded, and with short-sighted presumption promised themselves immortality! Posterity can hardly trace the situation of some; the sorrowful traveller wanders over the awful

---

[1] First printed in No. IV. of *The Bee*, with the following motto:
"Ille dolet verè, qui sine teste dolet."—MART.
[2] See Vol. I. p. 164, and Vol. III. pp. 72 and 480.

ruins of others; and, as he beholds, he learns wisdom, and feels the transience of every sublunary possession.

"Here," he cries, "stood their citadel, now grown over with weeds; there, their senate-house, but now the haunt of every noxious reptile; temples and theatres stood here, now only an undistinguished heap of ruin. They are fallen; for luxury and avarice first made them feeble. The rewards of the state were conferred on amusing and not on useful members of society. Their riches and opulence invited the invaders, who, though at first repulsed, returned again, conquered by perseverance, and at last swept the defendants into undistinguished destruction."

How few appear in those streets which, but some few hours ago, were crowded! and those who appear now no longer wear their daily mask, nor attempt to hide their lewdness or their misery.

But who are those who make the streets their couch, and find a short repose from wretchedness at the doors of the opulent? These are strangers, wanderers, and orphans, whose circumstances are too humble to expect redress, and whose distresses are too great even for pity. Their wretchedness rather excites horror than pity. Some are without the covering even of rags, and others emaciated with disease: the world has disclaimed them; society turns its back upon their distress, and has given them up to nakedness and hunger. These poor shivering females have once seen happier days and been flattered into beauty. They have been prostituted to the gay, luxurious villain, and are now turned out to meet the severity of winter. Perhaps, now lying at the doors of their betrayers, they sue to wretches whose hearts are insensible, or debauchees who may curse but will not relieve them.[1]

---

[1]   " Ah, turn thine eyes
Where the poor houseless shivering female lies.
She once, perhaps, in village plenty blest,
Has wept at tales of innocence distrest;
Her modest looks the cottage might adorn,
Sweet as the primrose peeps beneath the thorn;
Now lost to all; her friends, her virtue fled,
Near her betrayer's door she lays her head."—*The Deserted Village.*

Why, why was I born a man, and yet see the sufferings of wretches I cannot relieve! Poor houseless creatures! the world will give you reproaches, but will not give you relief. The slightest misfortunes of the great, the most imaginary uneasinesses of the rich, are aggravated with all the power of eloquence, and held up to engage our attention and sympathetic sorrow. The poor weep unheeded, persecuted by every subordinate species of tyranny; and every law, which gives others security, becomes an enemy to them.

Why was this heart of mine formed with so much sensibility! or why was not my fortune adapted to its impulse! Tenderness, without a capacity of relieving, only makes the man who feels it more wretched than the object which sues for assistance.[1] Adieu.

LETTER CXVIII.

ON THE MEANNESS OF THE DUTCH AT THE COURT OF JAPAN.

From Fum Hoam to Lien Chi Altangi, the discontented Wanderer, by the Way of Moscow, etc.

I HAVE been just sent upon an embassy to Japan. My commission is to be despatched in four days, and you can hardly conceive the pleasure I shall find upon revisiting my native country. I shall leave with joy this proud, barbarous, inhospitable region, where every object conspires to diminish my satisfaction and increase my patriotism.

---

[1] The following paragraph, with which (in *The Bee*) the paper originally concluded, had, probably, some personal allusion:

"But let me turn from a scene of such distress to the sanctified hypocrite, *who has been talking of virtue till the time of bed*, and now steals out, to give a loose to his vices, under the protection of midnight; vices more atrocious, because he attempts to conceal them. See how he pants down the dark alley, and, with hastening steps, fears an acquaintance in every face. He has passed the whole day in company he hates, and now goes to prolong the night among company that as heartily hate him. May his vices be detected; may the morning rise upon his shame! Yet I wish to no purpose; villany, when detected, never gives up, but boldly adds impudence to imposture."

But though I find the inhabitants savage, yet the Dutch merchants who are permitted to trade hither seem still more detestable. They have raised my dislike to Europe in general; by them I learn how low avarice can degrade human nature; how many indignities a European will suffer for gain.

I was present at an audience given by the emperor to the Dutch envoy, who had sent several presents to all the courtiers some days previous to his admission; but he was obliged to attend those designed for the emperor himself. From the accounts I had heard of this ceremony my curiosity prompted me to be a spectator of the whole.

First went the presents, set out on beautiful enamelled tables, adorned with flowers, borne on men's shoulders, and followed by Japanese music and dancers. From so great respect paid to the gifts themselves, I had fancied the donors must have received almost divine honors. But, about a quarter of an hour after the presents had been carried in triumph, the envoy and his train were brought forward. They were covered from head to foot with long black veils, which prevented their seeing, each led by a conductor, chosen from the meanest of the people. In this dishonorable manner, having traversed the city of Jeddo, they at length arrived at the palace gate, and, after waiting half an hour, were admitted into the guard-room. Here their eyes were uncovered, and in about an hour the gentleman-usher introduced them into the Hall of Audience.[1] The emperor was at length shown, sitting in a kind of alcove at the upper end of the room, and the Dutch envoy was conducted toward the throne.

As soon as he had approached within a certain distance the gentleman-usher cried out with a loud voice, " Holanda Capitan !" Upon these words the envoy fell flat upon the ground, and crept upon his hands and feet toward the throne. Still approaching, he reared himself upon his knees and then bowed his forehead to the ground. These ceremonies being over,

---

[1] "Otherwise, the Hall of a Hundred Mats."—KÆMPFER, *History of Japan*, vol. ii. p. 531.

he was directed to withdraw, still grovelling on his belly, and going backward like a lobster.[1]

Men must be excessively fond of riches, when they are earned with such circumstances of abject submission. Do the Europeans worship Heaven itself with marks of more profound respect? Do they confer those honors on the Supreme of Beings which they pay to a barbarous king, who gives them a permission to purchase trinkets and porcelain? What a glorious exchange, to forfeit their national honor, and even their title to humanity, for a screen or a snuffbox!

If these ceremonies essayed in the first audience appeared mortifying, those which are practised in the second were infinitely more so. In the second audience the emperor and the ladies of court were placed behind lattices, in such a manner as to see without being seen. Here all the Europeans were directed to pass in review, and grovel and act the serpent as before: with this spectacle the whole court seemed highly delighted. The strangers were asked a thousand ridiculous questions, as their names and their ages; they were ordered to write, to stand upright, to sit, to stoop, to compliment each other, to be drunk, to speak the Japanese language, to talk Dutch, to sing, to eat; in short, they were ordered to do all that could satisfy the curiosity of women.[2]

Imagine, my dear Altangi, a set of grave men thus transformed into buffoons, and acting a part every whit as honorable as that of those instructed animals which are shown in the streets of Pekin to the mob on a holiday. Yet the ceremony did not end here, for every great lord of the court was to be visited in the same manner; and their ladies, who took the whim from their husbands, were all equally fond of see-

[1] See Kæmpfer's History of Japan, vol. ii. p. 532.

[2] We obeyed the emperor's commands in the best manner we could. I joined to my dance a love-song in High Dutch. In this manner, and with innumerable such other apish tricks, did we suffer ourselves to contribute to the emperor and the court's diversion. As I was dancing," continues the grave doctor, "I had an opportunity twice of seeing the empress through the slits of the lattices, and took notice that she was of a brown and beautiful complexion, with black European eyes, full of fire, and from the proportion of her head, which was pretty large, I judged her to be a tall woman, and about thirty-six years of age."—KÆMPFER, vol. ii. p. 535.

ing the strangers perform; even the children seemed highly diverted with the dancing Dutchmen.

"Alas!" cried I to myself, upon returning from such a spectacle, "is this the nation which assumes such dignity at the court of Pekin? Is this that people that appear so proud at home, and in every country where they have the least authority? How does a love of gain transform the gravest of mankind into the most contemptible and ridiculous! I had rather continue poor all my life than become rich at such a rate. Perish those riches which are acquired at the expense of my honor or my humanity! Let me quit," said I, "a country where there are none but such as treat all others like slaves, and more detestable still, in suffering such treatment. I have seen enough of this nation to desire to see more of others. Let me leave a people suspicious to excess, whose morals are corrupted, and equally debased by superstition and vice; where the sciences are left uncultivated; where the great are slaves to the prince, and tyrants to the people; where the women are chaste only when debarred of the power of transgression; where the true disciples of Confucius are not less persecuted than those of Christianity; in a word, a country where men are forbidden to think, and consequently labor under the most miserable slavery—that of mental servitude." Adieu.

LETTER CXIX.

ON THE DISTRESSES OF THE POOR; EXEMPLIFIED IN THE LIFE OF A COMMON SOLDIER.[1]

From Lien Chi Altangi to Fum Hoam, etc.

THE misfortunes of the great, my friend, are held up to engage our attention; are enlarged upon in tones of declamation, and the world is called upon to gaze at the noble suf-

---

[1] First printed in *The British Magazine*, 1760; and reprinted by its author in 1765, with many alterations, as Essay XXIV.

ferers: they have at once the comfort of admiration and pity.

Yet where is the magnanimity of bearing misfortunes when the whole world is looking on? Men in such circumstances can act bravely, even from motives of vanity. He only who, in the vale of obscurity, can brave adversity, who, without friends to encourage, acquaintances to pity, or even without hope to alleviate his distresses, can behave with tranquillity and indifference, is truly great: whether peasant or courtier, he deserves admiration, and should be held up for our imitation and respect.

The miseries of the poor are, however, entirely disregarded, though some undergo more real hardships in one day than the great in their whole lives. It is, indeed, inconceivable what difficulties the meanest English sailor or soldier endures without murmuring or regret. Every day is to him a day of misery, and yet he bears his hard fate without repining.

With what indignation do I hear the heroes of tragedy[1] complain of misfortunes and hardships, whose greatest calamity is founded in arrogance and pride! Their severest distresses are pleasures, compared to what many of the adventuring poor every day sustain without murmuring. These may eat, drink, and sleep; have slaves to attend them, and are sure of subsistence for life; while many of their fellow-creatures are obliged to wander, without a friend to comfort or to assist them, find enmity in every law, and are too poor to obtain even justice.

I have been led into these reflections from accidentally meeting, some days ago, a poor fellow begging at one of the outlets of this town with a wooden leg. I was curious to learn what had reduced him to his present situation; and, after giving him what I thought proper, desired to know the history of his life and misfortunes, and the manner in which he was reduced to his present distress. The disabled soldier,

---

[1] "With what indignation do I hear an Ovid, a Cicero, or a Rabutin complain of their misfortunes and hardships, whose greatest calamity was that of being unable to visit a certain spot of earth, to which they had foolishly attached an idea of happiness."—*Essays*, 12mo., 1765, p. 215.

for such he was, with an intrepidity truly British, leaning on his crutch, put himself into an attitude to comply with my request, and gave me his history as follows:

"As for misfortunes, sir, I cannot pretend to have gone through more than others. Except the loss of my limb, and my being obliged to beg, I don't know any reason, thank Heaven, that I have to complain: there are some who have lost both legs and an eye; but, thank Heaven, it is not quite so bad with me.

"My father was a laborer in the country, and died when I was five years old; so I was put upon the parish. As he had been a wandering sort of a man, the parishioners were not able to tell to what parish I belonged, or where I was born; so they sent me to another parish, and that parish sent me to a third; till at last it was thought I belonged to no parish at all. At length, however, they fixed me. I had some disposition to be a scholar, and had actually learned my letters; but the master of the workhouse put me to business as soon as I was able to handle a mallet.

"Here I lived an easy kind of a life for five years. I only wrought ten hours in the day, and had my meat and drink provided for my labor. It is true, I was not suffered to stir far from the house, for fear I should run away; but what of that? I had the liberty of the whole house, and the yard before the door, and that was enough for me.

"I was next bound out to a farmer, where I was up both early and late, but I ate and drank well, and liked my business well enough, till he died. Being then obliged to provide for myself, I was resolved to go and seek my fortune. Thus I lived, and went from town to town, working when I could get employment, and starving when I could get none, and might have lived so still; but happening one day to go through a field belonging to a magistrate, I spied a hare crossing the path just before me. I believe the devil put it in my head to fling my stick at it: well! what will you have on't? I killed the hare, and was bringing it away in triumph, when the justice himself met me: he called me a villain, and, collaring me, desired I would give an account of myself. I began immediately to give a full account of all that I knew of my breed, seed, and generation; but though I gave a very long account, the justice said, I could give no account of myself; so I was indicted, and found guilty of being poor, and sent to Newgate, in order to be transported to the plantations.

"People may say this and that of being in jail; but for my part I found Newgate as agreeable a place as ever I was in, in all my life. I had my bellyful to eat and drink, and did no work; but alas! this kind of life was too good to last forever: I was taken out of prison, after five months, put on board of a ship, and sent off with two hundred more. Our passage was but indifferent, for we were all confined in the hold, and died very fast, for want of sweet air and provisions; but, for my part, I did not want meat, because I had a fever all the way. Providence was kind; when provisions grew short, it took away my desire of eating. When we came ashore, we were sold to the planters. I was bound for seven years; and as I was no scholar, for I had forgotten my letters, I was obliged to work among the negroes, and served out my time, as in duty bound to do.

"When my time was expired I worked my passage home, and glad I was to see Old England again, because I loved my country. O liberty! liberty! liberty! that is the property of every Englishman, and I will die in its defence. I was afraid, however, that I should be indicted for a vagabond once more, so did not much care to go into the country, but kept about town, and did little jobs when I could get them. I was very happy in this manner for some time; till one evening, coming home from work, two men knocked me down, and then desired me to stand still. They belonged to a press-gang: I was carried before the justice, and as I could give no account of myself (that was the thing that always hobbled me), I had my choice left, whether to go on board a man-of-war or list for a soldier. I chose to be a soldier; and in this post of a gentleman I served two campaigns in Flanders, was at the battles of Val and Fontenoy, and received but one wound through the breast, which is troublesome to this day.

"When the peace came on I was discharged; and as I could

not work, because my wound was sometimes painful, I listed
for a landman in the East India Company's service. I here
fought the French in six pitched battles; and verily believe
that if I could read or write our captain would have given
me promotion and made me a corporal. But that was not my
good-fortune; I soon fell sick, and, when I became good for
nothing, got leave to return home again, with forty pounds
in my pocket, which I saved in the service. This was at the
beginning of the present war, so I hoped to be set on shore,
and to have the pleasure of spending my money; but the Government wanted men, and I was pressed again before ever I
could set foot on shore.

"The boatswain found me, as he said, an obstinate fellow :
he swore that I understood my business perfectly well, but
that I shammed Abraham,[1] merely to be idle. God knows, I
knew nothing of sea-business : he beat me without considering what he was about. But still my forty pounds was some
comfort to me under every beating : the money was my comfort, and the money I might have had to this day, but that
our ship was taken by the French, and so I lost it all.

"Our crew was carried into a French prison, and many of
them died because they were not used to live in a jail; but
for my part it was nothing to me, for I was seasoned. One
night, however, as I was sleeping on the bed of boards, with a
warm blanket about me (for I always loved to lie well), I was
awakened by the boatswain, who had a dark lantern in his
hand. 'Jack,' says he to me, 'will you knock out the French
sentry's brains?' 'I don't care,' says I, striving to keep myself awake, 'if I lend a hand.' 'Then follow me,' says he,
'and I hope we shall do business.' So up I got, and tied my
blanket, which was all the clothes I had, about my middle, and
went with him to fight the Frenchmen.[2] We had no arms;
but one Englishman is able to beat five French at any time;
so we went down to the door, where both the sentries were
posted, and rushing upon them, seized their arms in a moment

---

[1] That is, assumed infirmity.

[2] Here Essay XXIV. adds, "I hate the French because they are all slaves and
wear wooden shoes."

and knocked them down. From thence nine of us ran together to the quay, and seizing the first boat we met, got out of the harbor, and put to sea. We had not been here three days before we were taken up by an English privateer, who was glad of so many good hands; and we consented to run our chance. However, we had not so much luck as we expected. In three days we fell in with a French man-of-war, of forty guns, while we had but twenty-three; so to it we went. The fight lasted for three hours; and I verily believe that we should have taken the Frenchman, but unfortunately we lost almost all our men just as we were going to get the victory. I was once more in the power of the French, and I believe it would have gone hard with me had I been brought back to my old jail in Brest; but, by good-fortune, we were retaken, and carried to England once more.

"I had almost forgotten to tell you that in this last engagement I was wounded in two places: I lost four fingers of the left hand, and my leg was shot off. Had I had the good fortune to have lost my leg and use of my hand on board a king's ship and not a privateer, I should have been entitled to clothing and maintenance during the rest of my life; but that was not my chance: one man is born with a silver spoon in his mouth, and another with a wooden ladle. However, blessed be God! I enjoy good health, and have no enemy in this world, that I know of, but the French and the justice of peace."

Thus saying, he limped off, leaving my friend and me in admiration of his intrepidity and content; nor could we avoid acknowledging that an habitual acquaintance with misery is the truest school of fortitude and philosophy. Adieu.

LETTER CXX.

ON THE ABSURDITY OF SOME LATE ENGLISH TITLES.

From the Same.

THE titles of European princes are rather more numerous than ours of Asia, but by no means so sublime. The King of Visapour, or Pegu, not satisfied with claiming the globe and all its appurtenances to him and his heirs, asserts a property even in the firmament, and extends his orders to the milky-way. The monarchs of Europe, with more modesty, confine their titles to earth, but make up by number what is wanting in their sublimity. Such is their passion for a long list of these splendid trifles, that I have known a German prince with more titles than subjects, and a Spanish nobleman with more names than shirts.

Contrary to this, "the English monarchs," says a writer of the last century, "disdain to accept of such titles, which tend only to increase their pride without improving their glory; they are above depending on the feeble helps of heraldry for respect, perfectly satisfied with the consciousness of acknowledged power." At present, however, these maxims are laid aside: the English monarchs have of late assumed new titles, and have impressed their coins with the names and arms of obscure dukedoms, petty states, and subordinate employments. Their design in this, I make no doubt, was laudably to add new lustre to the British throne; but, in reality, paltry claims only serve to diminish that respect they are designed to secure.

There is in the honors assumed by kings, as in the decorations of architecture, a majestic simplicity, which best conduces to inspire our reverence and respect: numerous and trifling ornaments in either are strong indications of meanness in the designer, or of concealed deformity. Should, for instance, the Emperor of China, among other titles, assume

that of Deputy Mandarin of Maccau, or the Monarch of Great
Britain, France, and Ireland desire to be acknowledged as
Duke of Brentford, Lunenburg, or Lincoln, the observer re-
volts at this mixture of important and paltry claims, and
forgets the emperor in his familiarity with the duke or
the deputy.

I remember a similar instance of this inverted ambition in
the illustrious King of Manacabo, upon his first treaty with
the Portuguese. Among the presents that were made him
by the ambassador of that nation was a sword, with a brass
hilt, which he seemed to set a peculiar value upon. This he
thought too great an acquisition to his glory to be forgotten
among the number of his titles. He therefore gave orders
that his subjects should style him, for the future, "Talipot,
the immortal Potentate of Manacabo, Messenger of the Morning, Enlightener of the Sun, Possessor of the whole Earth,
and mighty Monarch of the brass-handled Sword."

This method of mixing majestic and paltry titles, of quar-
tering the arms of a great empire and an obscure province
upon the same medal here, had its rise in the virtuous partiality of their late monarchs. Willing to testify an affection
to their native country, they gave its name and ensigns a
place upon their coins, and thus in some measure ennobled
its obscurity. It was, indeed, but just that a people which
had given England up their king, should receive some honor-
ary equivalent in return; but at present these motives are no
more: England has now a monarch wholly British, and has
some reason to hope for British titles upon British coins.

However, were the money of England designed to circulate
in Germany, there would be no flagrant impropriety in impressing it with German names and arms; but though this
might have been so upon former occasions, I am told there
is no danger of it for the future. As England, therefore,
designs to keep back its gold, I candidly think Lunenburg,
Oldenburg, and the rest of them may very well keep back
their titles.

It is a mistaken prejudice in princes to think that a number of loud-sounding names can give new claims to respect.

The truly great have ever disdained them. When Timur the Lame had conquered Asia, an orator by profession came to compliment him upon the occasion. He began his harangue by styling him the most omnipotent and the most glorious object of the creation. The emperor seemed displeased with his paltry adulation; yet still he went on, complimenting him as the most mighty, the most valiant, and the most perfect of beings. "Hold there, my friend," cries the late emperor; "hold there, till I have got another leg." In fact, the feeble or the despotic alone find pleasure in multiplying these pageants of vanity; but strength and freedom have nobler aims, and often find the finest adulation in majestic simplicity.

The young monarch of this country has already testified a proper contempt for several unmeaning appendages on royalty: cooks and scullions have been obliged to quit their fires; gentlemen's gentlemen, and the whole tribe of necessary people who did nothing, have been dismissed from further services. A youth who can thus bring back simplicity and frugality to a court will soon, probably, have a true respect for his own glory; and while he has dismissed all useless employments, may disdain to accept of empty or degrading titles. Adieu.

LETTER CXXI.

THE IRRESOLUTION OF THE ENGLISH ACCOUNTED FOR.

From the Same.

WHENEVER I attempt to characterize the English in general, some unforeseen difficulties constantly occur to disconcert my design; I hesitate between censure and praise. When I consider them as a reasoning, philosophical people, they have my applause; but when I reverse the medal, and observe their inconstancy and irresolution, I can scarcely persuade myself that I am observing the same people.

Yet, upon examination, this very inconstancy, so remarkable here, flows from no other source than their love of reason-

ing. The man who examines a complicated subject on every
side, and calls in reason to his assistance, will frequently
change; will find himself distracted by opposing probabili-
ties and contending proofs: every alteration of place will
diversify the prospect, will give some latent argument new
force, and contribute to maintain an anarchy in the mind.

On the contrary, they who never examine with their own
reason act with more simplicity. Ignorance is positive, instinct perseveres, and the human being moves in safety, within the narrow circle of brutal uniformity. What is true with
regard to individuals is not less so when applied to states. A
reasoning government like this is in continual fluctuation,
while those kingdoms where men are taught, not to contro-
vert, but obey, continue always the same. In Asia, for instance, where the monarch's authority is supported by force
and acknowledged through fear, a change of government is
entirely unknown. All the inhabitants seem to wear the
same mental complexion, and remain contented with heredi-
tary oppression. The sovereign's pleasure is the ultimate
rule of duty; every branch of the administration is a perfect
epitome of the whole; and if one tyrant is deposed, another
starts up in his room, to govern as his predecessor. The English, on the contrary, instead of being led by power, endeavor
to guide themselves by reason; instead of appealing to the
pleasure of the prince, appeal to the original rights of mankind. What one rank of men assert is denied by others, as
the reasons on opposite sides happen to come home with
greater or less conviction. The people of Asia are directed
by precedent, which never alters; the English by reason,
which is ever changing its appearance.

The disadvantages of an Asiatic government, acting in this
manner by precedent, are evident: original errors are thus
continued without hopes of redress, and all marks of genius
are levelled down to one standard, since no superiority of
thinking can be allowed its exertion in mending obvious defects. But to recompense those defects their governments
undergo no new alterations; they have no new evils to fear,
nor no fermentations in the constitution that continue; the

struggle for power is soon over, and all becomes tranquil as before; they are habituated to subordination, and men are taught to form no other desires than those which they are allowed to satisfy.

The disadvantages of a government acting from the immediate influence of reason, like that of England, are not less than those of the former. It is extremely difficult to induce a number of free beings to co-operate for their mutual benefit; every possible advantage will necessarily be sought, and every attempt to procure it must be attended with a new fermentation; various reasons will lead different ways, and equity and advantage will often be balanced by a combination of clamor and prejudice. But though such a people may be thus in the wrong, they have been influenced by a happy delusion; their errors are seldom seen till they are felt; each man is himself the tyrant he has obeyed, and such a master he can easily forgive. The disadvantages he feels may, in reality, be equal to what is felt in the most despotic government; but man will bear every calamity with patience when he knows himself to be the author of his own misfortunes. Adieu.

LETTER CXXII.

THE MANNER OF TRAVELLERS IN THEIR USUAL RELATIONS RIDICULED.

From the Same.

My long residence here begins to fatigue me. As every object ceases to be new, it no longer continues to be pleasing; some minds are so fond of variety that pleasure itself, if permanent, would be insupportable, and we are thus obliged to solicit new happiness even by courting distress. I only, therefore, wait the arrival of my son to vary this trifling scene, and borrow new pleasure from danger and fatigue. A life, I own, thus spent in wandering from place to place is at best but empty dissipation. But to pursue trifles is the lot of humanity; and whether we bustle in a pantomime or strut at a cor-

II.—33

onation, whether we shout at a bonfire or harangue at a senate-house, whatever object we follow, it will at last surely conduct us to futility and disappointment. The wise bustle and laugh as they walk in the pageant, but fools bustle and are important; and this probably is all the difference between them.

This may be an apology for the levity of my former correspondence; I talked of trifles, and I knew that they were trifles: to make the things of this life ridiculous it is only sufficient to call them by their names.

In other respects, I have omitted several striking circumstances in the description of this country, as supposing them either already known to you, or as not being thoroughly known to myself; but there is one omission, for which I expect no forgiveness, namely, my being totally silent upon their buildings, roads, rivers, and mountains. This is a branch of science on which all other travellers are so very prolix that my deficiency will appear the more glaring. With what pleasure, for instance, do some read of a traveller in Egypt measuring a fallen column with his cane, and finding it exactly five feet nine inches long; of his creeping through the mouth of a catacomb, and coming out by a different hole from that he entered; of his stealing the finger of an antique statue in spite of the janizary that watched him; or his adding a new conjecture to the hundred and fourteen conjectures already published upon the names of Osiris and Isis.

Methinks I hear some of my friends in China demanding a similar account of London and the adjacent villages; and if I remain here much longer it is probable I may gratify their curiosity. I intend, when run dry on other topics, to take a serious survey of the City Wall, to describe that beautiful building, the Mansion House; I will enumerate the magnificent squares in which the nobility chiefly reside, and the royal palaces appointed for the reception of the English monarch; nor will I forget the beauties of Shoe Lane, in which I myself have resided since my arrival. You shall find me in no way inferior to many of my brother travellers in the arts of description. At present, however, as a specimen of this way of writing I send you a few hasty remarks, collected in a late journey I made to Kentish Town[1]—and this in the manner of modern voyagers:

"Having heard much of Kentish Town, I conceived a strong desire to see that celebrated place. I could have wished, indeed, to satisfy my curiosity without going thither; but that was impracticable, and therefore I resolved to go. Travellers have two methods of going to Kentish Town: they take coach, which costs ninepence, or they may go afoot, which costs nothing; in my opinion a coach is by far the most eligible convenience; but I was resolved to go on foot, having considered with myself that going in that manner would be the cheapest way.

"As you set out from Dog House Bar[2] you enter upon a fine level road, railed in on both sides, commanding on the right a small prospect of groves and fields enamelled with flowers, which would wonderfully charm the sense of smelling were it not for a dunghill on the left, which mixes its effluvia with their odors. This dunghill is of much greater antiquity than the road; and I must not omit a piece of injustice I was going to commit upon this occasion. My indignation was levelled against the makers of the dunghill, for having brought it so near the road; whereas, it should have fallen upon the makers of the road, for having brought that so near the dunghill.

"After proceeding in this manner for some time, a building resembling somewhat a triumphal arch salutes the traveller's view. This structure, however, is peculiar to this country, and vulgarly called a turnpike-gate; I could perceive a long inscription in large characters on the front, probably upon the occasion of some triumph, but, being in haste, I left it to

---

[1] A hamlet and prebendal manor of St. Paul's, north-west of St. Pancras, and written in Court-rolls of the 14th century as Kaunteloe or De Kaunteloe. The lease passed in 1670 into the hands of the Jeffreys family, and subsequently, by marriage, to the first Earl Camden, in whose family it still remains. Kentish Town is now (1854) part of modern London.

[2] Dog House Bar stood across the City Road, where Old Street and Old Street Road now unite. It is marked in the maps of London engraved in the reign of George II.

be made out by some subsequent adventurer who may happen to travel this way; so, continuing my course to the west, I soon arrived at an unwalled town called Islington.[1]

"Islington is a pretty, neat town, mostly built of brick, with a church and bells; it has a small lake, or rather pond,[2] in the midst, though at present very much neglected. I am told it is dry in summer; if this be the case, it can be no very proper receptacle for fish, of which the inhabitants themselves seem sensible, by bringing all that is eaten there from London.

"After having surveyed the curiosities of this fair and beautiful town, I proceeded forward, leaving a fair stone building, called the White Conduit House,[3] on my right. Here the inhabitants of London often assemble to celebrate a feast of hot rolls and butter: seeing such numbers, each with their little tables before them, employed on this occasion, must, no doubt, be a very amusing sight to the looker-on, but still more so to those who perform in the solemnity.

"From hence I parted with reluctance to *Pancras*,[4] as it is

---

[1] "The monster London" of Cowley's poem upon "Solitude:"

"Let but thy wicked men from out thee go,
  And all the fools that crowd thee so,
    Even thou, who dost thy millions boast,
  A village less than Islington wilt grow,
    A solitude almost."

[2] "*Master Stephen.* What do you talk on it? Because I dwell at Hogsden, I shall keep company with none but the archers of Finsbury or the citizens that come ducking to Islington Ponds."—BEN JONSON, *Every Man in his Humor.*

"*27th March*, 1664.—Walked through the Ducking Pond Fields; but they are so altered since my father used to carry us to Islington, to the old man's, at the King's Head, to eat cakes and ale (his name was Pitts), that I did not know which was the Ducking Pond (*see* Ball's Pond), nor where I was."—PEPYS.

[3] A kind of minor Vauxhall, for Londoners who went for cakes and cream to Islington. The gardens lost their rank and reputation early in the present century; and the house, before it was pulled down (January, 1849) to make way for a new street, was nothing more than a large tavern, with a large room for suburban entertainments and political meetings. — See *The Bee*, No. II., and art. "White Conduit House," in CUNNINGHAM's *Hand-book of London,* ed. 1850, p. 547.

[4] "Pancras Church standeth all alone, as utterly forsaken, old and weather-beaten, which, for the antiquity thereof, is thought not to yield to Paul's in London. About this church have bin many buildings now decayed, leaving poor

written, or *Pancridge,* as it is pronounced; but which should be both pronounced and written *Pangrace:* this emendation I will venture *meo arbitrio;* Παν, in the Greek language, signifies *all,* which, added to the English word *grace,* maketh *all grace,* or *Pangrace;* and, indeed, this is a very proper appellation to a place of so much sanctity as Pangrace is universally esteemed. However this be, if you except the parish church and its fine bells, there is little in Pangrace worth the attention of the curious observer.

"From Pangrace to Kentish Town is an easy journey of one mile and a quarter: the road lies through a fine champaign country, well watered with beautiful drains, and enamelled with flowers of all kinds, which might contribute to charm every sense, were it not that the odoriferous gales are often more impregnated with dust than perfume.

"As you enter Kentish Town the eye is at once presented with the shops of artificers, such as venders of candles, small-coal, and hair-brooms; there are also several august buildings of red brick, with numberless sign-posts, or rather pillars, in a peculiar order of architecture; I send you a drawing of several, *vide* A, B, C. This pretty town probably borrows its name from its vicinity to the county of Kent; and, indeed, it is not unnatural that it should, as there are only London and the adjacent villages that lie between them. Be this as it will, perceiving night approach, I made a hasty repast on roasted mutton and a certain dried fruit called potatoes, resolving to protract my remarks upon my return; and this I would very willingly have done, but was prevented by a circumstance which, in truth, I had for some time foreseen; for, night coming on, it was impossible to take a proper survey of the country, as I was obliged to return home in the dark." Adieu.

Pancras without companie or comfort, yet it is now and then visited with Kentish-towne and Highgate, which are members thereof; but they seldom come there, for they have chapels of ease within themselves; but when there is a corpse to be interred, they are forced to leave the same within this forsaken church or church-yard, where (no doubt) it resteth as secure against the day of resurrection as if it laie in stately Paule's."—NORDEN, *Spec. Brit.*, 4to, 1593.

LETTER CXXIII.

THE CONCLUSION.

To the Same.

AFTER a variety of disappointments, my wishes are at length fully satisfied. My son, so long expected, is arrived; at once, by his presence, banishing my anxiety and opening a new scene of unexpected pleasure. His improvements in mind and person have far surpassed even the sanguine expectations of a father. I left him a boy, but he is returned a man: pleasing in his person, hardened by travel, and polished by adversity. His disappointment in love, however, had infused an air of melancholy into his conversation, which seemed at intervals to interrupt our mutual satisfaction. I expected that this could find a cure only from time; but Fortune, as if willing to load us with her favors, has in a moment repaid every uneasiness with rapture.

Two days after his arrival, the man in black, with his beautiful niece, came to congratulate us upon this pleasing occasion; but, guess our surprise when my friend's lovely kinswoman was found to be the very captive my son had rescued from Persia, and who had been wrecked on the Wolga, and was carried by the Russian peasants to the port of Archangel. Were I to hold the pen of a novelist I might be prolix in describing their feelings at so unexpected an interview; but you may conceive their joy without my assistance; words were unable to express their transports; then how can words describe it?

When two young persons are sincerely enamored of each other, nothing can give me such pleasure as seeing them married: whether I know the parties or not, I am happy at thus binding one link more in the universal chain. Nature has in some measure formed me for a match-maker, and given me a soul to sympathize with every mode of human felicity. I instantly, therefore, consulted the man in black, whether we might not crown their mutual wishes by marriage: his soul seems formed of similar materials with mine—he instantly gave his consent, and the next day was appointed for the solemnization of their nuptials.

All the acquaintances which I had made since my arrival were present at this gay solemnity. The little beau was constituted master of the ceremonies, and his wife, Mrs. Tibbs, conducted the entertainment with proper decorum. The man in black and the pawnbroker's widow were very sprightly and tender upon this occasion. The widow was dressed up under the direction of Mrs. Tibbs; and as for her lover, his face was set off by the assistance of a pig-tail wig, which was lent by the little beau, to fit him for making love with proper formality. The whole company easily perceived that it would be a double wedding before all was over; and indeed my friend and the widow seemed to make no secret of their passion: he even called me aside, in order to know my candid opinion, whether I did not think him a little too old to be married. "As for my own part," continued he, "I know I am going to play the fool, but all my friends will praise my wisdom, and produce me as the very pattern of discretion to others."

At dinner everything seemed to run on with good-humor, harmony, and satisfaction. Every creature in company thought themselves pretty, and every jest was laughed at. The man in black sat next his mistress, helped her plate, chimed her glass; and, jogging her knees and her elbow, he whispered something arch in her ear, on which she patted his cheek: never was antiquated passion so playful, so harmless, and amusing, as between this reverend couple.

The second course was now called for, and, among a variety of other dishes, a fine turkey was placed before the widow. The Europeans, you know, carve as they eat; my friend, therefore, begged his mistress to help him to a part of the turkey. The widow, pleased with an opportunity of showing her skill in carving (an art upon which, it seems, she piqued herself) began to cut it up, by first taking off the leg. "Madam," cried my friend, "if I might be permitted to advise, I would begin by cutting off the wing, and then the leg will come off more easily." "Sir," replies the widow, "give me leave to understand cutting up a fowl; I always begin with the leg." "Yes, madam," replies the lover, "but if the wing be the most convenient manner, I would begin with the wing." "Sir," interrupts the lady, "when you have fowls of your own, begin with the wing, if you please; but give me leave to take off the leg: I hope I am not to be taught at this time of day!" "Madam," interrupts he, "we are never too old to be instructed." "Old, sir!" interrupts the other, "who is old, sir? When I die of age, I know of some that will quake for fear: if the leg does not come off, take the turkey to yourself." "Madam," replied the man in black, "I don't care a farthing whether the leg or the wing comes off; if you are for the leg first, why, you shall have the argument, even though it be as I say." "As for the matter of that," cries the widow, "I don't care a fig, whether you are for the leg off or on; and, friend, for the future keep your distance!" "Oh," replied the other, "that is easily done; it is only removing to the other end of the table; and so, madam, your most obedient, humble servant."

Thus was this courtship of an age destroyed in one moment; for this dialogue effectually broke off the match between this respectable couple that had been just concluded. The smallest accidents disappoint the most important treaties; however, though it in some measure interrupted the general satisfaction, it no ways lessened the happiness of the youthful couple; and by the young lady's looks I could perceive she was not entirely displeased with this interruption.

In a few hours the whole transaction seemed entirely forgotten, and we have all since enjoyed those satisfactions which result from a consciousness of making each other happy. My son and his fair partner are fixed here for life; the man in black has given them up a small estate in the country, which, added to what I was able to bestow, will be capable of supplying all the real, but not the fictitious, demands of happiness. As for myself, the world being but one city to me, I do not much care in which of the streets I happen to reside. I shall therefore spend the remainder of my days in examining the manners of different countries, and have prevailed upon the man in black to be my companion. "They must often change," says Confucius, "who would be constant in happiness or wisdom." Adieu.

END OF VOL. II.